Organic Pesticides
in the Environment

A symposium co-sponsored by
the Division of Water, Air,
and Waste Chemistry and the
Pesticide Subdivision of the
Division of Agricultural and
Food Chemistry at the 150th
Meeting of the American
Chemical Society, Atlantic
City, N. J., Sept. 13–15, 1965

Aaron A. Rosen and H. F. Kraybill
Symposium Chairmen

ADVANCES IN CHEMISTRY SERIES **60**

AMERICAN CHEMICAL SOCIETY

WASHINGTON, D.C.   1966

Library of Congress Catalog Card 66-30613

PRINTED IN THE UNITED STATES OF AMERICA

Second Printing 1970

Advances in Chemistry Series

Robert F. Gould, *Editor*

AMERICAN CHEMICAL SOCIETY | PUBLICATIONS

FOREWORD

ADVANCES IN CHEMISTRY SERIES was founded in 1949 by the
American Chemical Society as an outlet for symposia and
collections of data in special areas of topical interest that could
not be accommodated in the' Society's journals. It provides a
medium for symposia that would otherwise be fragmented,
their papers distributed among several journals or not published at all. Papers are refereed critically according to ACS
editorial standards and receive the careful attention and
processing characteristic of ACS publications. Papers published
in ADVANCES IN CHEMISTRY SERIES are original contributions
not published elsewhere in whole or major part and include
reports of research as well as reviews since symposia may
embrace both types of presentation.

CONTENTS

PREFACE

When historians of future generations write of our era, they will note wryly how much of our technical capability was devoted to producing commodities inevitably destined to contaminate our environment. The most spectacular example must be the automobile. Its exhaust pollutes our atmosphere; it has brought about the need for ever-spreading highways, which are indeed rapidly "autodegradable," but are still permanent scars on the environment. Ultimately, it is discarded in a junkyard, which detracts from the beauty of the landscape. Another offending commodity, synthetic detergents, has a particularly striking propensity to affect the purity of our water resources. Detergents are produced with the specific intention that after a single use, and virtually undiminished in quantity, they will be promptly discharged to the most convenient watercourse.

Chemical pesticides hold a unique position among the environmental contaminants since distribution in the environment is the way they are used. Adding to their impact is the fact that pesticides are fashioned and valued for their deadly effect on living organisms. The result is of inevitable concern to both laymen and scientists. There is good cause for concern about the kind and extent of defilement of the environment that pesticides can produce.

Pesticides have been spread throughout the environment; they have been found in the air we breathe, in the streams and lakes that supply our drinking water, in the clothing we wear, and, indeed, in our very bodies. Large numbers of birds, fish, and forest animals have succumbed to these poisons. The same poisons have been found in the bodies of creatures in the remote reaches of the world—fish in the Mid-Pacific and water fowl in the Antarctic.

The concern over the threats of pesticide danger implied in these discoveries includes, of course, apprehension about the less obvious consequences to humans. This general concern evoked this symposium, which was designed to present a clear perspective on the environmental hazards of organic pesticides, the necessary background knowledge, and the approaches to be used in assessing the problem. The problems of pesticides in foods have long been recognized and studied extensively; therefore, this symposium was devoted only to nonfood aspects of the environment.

The symposium was arranged to include each of the major elements of the pesticide problem. Some organic compounds are used as pesticides because they have a useful combination of chemical, physical, and biological properties. The chemical and physical properties determine how these materials spread in the environment by volatility and solubility; these properties also affect the persistence of pesticides in terms of hydrolysis, oxidation, and removal by adsorption. The biological properties determine not only the purpose for which pesticides are used, but also the degree of incidental hazard to other living things, even in minute traces in the environment and in animal tissues. The method of use is an important factor in determining what part of the environment becomes contaminated. Aerial dusting is obviously a greater hazard than careful, direct application to crops since the airplane contaminates air, soil and surface water simultaneously.

To appraise the extent of environmental contamination is a problem in organic pesticide analysis. Analytical methods for such diverse samples as air and human tissue have been developed and are yielding important information. The fate and persistence of pesticides constitutes another complex problem. It includes consideration of environmental and biological effects upon pesticides, how they move in rivers, and how they are translocated from one environmental medium to another. Finally, there is the question of damage control. Can we reduce the introduction of pesticides into air and water? If not, can we effectively remove these poisons from the parts we consume?

These are the considerations that prevailed in arranging this symposium. All were represented in the various presentations. The extent of knowledge is not uniform in these fields, but the study of pesticides in the environment is a relatively new endeavor. Progress has already been made, both in delineating the problem and in developing specific knowledge, and the work reported here is an account of that progress.

A. A. ROSEN

Cincinnati, Ohio
March 1966

INTRODUCTION

A mong the many technological achievements of our era is the remarkable acceleration of food and fiber production and the control of pest-vectored diseases by the wide scale acceptance and use of chemical pesticides. Over the past 15 years, however, pest control with these remarkable agents has inadvertently contributed to a remarkable proliferation of these chemicals in our environment, culminating in the ever increasing problems of environmental pollution.

The tempo of interest has been accelerated not only by concern for the quality of our environment but by the potential impact on public health and the survival of fish and wildlife. For the general public, interest in environmental pollution was awakened by the publication of "Silent Spring." The appearance of the President's Science Advisory Committee Report on "Use of Pesticides" reflected this concern and the need for national programs and policies dealing with pest control and associated biomedical problems. However, neither of these publications really provided the initial thrust for exploratory research in this area of toxicology and epidemiology. Over the past decade a gradual evolution in the fields of cellular biology cytogenetics and biochemistry-pharmacology has focused attention on the significance of sub-threshold toxic effects and the ability of a single toxicant or integration of several toxic stresses to induce responses and pathological changes at the cellular level.

Toxicological research a decade ago lacked the current conceptual approaches which provide a fuller appreciation of the mechanisms involved in cellular biochemistry relating to cellular alteration and ultimately, disease states. Unfortunately, some of the current toxicological research on pesticides fails to comprehend the more imaginative approaches provided by subliminal pharmacology. Perhaps carcinogenesis research has done more to demonstrate the capacities of various stress agents, such as chemicals, viruses, bacterial toxins and/or metabolites, for altering cellular protein or deoxyribonucleic acid (DNA). The separate action of a virus or the tandem effect of a virus and a chemical has been implicated in subtle cellular changes which, over an extended span, fulminate into a clinically recognizable response or specific disease.

Realizing that protracted cellular insults may occur from chronic exposure to pesticides, one certainly is not justified in making sweeping conclusions on safety based on short term observations of single or multiple exposures to a chemical pesticide. In advancing our knowledge of cellular responses, the elucidation of the structure of DNA and appreciation of the mechanisms of action of DNA with various exogenous agents have done much to open up wide vistas for biochemical, toxicological, and epidemiological research.

Concurrent with these biomethodological approaches to research has been the rapid advance of physicochemical methodology. These sophisticated techniques of detection have provided means for identifying and measuring infinitely small amounts of pesticides and other environmental toxicants and their metabolites, which may be involved in micro insults to cellular response in various species, including man.

The biomedical research session of this broad symposium presents some of the progress made by an expanding and comprehensive research program designed to study the biological impact of chemical pesticides on man and his environment. In a toxicological-epidemiological assessment of the problem of environmental pollutants, pesticides are just one category in a wide spectrum of such agents. Obviously, the experimental designs and the methodological approaches used should provide a model for exploring the biological action of other contaminants.

Washington, D. C.　　　　　　　　　　　　　　　　H. F. KRAYBILL
March 1966

Pesticides: Properties and Prognosis

L. E. MITCHELL

Shell Chemical Co., Agricultural Chemicals Division, New York, N. Y.

Approximately 300 organic pesticide chemicals are being marketed in more than 10,000 different formulations. Last year over 750 million pounds were used in the United States. Insecticides account for nearly half this amount, but herbicides will far surpass them in tonnage within a few years. The chlorinated hydrocarbon insecticides have attracted attention because of their so-called "persistence." However, unlike some of their inorganic predecessors, organic pesticides are decomposed in the environment by biological and physicochemical processes which influence the amounts that will be found in the environment. Their mere presence in the environment does not necessarily jeopardize the public health. The amounts present, their toxicities, and the rate of detoxification and decomposition must be considered to assess their significance in the environment.

It has been only a few short years since DDT was lauded as one of the great contributions to the welfare of mankind. The scientific as well as the popular literature was filled with glowing reports of its enormous value for controlling a wide range of insect pests and saving countless lives throughout the world. In this same literature, however, reports of resistance of a few insect species to DDT began appearing. Soon afterward, some analytical chemist found a trace of DDT in some animal fat. Before long, his colleagues found not only DDT, but metabolites of DDT as well, in both animal and human fat. Suddenly, DDT and most of the pesticides that were subsequently discovered and used for the protection of man himself, his food and fiber supplies, and his forests and livestock became looked upon as insidious, uncontrollable poisons.

It is becoming increasingly difficult to find a paper in the current literature that puts pesticides in a favorable light. It is now fashionable to condemn them. If one can show that a handful of some pesticide dropped into a tank or a pond will kill some fish, the data are soon extrapolated to all the rivers and lakes in North America, to the surrounding oceans, and to both polar regions.

If the pesticide happens to accumulate in animal tissue, there is no end to the allegations that are made. Many of the diseases and maladies for which the causes are unknown have at one time or another been attributed to pesticides. For example, a few years ago poliomyelitis was alleged to be caused by pesticides. Once a successful vaccine was discovered, these charges, of course, were dropped.

However, pesticides are chemicals. Like other chemicals, they have certain properties that govern their effectiveness and fate in any given system. They vaporize, oxidize, hydrolyze, and metabolize. The differences in properties and reaction rates are what make them useful as pesticides under given conditions and influence their importance as contaminants of the environment.

In assessing the extent to which any chemical might pervade the environment, the first consideration, of course, is to determine how much has been used. Figure 1 illustrates the rapid growth rate of the organic pesticide industry (23). In 1940 the total usage of synthetic organic pesticides in the United States was approximately 140 tons. In 1944 over 8000 tons were used. By that time 2,4-D had been discovered, and the organic pesticide industry was off to a fast start.

At the present time there are approximately 300 organic pesticide chemicals in general use, marketed in more than 10,000 different formulations. A breakdown of the approximate number of chemicals in general use in each class is shown in Table I. There are many more than 10,000 pesticidal products registered with the United States Department of Agriculture, but many of them have relatively limited use and at the present time can probably be disregarded in so far as finding them anywhere, except possibly in a few isolated spots in the environment.

The relative growth of the major classes of pesticides over the last few years is illustrated in Figure 2.

Of the 750 million pounds of pesticides used in 1964, insecticides accounted for nearly half, with herbicides and fungicides comprising most of the balance (23). The markets for fungicides and chlorinated hydrocarbon insecticides have apparently reached a peak while the markets for organophosphorus insecticides and herbicides are increasing. It is predicted that the domestic use of herbicides will far surpass that of insecticides within a few years.

Because of recent adverse publicity and criticism, the public has the misconception that pesticides have been spread with reckless abandon all over the landscape, contaminating all food and fiber crops, decimating the fish and wildlife, exterminating the songbirds, and polluting the entire

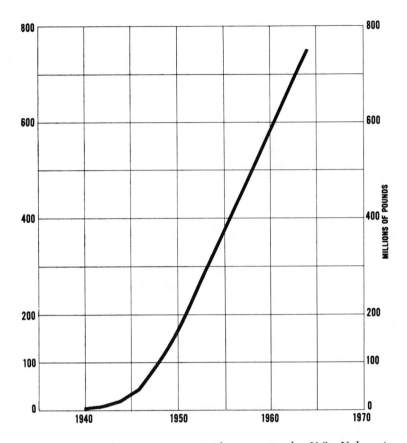

Figure 1.   Trend of organic pesticide usage in the U.S. Values in millions of pounds of technical products.

environment beyond reclamation. Actually, in any given year pesticides are applied to only a small percentage of the land used for food and fiber. Of all the insecticides used in this country, 75% are applied to less than 2% of the land. Table II shows a breakdown of the insecticide usage for a typical year on farms in the United States. Of the 457 million acres of farmland in the United States, it is estimated that pesticides are used on only 15% of the total crop acreage. Of the 758 million acres of forest land, less than 0.3% is subjected to any pesticide treatment in any one year. Ninety-seven percent of our native grasslands have never had a pesticide applied to them. Of the total land area of the United States, about 75% has never had any pesticide applied to it (24).

Although pesticides are alleged to have had detrimental effects on wildlife, the fact is that in recent years the population of deer, bear, ante-lope, elk, moose, and other big game has been at one of the highest levels

Table I. Organic Pesticide Chemicals in General Use

Classification	Approximate No. in Use
Insecticides	95
Miticides	17
Nematocides	12
Rodenticides	9
Fungicides	68
Herbicides	86
Miscellaneous	8
(Repellants, Fish Toxicants, Etc.)	
	295

recorded in the past two decades, according to U.S. Forest Service estimates (24).

Of 84 species of wild birds studied in 1960 by the National Audubon Society in conjunction with the United States Fish and Wildlife Service,

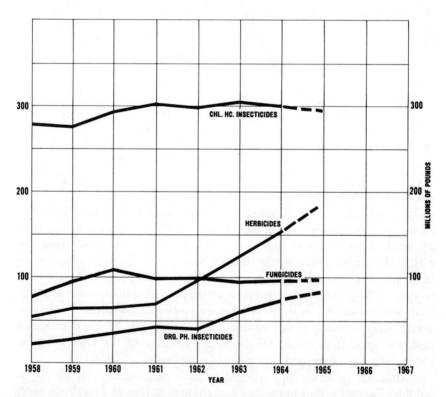

Figure 2.   Organic pesticide chemicals sold annually in the U.S. Values in millions of pounds of technical products.

71 were either increasing in number or remained constant. Frequently, pesticides have been alleged to be responsible for the deaths of large numbers of bald eagles, whooping cranes, and ospreys. Information released by knowledgeable authorities in the latter part of 1965 shows that by far the greatest toll of eagles is from hunters, while the osprey has been driven from its former nesting areas by invasions of gulls. The whooping cranes, which have been poised on the edge of extinction for more than 30 years, are actually increasing. In 1938 at their low point there were only 14 known wild whooping cranes in North America. In 1965 the Interior Department announced a record 44 whooping cranes in the Arkansas National Wildlife Refuge on the Gulf Coast of Texas, the wintering home of these cranes (*19*). The significance of this increase is immediately apparent since it occurred during the period of intensive growth of the pesticide industry.

Table II. Insecticide Usage by U.S. Farmers in Typical Year

Millions of Pounds Applied	Crops and Possessions Protected
6.2	Vegetable crops
15.8	Fruit and nut crops
32.4	Grain Crops
90.0	Cotton
10.3	Hay, soybeans, seed and sugar crops, etc.
2.1	Livestock
7.8	Farm buildings and structures
164.6	

Chlorinated Hydrocarbon Insecticides

The chlorinated hydrocarbon insecticides, because of their low cost and broad spectrum, have found a unique place in the control of insect pests. However, the aggregate domestic uses for which these compounds are eligible on the basis of their performance, toxicology, and cost characteristics are apparently fully developed. Figure 3 illustrates the trend of chlorinated hydrocarbon usage in the United States over the last few years (*23*). The tendencies for growth are being overcome by obsolescence and by attrition owing to new products which are better, cheaper, or less toxic. It is interesting to superimpose Figure 3 onto Figure 1. The result is shown in Figure 4. This vividly demonstrates not only the decreasing share of the market held by the chlorinated insecticides, but its rate of growth compared to that for the total pesticide market.

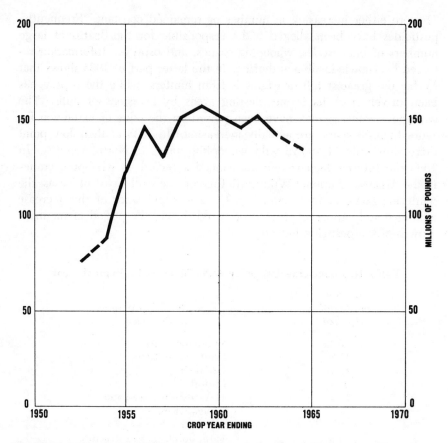

Figure 3. Trend of chlorinated hydrocarbon insecticide usage in the U.S. Values in millions of pounds of technical products—DDT, BHC, lindane, aldrin, chlordan, dieldrin, endrin, heptachlor, toxaphene.

There are essentially three classes of chlorinated hydrocarbon insecticides, as shown in Table III. With the present methodology, occasional traces of some of these compounds have been found in unexpected places. As a result, the agricultural application of this group of compounds has been cited as being responsible for substantial contamination of our environment.

Beginning with World War II, the armed forces have carried chlorinated hydrocarbon insecticides wherever they have gone for personnel protection, premise treatment, and area control (9). Many of these compounds have been manufactured in several countries and used for disease-vector control on the land, in the home, in water resources, and directly on people by a number of international agencies, as well as by individual nations.

In the United States chlorinated hydrocarbons have been used in a number of large scale programs, such as the Dutch elm disease program, fire-ant control program, gypsy moth control program, and many others. Few, if any, of these projects have dealt directly with farm crop insect problems. Yet, practically all the complaints about environmental contamination have been attributed to agricultural usage, and it has been recommended that the chlorinated hydrocarbons be "phased out" as a means of solving one set of problems. This recommendation is no more logical than would be a recommendation for banning cars A and B because they are involved in more accidents than other makes of autos. (This, of course, is assumed because there are more cars A and B on the road than any other make).

There is a misconception that agricultural usage of chlorinated hydrocarbon insecticides will result in their accumulation in the soil *ad infini-*

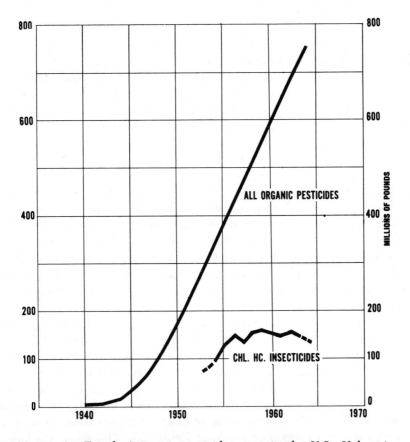

Figure 4.   Trend of organic pesticide usage in the U.S. Values in millions of pounds of technical products.

Table III. Classes of Chlorinated Hydrocarbon Insecticides

Class I.   Oxygenated Compounds

Chlorobenzilate	Methoxychlor
Dicofol	Neotran
Dieldrin	Ovex
Endosulfan	Sulfenone
Endrin	Tetradifon
Kepone	

Class II.   Benzenoid, Nonoxygenated Compounds

BHC	Perthane
Chlorbenside	TDE
DDT	Zectran
Lindane	

Class III.   Nonoxygenated, Nonbenzenoid Compounds

Aldrin	Mirex
Chlordan	Strobane
Heptachlor	Toxaphene

tum, and that the soil provides an insecticide reservoir for water contamination. However, available data indicate that water causes a deactivation of the soil particles which enhances the vaporization rate. Once this is accomplished by irrigation or rainfall, a major part of the insecticide is lost to the atmosphere by this volatilization process and is further degraded by ultraviolet light when exposed to the atmosphere (20).

Under normal agricultural practices aldrin and dieldrin, for example, are not transported appreciably by water within the soil. They tend to move upward in the soil and are located in the upper 2-inch layer even after having been worked into soils to a depth of 5 inches. They are degraded by microbiological activities, chemical degradation, and ultraviolet light, and are volatilized at the soil-air interface when displaced by water (3). Cultivation reduces the residue level, but the insecticides do not move appreciably into contiguous waters largely because of their insolubility and their sorption onto soil particles (10,14). Thus, under normal agricultural practices, these insecticides do not accumulate in the soil *ad infinitum.*

Another common misconception about the fate of chlorinated hydrocarbon insecticides in water is that they remain there forever. Like the soil, aquatic environments are dynamic systems. Residues of chlorinated hydrocarbons dissipate from aquatic environments by codistillation phenomena, metabolism, decomposition, and absorption on surfaces where they are subject to like dissipation forces. Table IV shows the loss of various insecticides by codistillation 20 hours after they were introduced into a jar of water containing mosquito larvae (2). This work was based on still systems. Recent work by investigators at Washington University in St. Louis shows that aldrin and dieldrin are nearly quantitatively removed from water by aeration under laboratory conditions in 1 to 2 hours. The initial concentrations were near saturation (20 p.p.b. of aldrin and 210 p.p.b. of dieldrin) (6).

Even endrin, which received much notoriety during 1964 in connection with the Mississippi River fish kill, is only a temporary resident in the aquatic environment. A study was conducted by the Fish and Wildlife Service on a pond in Colorado that had been accidentally sprayed with endrin. The water, which originally contained 40 p.p.b. of endrin, was entirely free of endrin within a month. The mud was free of endrin within 3 months, the vegetation within 2 months, and the fish within 4 months (4).

Table IV. Loss of Insecticides from Water by Codistillation

Insecticide	Original Concn., p.p.m.	% Codistilled, 20 Hours at 26.5°C.
Aldrin	0.024	93
Dieldrin	0.024	55
Heptachlor	0.21	91
Heptachlor epoxide	0.25	42
p,p'-DDT	0.0056	30
γ-Chlordan	0.20	70
Lindane	0.023	30

It is well known that the chlorinated hydrocarbon insecticides accumulate in the fatty tissues of the animal body and that their propensity for storage varies from compound to compound. There is ample evidence to show that most, and probably all, of the chlorinated hydrocarbon insecticides, when fed regularly at any given concentration in the diet, will reach an equilibrium in the fat. In fact, there is increasing evidence that the animal body will adapt to the toxicant and gradually metabolize the chemical at a faster rate. Figure 5 illustrates this point. Dieldrin fed to rats at a given level in their diets will show a rapid rate of accumulation in the fat for a few weeks and then will decline almost as rapidly until it reaches equilibrium (22).

The same thing apparently occurs in birds that are fed dieldrin for long periods, as illustrated in Figure 6. Eggs laid by chickens that were fed 1 p.p.m. of dieldrin for nearly 2 years show a tendency to accumulate dieldrin in the yolk for several months. Then the hen begins to metabolize the dieldrin at a faster rate, and the dieldrin content in the eggs rapidly declines. There was no significant difference in viability or hatchability of eggs laid by the chickens in these trials as compared with the controls at any time during the 700-day feeding trials. The young chicks were reared for 12 weeks after hatching and showed no adverse effects during the entire period (5).

These findings are highly significant. The fact that domestic usage of the chlorinated hydrocarbon insecticides has reached a peak and is on the decline can only mean that the maximum amounts of this class of pesticide chemicals in the environment have already been reached and can only decline in the future. It stands to reason, therefore, that the residue levels of these compounds have reached a peak in the fatty tissues of humans, wildlife, and domestic animals that have had access to residues of these pesticide chemicals in the environment and are probably declining. From the standpoint of public health, there is not one shred of evidence that the traces of these compounds in the body fat have any detrimental effect. Of course, it cannot be stated absolutely that some effect will not be discovered in the future. However, by the same token, it cannot be stated absolutely that this effect will not be beneficial!

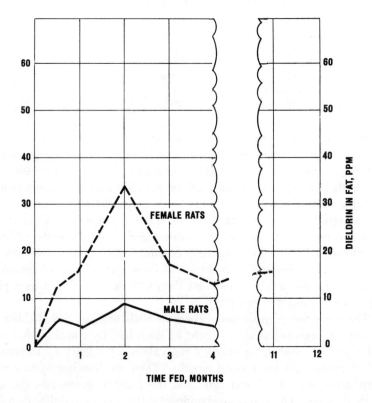

Figure 5.   Dieldrin in fat of rats fed 5 p.p.m. dieldrin in daily diets

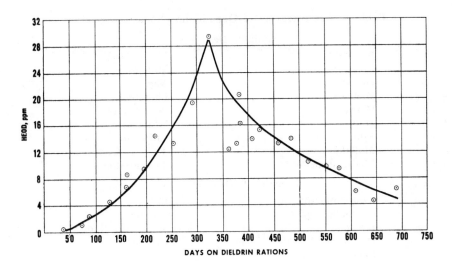

Figure 6.   Residues (HEOD) in eggs (yolk) of a chicken fed 1 p.p.m.
dieldrin for 700 days

Organophosphorus Insecticides

The organophosphorus insecticides are all structurally related and undergo similar reactions. The chemical classification of the most widely used compounds of this type is given in Table V. These compounds can also be differentiated on the basis of whether they are largely effective *per se* or undergo oxidative conversions in plants or animals. All are inhibitors of the enzyme, cholinesterase. Their potency depends not only upon their intrinsic enzyme affinity but also on anticholinesterase properties acquired through in vivo metabolism.

There seems to be no limit to the number of toxic organophosphorus compounds that can be synthesized and that exhibit insecticidal activity. While many compounds of this type have been marketed, only about 20 of them comprise the bulk of the total tonnage. Parathion, methyl parathion, and malathion are perhaps the best known and most widely used of this class of insecticides. The relatively low cost of the first two, combined with their good performance against a broad spectrum of insects, probably accounts for their continuing popularity. The low order of toxicity of malathion to mammals has made it acceptable under many conditions where other, perhaps more insecticidally active, insecticides are restricted.

Some of the highly toxic insecticides of this type are used on many vegetable and fruit crops close to harvest because of their high degree of volatility; examples are tepp and mevinphos. Other insecticides of this

Table V. Classification of Organophosphorus Insecticides

Aliphatic Derivatives

Butonate	Mevinphos
Demeton	Mipefox
Dichlorvos	Naled
Dimefox	Phorate
Dimethoate	Phosphamidon
Dithiodemeton	Schradan
Ethion	Sulfotepp
Malathion	Tepp
Methyl demeton	Trichlorofon

Aromatic (Cyclic) Derivatives

Azinphosmethyl	EPN
Carbophenothion	Fenthion
Diazinon	Methyl parathion
Dicapthon	Parathion
Endothion	Ronnel

type which are much less toxic are used primarily to control insects that attack livestock; examples are ronnel, dichlorvos, coumaphos, Ciodrin, and trichlorfon. Still another group of these compounds is being developed for use in the soil to control soil-borne insects. Typical soil insecticides of this type are parathion, diazinon, and phorate.

These insecticides range from completely water-miscible compounds to essentially insoluble ones, as indicated in Table VI. Most highly water-soluble insecticides are systemic, that is, they are absorbed into the tissues of the growing crop, either through the leaves or through the roots. But some water-miscible compounds are so unstable that their toxicity is destroyed before systemic activity can be observed (12, 18). Tepp, for example, has a half life in water of only 8 hours. While many other compounds in this class have only limited solubility in water, they are still effective systemics. Examples are demeton, methyl demeton, and phorate.

Table VI. Water Solubilities of Some Organophosphorus Insecticides

	p.p.m.		p.p.m.
Carbophenothion	2	Phorate	85
Parathion	24	Malathion	145
Azinphosmethyl	33	Dichlorvos	1000
Diazinon	40	Dimethoate	7000
Methyl Parathion	50	Mevinphos	∞

Oxidation increases both the water solubility and the anticholinesterase activity. Appreciable water solubility is necessary if a compound is to be readily translocated. Oxidation therefore converts several insecticides in this class into systemic ones. These insecticides can be divided into those which are systemic in themselves and those which are systemic only after oxidation. The organophosphorus insecticides are also subject to hydrolysis, and in many cases this is the main reaction. Those compounds in this class which contain methylamino groups appear to undergo demethylation more readily than either hydrolysis or oxidation, at least under some conditions. The new crotonamide, Bidrin insecticide, is an example. The dimethylamino group (—NMe₂) metabolizes in both plants and animals to the methylamino group (—NHMe) before further degradation takes place (*16*). However, this breakdown apparently does not occur in soil. These reactions are illustrated in Figure 7.

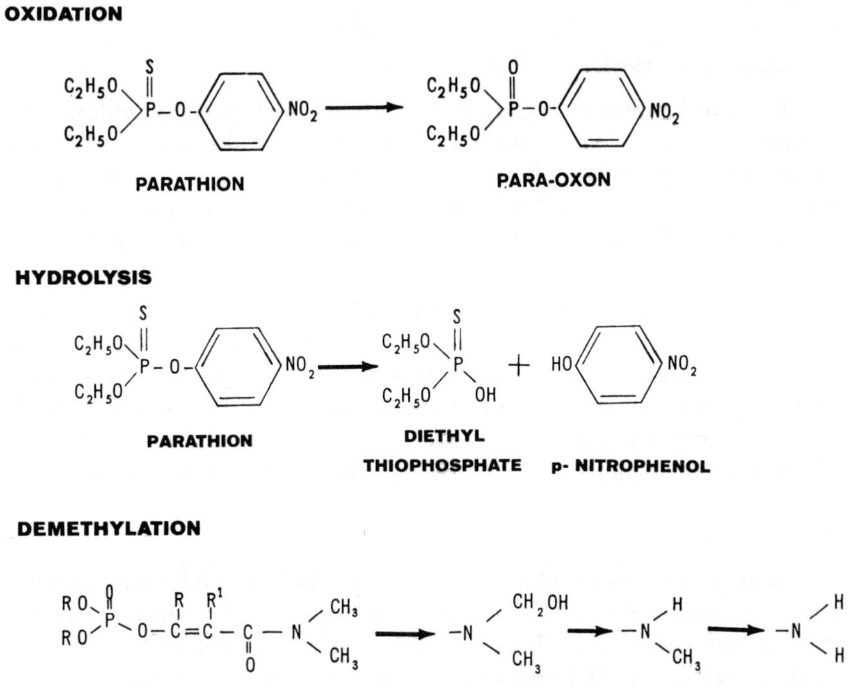

OXIDATION

HYDROLYSIS

DEMETHYLATION

Figure 7.   Typical reactions of organophosphorus insecticides

Plant enzymes do not catalyze the hydrolysis of organophosphorus compounds greatly, but they do catalyze their oxidation. Consequently, the oxidation products accumulate more in plants than in animals, but they appear to be generally the same as those produced by animals.

   Soil microorganisms metabolize the organophosphorus compounds fairly rapidly. In general, the drier the soil is, the slower the rate of degradation. Also, the higher the pH of the soil, the faster the rate of hydrolysis. Thus, under practical field conditions it is unlikely that most of these compounds will remain for any great length of time in soil or water supplies. There are, of course, variations in the group. Parathion has been found in trace amounts in subterranean water. Also, as mentioned, a few members of this class of compounds are sufficiently stable to be used as effective soil insecticides. These have been found useful for controlling certain soil insects that have become resistant to the chlorinated hydrocarbons.

Most of the organophosphorus insecticides are toxic to fish, but do not accumulate in animal tissues. There are, of course, a few exceptions like Guthion, which has been found in fish several weeks after being exposed in laboratory experiments to sub-lethal concentrations in water (25).

Carbamate Insecticides

The development of resistance by certain insect species to chlorinated hydrocarbon insecticides aroused research into alternative chemical classes of compounds. This research led to the development of the carbamates as useful broad-spectrum insecticides. The best known of this class is carbaryl (Sevin), which has emerged as one of the most extensively used insecticides.

The carbamates, like the organophosphorus insecticides, are cholinesterase inhibitors. However, the reaction is rapidly reversible. Carbaryl has a half life in the soil of about 8 days and is decomposed by ultraviolet light. The carbamates metabolize rapidly in animals and show little, if any, propensity for storage in animal tissues. Additional properties and reactions of carbamates are discussed in the section on fungicides.

Nematocides

Most of the nematocides marketed are halogenated hydrocarbons. They are either saturated organic halides, such as methyl bromide, ethylene dibromide, and dibromochloropropane, or unsaturated organic halides, such as dichloropropene and dibromobutene. Among the nematocides, a few exceptions to this class of compounds are chloropicrin, a thiocarbamate (Vapam), two organophosphates (V-C 13 and Zinophos), and a thiadiazine (Mylone).

These compounds, in general, have relatively high vapor pressures and are lost from the soil within a few hours or days after application. Some of them are used principally on seed beds and in greenhouses. Because of their properties and/or limited use, there is little chance that they will become significant contaminants of the environment.

Fungicides

The organic compounds used as fungicides consist principally of dithiocarbamates, dicarboximides, chlorinated phenols, and several organic mercurials. Recent entries into the fungicide field include derivatives of guanidine, triazine, and anthraquinone. The dithiocarbamates fall into two distinct classes, typified by sodium dimethyl dithiocarbamate and disodium ethylenebisdithiocarbamate (Nabam), as illustrated in Figure 8. While these compounds possess outstanding toxicity to fungi, they are water-soluble and relatively unstable; it is believed that they would have fallen by the wayside if it had not been for the discovery of the stabilizing influence of zinc sulfate and lime. This finding led to the stable, insoluble dithiocarbamate, metal-complex fungicides: ferbam, maneb, ziram, zineb, and thiram. These compounds, in general, break down under acid conditions to give dimethylamine and carbon disulfide.

SODIUM DIMETHYL
DITHIOCARBAMATE

DISODIUM ETHYLENEBIS-
DITHIOCARBAMATE
(NABAM)

Figure 8.   *Basic structures typical of the dithiocarbamate
fungicides*

However, there are indications that this breakdown must be considered as an equilibrium capable of reversal under the appropriate biological conditions. As the pH increases, the stability increases substantially. There is also some evidence that these compounds undergo replacement of the metal ion by copper, with the formation of highly stable copper complexes which conceivably could remain in the environment for long periods.

A number of dicarboximide compounds are also of commercial importance. Captan and folpet probably comprise the largest uses of this class. In general, these compounds are subject to breakdown by soil microorganisms and do not appear likely to be retained in the environment to any significant degree.

A number of chlorinated phenols are also important as fungicides. These include pentachlorophenol, tetrachlorophenol, and trichlorophenol. In addition, organic mercurials have been in use for years. A few compounds of this class are shown in Figure 9. Some of these compounds are water-soluble and are used as slimicides in paper mills; most are insoluble and are used to control soil-borne diseases. Some also have comparatively high vapor pressures and readily sublime. In general, the mercurials are toxic to man and animals (*11,17*).

The discovery of fungicidal activity in guanidine, triazine, and anthraquinone derivatives is opening new areas of fungicide research, and a few pesticides of these types are being developed commercially.

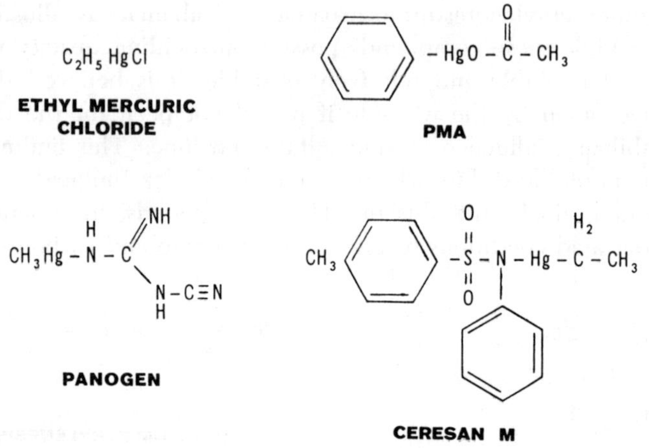

Figure 9.   Structures of some organic mercurial fungicides

Herbicides

Herbicides can be classed into two categories, selective and nonselective. With many herbicides, however, there are only quantitative differences between the two categories. In other words, many selective herbicides when used in higher dosages become nonselective.

With the array of molecular configurations, possible formulation procedures, physiological requirements, and specific responses found among the organic herbicides, the most useful scheme of classification to the chemist is one that will place herbicides in groups having similar chemical properties. One such classification is shown in Table VII.

Table VII. Chemical Classification of Herbicides

Substituted phenols
Chlorophenoxy compounds
Substituted acetic and propionic acids
Amides and thioamides
Substituted ureas
Carbamates and dithiocarbamates
Symmetrical triazines
Benzoic acid derivatives
Miscellaneous herbicides

For use on croplands, the ideal soil-borne herbicide is selective against the weeds, is tolerated by the crop, and at practical dosages should break down in the soil within one season so as not to leave a toxic residue for a subsequent crop. For use as a soil sterilant, a compound should resist leaching and breakdown so as to remain active in the soil for many years.

The substituted phenols are practically insoluble in water; however, being phenols, they readily form salts with organic and inorganic bases, most of which are water-soluble. Since they must utilize water as a carrier in order to be selective and yet penetrate the leaf cuticle, they all respond to activation by buffering on the acid side of neutrality. Ammonium sulfate is the common compound used to bring about this activation. In this water-soluble form they are subject to leaching and runoff from the soil. Some, but not all, of the chlorophenols are oxidized by the soil microflora. For example, 2,6-dichlorophenol is readily destroyed while the 2,3-, 3,4-, and 3,5-dichlorophenols persist for long periods (15).

The chlorophenoxy groups of herbicides includes 2,4-D, 2,4,5-T, and many other chemically related compounds. The chlorophenoxy compounds are primarily selective herbicides and comprise approximately half the total domestic herbicide market. Although 2,4-D is essentially insoluble in water, its esters are slightly water-soluble, and salts of 2,4-D are completely water-soluble. Several of these compounds are used not only for application to plant foliage and soil but also as aquatic herbicides (8). Each year hundreds of tons of these compounds are applied directly to lakes, rivers, and other surface waters for weed control. Approximately 100,000 pounds of 2,4-D granules are applied annually to the lakes in the TVA system alone (7). The herbicide 2,4-D may persist for several months in lake water whereas the esters of 2,4-D are usually broken down in a few days (1). When applied to watershed areas, the phenoxy herbicides are not likely to constitute a major water pollution hazard since the rate of bacterial degradation is sufficiently rapid to destroy them within a few days (26). However, a few of these compounds can remain in the environment for a year or more.

Dalapon is a member of the propionic acid group. Compounds in this class are water-soluble and relatively stable. They are subject to hydrolysis, but the rate is slow at lower temperatures. Also, they are sorbed to an appreciable extent on soils having high organic content, and a few of them remain active for several seasons.

The amides and thioamides have a low order of solubility and a somewhat greater vapor pressure than most other herbicides. They do not appear to be strongly fixed to soils having high organic matter and generally break down within a year to innocuous compounds.

Dichloral urea (DCU) is typical of the substituted ureas. These compounds vary in water solubility from about 5 to about 3000 p.p.m. Consequently, some of them are readily leached into the soil. They are stable to oxidation and hydrolysis and are relatively persistent. They are slowly broken down by soil microorganisms and are likely to remain active in the soil for several seasons.

The carbamate and thiocarbamate radicals have toxicity for weeds, fungi, and insects. In general, they are slightly soluble in water and somewhat more volatile than most other herbicides.

The symmetrical triazines, such as simazine, have a wide range of properties and are being used to cover a wide range of crops. They vary in water solubility from about 5 to 3500 p.p.m. The triazines are stable to aqueous alkali and dilute acids, but they are broken down gradually by catalysts in the soil and by microorganisms. They are not strongly fixed in soils, and some of them are relatively persistent, particularly in arid areas (8, 21).

The benzoic acid derivatives, such as 2,3,6-trichlorobenzoic acid, behave like the chlorophenoxy compounds. In general, they are slightly soluble in water but tend to leach readily into the soil. In areas of light rainfall some of these compounds may persist for five or more seasons; others are lost in one season. There is evidence that some of the loss may be caused by volatilization.

In general, most of the herbicides are only moderately to slightly toxic to fish, having median tolerance limits (Tlm) generally above 1 p.p.m. A few, however, exhibit Tlm's well below 1 p.p.m. When fed to dairy and meat animals at dietary concentrations of several parts per million, the herbicides, in general, are not excreted in milk and do not accumulate in tissues. While this seems to be the case for the herbicide *per se,* the metabolites of many of the herbicides have not been fully investigated.

Toxic Hazards of Pesticides in Environment

Because of the prowess of the analytical chemist, it is now possible to find residues of the chlorinated hydrocarbon insecticides in the environment at concentrations of a few parts per trillion. He is not so adept at finding nanogram quantities of some of the other classes of compounds; for many pesticides, the metabolites are not identified, so he doesn't know what to look for. There is little question, however, that many of the compounds that now escape detection are present in the environment, and it is only a matter of time until the analytical chemist finds them.

The real question, of course, is: What is the significance of traces of these compounds in the environment? To answer this, we must con-

Table VIII. Toxicity of Chlorinated Hydrocarbon Insecticides (*13*)

[Dietary levels (p.p.m.) producing minimal or no effect
after continuous feeding for 90 days to 2 years]

Cyclodiene compounds	*Rats*	*Dogs*
Aldrin	0.5	1
Chlordan	25	N.A.[a]
Dieldrin	0.5	1
Endosulfan	30	30
Heptachlor	0.5	4
(Heptachlor epoxide)	0.5	0.5
DDT-related compounds		
DDT	5	400
Chlorbenside [b]	20	1000
Chlorobenzilate [b]	<50	2564
DDD	10	N.A.[a]
Methoxychlor	100	4000
Kelthane [b]	20-100	300
Perthane	500	100
Miscellaneous compounds		
BHC	10	N.A.[a]
Lindane	50	> 15
Ovex [b]	25	200
Strobane	50	400
Sulfenone [b]	100	400
Tetradifon [b]	300	500
Toxaphene	10	400

[a] Data not available.
[b] Miticide.

sider the toxic properties of these pesticides from ingestion over long periods of time. Dr. Arnold Lehman of the Food and Drug Administration (USDHEW) recently published some chronic toxicity data for laboratory animals fed pesticides for long periods of time (*13*). Table VIII shows the maximum dietary levels of some chlorinated hydrocarbon insecticides that have been fed to laboratory test animals for periods up to 2 years without causing any significant effect on the animals or their functional organs.

Table IX shows the dietary levels of some of the organophosphorus insecticides that cause no effect on continued ingestion. These compounds, in general, show no-effect levels of the same order of magnitude as the chlorinated hydrocarbons. Similar data for some of the fungicides (Table X) indicate that the fungicides *per se* generally have a low order of toxicity. Similar toxicity data are shown in Table XI for a number of the herbicides.

Table IX. Toxicity of Some Organophosphorus Insecticides (13)

[Dietary levels (p.p.m.) producing minimal or no effect
after continuous feeding for 90 days to 2 years]

	Rats	Dogs
Carbophenothion	5	0.8
Demeton	1	1
Diazinon	1	0.75
Guthion	5	5
Dioxathion	4	1
EPN	5–25	50
Ethion	3	1
Malathion	100–1000	100
Phosdrin	0.8	1
Parathion	1	1

Table X. Toxicity of Some Miscellaneous Fungicides (13)

[Dietary levels (p.p.m.) producing minimal or no effect
after continuous feeding for 90 days to 2 years]

	Rats	Dogs
Captan	1000	4000
Dichlone (Phygon)	1580	500
Dyrene	5000	> 5000
Dodine (Cyprex)	200	> 50
Folpet (Phaltan)	3,200	10,000
Ferbam	250	200
Maneb	25	80
Thiram	100	200
Zineb	500	2000
Ziram	250	200

Table XI. Toxicity of Some Herbicides (13)

[Dietary levels (p.p.m.) producing minimal or no effect
after continuous feeding for 90 days to 2 years]

	Rats	Dogs
Chloro-IPC	2000	2000
Dalapon	300	2000
Diuron	50–500	N.A.[a]
Fenuron	500	N.A.[a]
Monuron	250	1000
2,4-D	300	400
Simazine	100	N.A.[a]
Trifluralin	2000	1000

[a] Data not available.

These values represent dietary levels that cause minimal or no effects on animals ingesting them every day for long periods of time. Substantially higher concentrations of pesticides in the diet may show effects which are not considered harmful on test animals. They are changes which can be detected while the animal is on the pesticide rations. These are apparently adaptive changes, since they disappear when the animals are taken off the pesticide rations.

No one will dispute the axiom that we must know as much about the risks in the use of pesticides as we know about the benefits. However, the risks must be determined from competent research and judged by knowledgeable scientists, not assumed by emotional authors and judged by ambitious politicians. As monitoring of the environment progresses, it must be expected that traces of pesticides will frequently be found wherever they are sought, provided the analytical tool is sufficiently sensitive. It is important that arbitrary, precipitous action be avoided on the basis of a positive finding, which will result in the loss of some of these valuable aids to agriculture. As each day passes, it must be recognized that one more increment of use experience has been acquired which can serve as a basis for judging the hazards to the public health of pesticide contaminants in the environment.

Literature Cited

(1) Aly, O. M., Fairst, S. D., *J. Agr. Food Chem.* **12**, 541 (1964).
(2) Bowman, M. C., Acree, F., Jr., Lofgren, C. S., Beroza, M., *Science* **146** (3650), 1480–1 (1964).
(3) Bowman, M. C., Schecter, M. S., Carter, R. L., *J. Agr. Food Chem.* **13**, 360 (1965)
(4) Bridges, W. R., *Trans. Am. Fish Soc.* **90** (3), 332–4 (1961).
(5) Brown, V. K., Richardson, A., Robinson, J., Stevenson, D. E., Shell Research, Ltd., Tunstall Laboratory, Sittingbourne, Kent, in press.
(6) Buescher, C. A., Jr., Bell, M.C., Berry, R. K., *J. Water Pollution Control Federation* **36** (8), 1005–14 (1964).
(7) Christopher, G. S., Tennessee Valley Authority, Wilson Dam, Ala., private communication, 1965.
(8) Crafts, A. S., "Chemistry and Mode of Action of Herbicides," Interscience New York, 1961.
(9) Cushing, E. C., "History of Entomology in World War II," Smithsonian Institute, Washington, D.C., 1957.
(10) Decker, G. C., Bruce, W. N., Bigger, J. H., "Accumulation and Dissipation of Residues Resulting from the Use of Aldrin in Soils," 17th Illinois Custom Spray Operation Training School, Urbana, Ill., p. 77–84, January, 1965.
(11) Frear, D. E. H., "Chemistry of the Pesticides," 3rd ed., Van Nostrand, New York, 1955.
(12) Heath, D. F., "Organophosphorus Poisons," Pergamon Press, New York, 1961.
(13) Lehman, A. J., "Toxicity of Pesticides," Association of Food and Drug Officials of the U.S., 1965.
(14) Lichtenstein, E. P., Schaltz, K. R., *J. Agr. Food Chem.* **13**, 57 (1965).

(15) MacRae, I. C., Alexander, M., *Ibid.*, **13**, 72 (1965).
(16) Menzer, R. E., Casida, J. E., *Ibid.*, **13**, 102 (1965).
(17) Metcalf, R. L., *Advan. Pest Control Res.* **3**, (1960).
(18) Metcalf, R. L., "Organic Insecticides," Interscience, New York, 1955.
(19) *New York Times* (July 25 and Nov. 23, 1965).
(20) Roburn, J., *Chem. Ind.* (London) **1963** 1555.
(21) Sheets, T. J., Crafts, A. S., Drever, H. R., *J. Agr. Food Chem* **10**, 458 (1962).
(22) Stanford Research Institute, "Effects of Pesticides on Animals and Human Beings," Tech. Rep. **6** (September 1963).
(23) U. S. Department of Agriculture, Agriculture Stabilization and Conservation Service, "The Pesticide Situation for 1961–1962" (also, 1962–1963, 1963–1964, 1964–1965).
(24) U. S. Department of Agriculture, Office of Information, Synthetic Organic Chemicals, "The War that Never Ends" (May 1965).
(25) U. S. Department of Interior, F.&W.S., Bur. Sport Fisheries and Wildlife, Cir. **178** (1963).
(26) Winston, A. W., Ritty, P. M., *Proc. N. E. Weed Control Conf.* **15**, 396 (Jan. 4–6, 1961).

RECEIVED December 20, 1965.

Sorption and Leaching of 4-Amino-3,5,6-trichloropicolinic Acid in Soils

JOHN W. HAMAKER, CLEVE A. I. GORING and
CHARLES R. YOUNGSON

Bioproducts Research Laboratory, The Dow Chemical Co.,
Walnut Creek, Calif.

*The greatest sorption of 4-amino-3,5,6-trichloropicolinic acid,
2,4-D, and 2,4,5-T was observed for soils containing a high
percentage of organic matter and for red and acidic soils.
Leaching from columns of these soils confirmed this order
of sorption. Maximum sorption was attained rapidly by red
soils but slowly by highly organic soils. Exhaustive washing
with hot water or treatment with sodium hydroxide quantitatively removed sorbed 4-amino-3,5,6-trichloropicolinic
acid from all but muck soils. The data suggest that sorption
of 4-amino-3,5,6-trichloropicolinic acid is primarily caused
by organic matter and hydrated metal oxides, with clays
probably playing a minor role. Sorption of unionized
4-amino-3,5,6-trichloropicolinic acid and its anion was
involved.*

A new, potent, persistent plant growth regulator and herbicide that
should eventually have considerable agronomic value throughout
the world is 4-amino-3,5,6-trichloropicolinic acid (4,5,6). Its biological
activity is associated largely with its uptake from soils by plants. Therefore, it is important to determine and understand its interactions with
soils and soil components and the effects of such interactions on the avail-
ability and leaching of the material in soils. Preliminary studies of this
nature are described in this report.

Sorption was determined using neutral (pH 7), 0.25 to 1.0 p.p.m.
stock solutions of C^{14}, carboxy-labeled herbicides, and Cl^{36} (lithium

salt). In neutral stock solutions, all of the herbicides used are present as salts.

Experimental Method of Measuring Sorption

A quantity of 2 ml. of a stock solution of the compound was added to 0.5 gram of soil or other material, and this mixture was allowed to equilibrate at 25°C. in a constant temperature water bath with intermittent shaking. The mixture was then centrifuged for 20 minutes, and an 0.25-ml. aliquot was evaporated on lens paper in a planchet for counting. The sorption of 4-amino-3,5,6-trichloropicolinic acid, 2,4-D, 2,4,5-T, and Cl⁻ was determined on a number of soils using this technique, and the results are shown in Table I.

Table I. Sorption of Cl⁻, 2,4-D, 2,4,5-T, and 4-Amino-3,5,6-trichloropicolinic Acid by Various Soils

| | | % Sorbed in 1 Hour | | |
| | | | | |
Soil	% Organic Matter	1 p.p.m. Cl⁻	0.94 p.p.m. 2,4-D	1.34 p.p.m. 2,4,5-T	0.4 p.p.m. 4-Amino-3,5,6-trichloropicolinic acid
4	0.2	1	3	Nil	Nil
3	0.3	22	10	23	17
7	0.4	2	1	3	1
D_1	1.0	7	5	6	3
N_1	2.7	Nil	9	5	8
B_2	4.1	6	13	20	12
B_1	10.7	Nil	45	47	35
Q_2	25.0	8	45	57	30
Q_1	32.2	2	43	52	39
Q_3	44.3	..	..	..	68

Several relationships are indicated by Table I:

4-amino-3,5,6-trichloropicolinic acid shows the same pattern of sorption as the herbicides, 2,4-D and 2,4,5-T.

With the exception of soil 3, the sorption of all three herbicidal materials is well correlated to the organic matter content of these soils.

Soil 3 is also exceptional in its capacity to sorb chloride ion.

The similarity of the three herbicides might be anticipated from the fact that they all behave as carboxylic acids. In spite of the presence of an amino group in its structure, 4-amino-3,5,6-trichloropicolinic acid does not show amphoteric behavior. In aqueous solution, it titrates as a monobasic acid with a pK_A of 4.1. The positive correlation of organic matter with sorption is consistent with the results of Sheets, Crafts, and Drever (7). They reported that organic matter was the best single predictor of sorption among the four factors: organic matter, total clay, soil pH, and cation exchange capacity.

Table II. Composition of Soils Used for Sorption Studies

Soil	pH [a]	% Clay [b]	% Silt [b]	% Sand [b]	% Organic Matter [c]
4	8.1	34	45	21	0.2
3	5.9	16	36	48	0.3
7	8.2	3	10	87	0.4
D_1	6.0	12	46	42	1.0
N_1	6.8	48	39	13	2.7
B_2	7.2	7	35	58	4.1
B_1	5.3	22	52	26	10.7
Q_2	5.5	16	48	36	25.0
Q_1	5.9	23	38	39	32.2
Q_3	5.1	6	26	68	44.3

[a] pH. Determined on saturated paste (2), p. 922.
[b] Mechanical analysis. Determined by hydrometer method (2), p. 562.
[c] Organic matter. Determined by wet ash method (2), p. 1374.

The composition and pH of these soils were determined by standard methods (3), and the results are presented in Table II. Comparing Tables I and II shows that there is no evident relationship between sorption and the proportions of sand, silt, and clay. However, soils showing high sorption for the three herbicidal materials are also acidic—e.g., soils 3 and B_1 through Q_3. This is caused partly by a tendency of highly organic soils to be acidic. A positive correlation between sorption and low pH would be expected from the number of instances reported in the review on sorption of organic pesticides by Bailey and White (2).

Influence of pH on Sorption

To test the effect of pH on sorption further, soils and soil components were adjusted to other than their natural pH values. Unless otherwise noted, 4.0 ml. of solution containing 4-amino-3,5,6-trichloropicolinate were added to 1.0 gram of solid—i.e., soil, clay, etc.—and the pH was adjusted with HNO_3 or NaOH to the desired value. The mixture was allowed to stand 1 hour with frequent stirring and readjustments of the pH, after which the supernatant was centrifuged for 20 minutes and an aliquot mounted for counting. The results of such measurements on four different soils for 4-amino-3,5,6-trichloropicolinic acid are shown in Figure 1. Also indicated on the figure is the percentage of the dissolved free acid as calculated for a pK_A of 4.1. It is evident that sorption of the unionized acid is correlated to the rapid increase of sorption with decreasing pH observed for all these soils. These results explain, in part, the higher sorption of 4-amino-3,5,6-trichloropicolinic acid observed in Table I on soil 3 and on the organic soils such as soil Q_1. They were acidic relative to the other soils. However, the organic soils, which soil

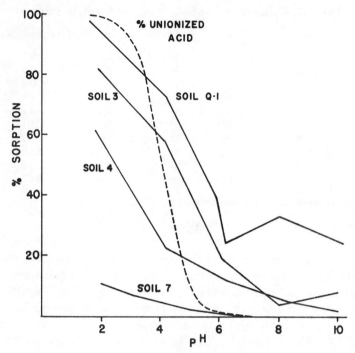

Figure 1.   Sorption of 4-amino-3,5,6-trichloropicolinic acid by soils as a function of pH

4 ml. of 1 p.p.m. solution + 1 gram of soil adjusted to pH with NaOH and HCl or HNO₃. Incubation 1 hour.

Q_1 represents, have some mechanism for sorbing the anion of 4-amino-3,5,6-trichloropicolinic acid as (to a lesser degree) do soils 3, 4, and 7.

Materials similar to possible soil components were also used to investigate the influence of pH on sorption. These results are presented in Figure 2, which shows that steer manure and Fe_2O_3 behave most similarly to soils. These data suggest a hypothesis to explain the sorption of 4-amino-3,5,6-trichloropicolinic acid and similar chemicals by soils—that organic matter and hydrated metal oxides are principally responsible, with clay minerals making a minor contribution in most cases. Thus, in the case of soil Q_1, organic matter is largely responsible while for soils 3 and 4 hydrated metal oxides are the main sorbing agent. For soil 7 not enough of either is present to cause significant sorption. It is instructive at this point to consider the nature of soil 3. This is a red, lateritic type that would be expected to contain the hydrated oxides of iron and aluminum.

Sorption of Cl⁻ by these soil components provides further evidence supporting this hypothesis. These data were determined by the same technique using Cl[36] and are presented in Figure 3. Only soil 3 showed much chloride sorption, and this is consistent with the high sorption of chloride by metallic oxides and low sorption by organic matter—i.e., manure. The sorption of Cl⁻ by a number of samples of clay minerals, kaolinite, montmorillonite, attapulgite, and illite, was determined both with and without pH variation, and none was found. Actually, a slight negative sorption was observed—a phenomenon that has been reported in the literature and attributed to increased concentration owing to preferential sorption of water from the solution. The chloride sorption observed in soils (*see* Table I) may indicate the hydrated metal oxide present. Because of the uncertain accuracy of low sorption values, no attempt is made to consider this quantitatively. Sorption is determined by a difference in solution concentration before and after treatment with soil, so that sorption of a few percent, being the difference between two relatively large numbers, is subject to large relative error.

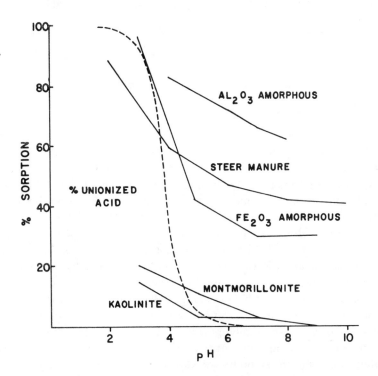

Figure 2.   Sorption of 4-amino-3,5,6-trichloropicolinic acid as a function of pH

4 ml. of 1 p.p.m. solution + 1 gram of solid adjusted to pH with NaOH and HNO₃ or HCl. Incubation 1 hour.

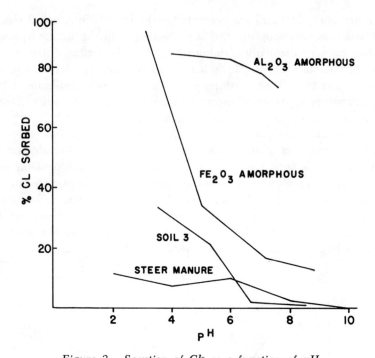

Figure 3.   Sorption of Cl⁻ as a function of pH

4 ml. of a 1 p.p.m. solution + 1 gram of solid adjusted to pH with NaOH and HCl or HNO₃. Incubation 1 hour.

Results of sorption measurements of 4-amino-3,5,6-trichloropicolinic acid by other samples of possible soil components or related materials at their natural pH values are collected in Table III. The same method was used as for the original soil measurements—i.e., Table I. The same general conclusions are indicated—namely, large sorption by organic matter and metallic oxides, especially at low pH, and low sorption on clay minerals. However, further work is needed to clarify the role of clay. The results with illite suggest that its sorption may possibly be much higher at low pH than other clay minerals. This is somewhat ambiguous since the sample showing high sorption showed also a relatively high carbon content (1.82%) compared with 0.83% carbon for the second sample. These clay mineral samples, with one exception, were natural materials, not highly purified samples, and possible impurities may be implicated in the sorption observed, at least partially. Since kaolinite and montmorillonite are clay minerals usually present in soil, in most cases clay minerals probably make only a minor contribution to the sorption of 4-amino-3,5,6-trichloropicolinic acid. The poor sorption of the 4-amino-3,5,6-trichloropicolinate anion by clay minerals and the strong sorption by hydrated metal oxides would appear to be consistent with a process of replacing OH⁻ from the metal oxide surface in more or less the same manner that chloride is sorbed. Since the clay minerals were not highly purified, the small sorption observed may have been caused by small amounts of metallic oxide impurity. The sorption of unionized acid would probably involve hydrogen bonds, which both clay and hydrated metal oxides would be expected to form. Thus, as observed, both should show increased sorption at low pH. With respect to sorption by organic matter, the anion and even the unionized acid could be subject to detergent-type adsorption—i.e., attachment to a lipid type surface through the hydrophobic end of the molecule—i.e., in opposition to the carboxylate group. Additionally, for the unionized 4-amino-3,5,6-tri-chloropicolinic acid, uptake could be increased by solution and migration into this lipid phase.

Table III. Sorption of 4-Amino-3,5,6-trichloropicolinic Acid by Possible Soil Components or Related Materials

(2.0 ml., 1.0 p.p.m.$C^{\pm 14}$-labeled chemical + 0.5 g. soil with 1-hour incubation and clarification by 20-minute centrifugation)

Type of Material	pH of Slurry	% Sorbed
Organic Amendment		
Steer manure	8.7	45
Oak leaf mold	7.3	22
Peat moss [a]	3.8	37
Hydrated Metal Oxides		
Fe_2O_3 1 [b] (amorphous)	. .	21
Fe_2O_3 2 (amorphous)	5.1	28
Fe_2O_3 3 [c] (partially crystalline)	2.9	34
Al_2O_3, crystalline [d] (gibbsite)	4.2	46
Al_2O_3, amorphous [e]	4.5	83
Clay Minerals		
Kaolinite 1	6.5	5
Kaolinite 2	4.7	9
Montmorillonite 1	8.1	14
Montmorillonite 2	6.0	Nil
Attapulgite	8.4	8
Illite 1 [f]	4.1	42
Illite 2 [f]	6.5	14
Illite purified	7.6	4

[a] 0.25 gram used because of large bulk volume.
[b] Ferric hydroxide precipitated with NH_3 and dried at 50°C.
[c] Air oxidation of moist precipitate from ferrous sulfate with NH_3. Dried at 50°C.
[d] Dialysis at 50°C. of $Al_2O_3 \cdot x \ H_2O$ suspension for 2 weeks. Freeze-dried.
[e] $0.5N$ $AlCl_3$ titrated to pH 5 with NaOH solution. Dried at 50°C.
[f] Illite 1, 1.82% carbon by combustion analysis.
Illite 2, 0.83% carbon by combustion analysis.

As a preliminary check on this latter hypothesis, an experiment was performed on extraction of 4-amino-3,5,6-trichloropicolinic acid from aqueous solution. A 0.4-p.p.m. solution of C^{-14}-labeled 4-amino-3,5,6-trichloropicolinic acid was buffered to a desired pH (formate or phosphate buffer) and extracted with an equal volume of ethyl acetate. After equilibration and separation of the phases, the pH of the aqueous phase was determined with a pH meter, and aliquots of both solutions were assayed by counting. The percentage extracted is shown in Figure 4

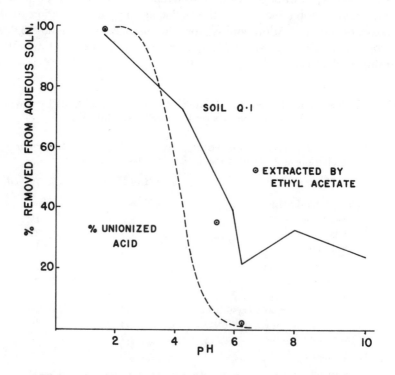

Figure 4. Extraction model for sorption of 4-amino-3,5,6-trichloropicolinic acid

Extract from 0.4 p.p.m. of 4-amino-3,5,6-trichloropicolinic acid by equal volume of ethyl acetate.

together with the sorption on soil Q_1 and the percentage of free 4-amino-3,5,6-trichloropicolinic acid in aqueous solution, both as a function of pH. Because of the shifting of the acid equilibrium, the amount extracted or sorbed is considerably larger than the equilibrium concentration of free acid in solution. The fact that a small amount apparently is not sorbed or extracted at pH 1.6 may be caused by colloidal material not removed by centrifuging or standing.

To test this hypothesis further, a partition or distribution coefficient was calculated from the sorption at pH 2 by a number of soils. The same experimental technique was used as previously described. A sorption index is calculated by the following expression:

$$\text{Sorption index} = \frac{\%\ \text{in solution}}{\%\ \text{sorbed}} \times \%\ \text{organic matter}$$

This is proportional to a partition coefficient between organic matter and solution as shown below:

$$\text{Partition coefficient} = \frac{\text{concn. in solution}}{\text{concn. in organic phase}}$$

$$= \frac{\text{concn. in solution}}{\text{concn. in soil}/\%\ \text{organic matter}}$$

$$= k \times \frac{\%\ \text{in solution}}{\%\ \text{sorbed}} \times \%\ \text{organic matter}$$

Since at pH 2 virtually all the 4-amino-3,5,6-trichloropicolinic acid will be in the free acid form, this partition coefficient—and therefore the sorption index—would be constant if extraction is the mechanism by which the free acid is absorbed. Table IV shows reasonable constancy for the sorption index over a wide range of organic contents except for the first three soils—i.e., soils 3, 4, and 7. There are at least two possible causes for failure of this relationship in these cases: other components contributing significantly to sorption, and analytical uncertainty in or-

Table IV. Sorption of 4-Amino-3,5,6-trichloropicolinic Acid by Soils at pH 2

(4 ml. 1.0 p.p.m. solution + 1 g. soil adjusted with HNO_3 and incubated 1 hour)

Soil	% Organic Matter	% in Solution	% Sorbed	Ratio [b]	Sorption Index [c]
4	0.2	38	62	0.62	0.12
3	0.3	19	81	0.23	0.070
7	0.4	90	10	9.0	3.6
D_1	1.0	51	49	1.04	1.1
N_1	2.7	23	77	0.29	0.79
B_2	4.1	11	89	0.13	0.53
B_1	10.7	5.8	94	0.062	0.66
Q_1	32.2	2	98	0.021	0.66

[a] Determined by wet ash method.
[b] $\text{Ratio} = \frac{\%\ \text{in solution}}{\%\ \text{sorbed}} = k_1 \times \frac{\text{solution concn.}}{\text{concn. in solid}}$
[c] Partition coefficient = $k_2 \times$ ratio $\times$ % organic matter.
= $k_2 \times$ sorption index.

ganic matter determination for such low values. The approximate constancy of what is here called a sorption index would follow from an extraction mechanism, but does not unequivocally determine that this mechanism was being followed. If, for example, monomolecular layer surface sorption occurred and a small proportion of the available surface were covered, we would also expect the sorption index to be constant.

This might be the case in alkaline solution where 4-amino-3,5,6-trichloropicolinic acid would be present in an anion form. Accordingly, sorption indices were also calculated for the same soils at pH 9 (Table V). In this case, there is a trend toward higher values for higher soil organic matter content, but the range of variation of the sorption index is less (27 to 1) than the range of variation of organic matter content (221 to 1). Since the index is proportional to concentration in solution/concentration in solid, the increase could be attributed to a relatively smaller contribution of sorption by materials other than organic matter at higher organic matter levels. It could also reflect a lower surface-weight ratio for organic matter owing to its occurrence in more concentrated form. It would be interesting to estimate the total surface of these components from sorption isotherm measurements.

Table V. Sorption of 4-Amino-3,5,6-trichloropicolinic Acid by soils at pH 9

(4 ml. 1 p.p.m. solution + 1 g. soil adjusted with NaOH and HNO_3. 1-hour incubation)

Soil	% Organic Matter	% Left in Solution	% Sorbed	Ratio [a]	Sorption Index [b]
4	0.2	96.3	3.7	26.0	5.2
3	0.3	94	6.0	15.2	4.5
7	0.4	96.6	3.4	28.2	11.2
N_1	2.7	98.8	1.2	82	22
B_2	4.1	88.8	11.2	7.93	32.5
B_1	10.7	80.3	19.7	4.08	43.6
Q_1	32.2	67	33	2.0	65
Q_3	44.3	60.7	39.3	1.54	68.2

[a] $\text{Ratio} = \dfrac{\% \text{ in solution}}{\% \text{ sorbed}} = k \times \dfrac{\text{solution concn.}}{\text{concn. in solid}}$

[b] $\text{Sorption index} \times \dfrac{\% \text{ in solution}}{\% \text{ sorbed} / \% \text{ organic matter}}$

If sorption is followed for long periods—i.e., weeks—it is found that the sorption increases significantly for organic soils but not for the lateritic soil 3. Table VI compares the results for soil Q_1 (32% organic matter) with soil 3 (0.3% organic matter). A number of test tubes containing 2.0 ml. of 1 p.p.m. C^{14}-labeled 4-amino-3,5,6-trichloropicolinic

**Table VI. Sorption of 4-Amino-3,5,6-trichloropicolinic Acid
as a Function of Time**

(0.5 g. soil + 2.0 ml. 0.25 p.p.m. neutral solution
incubated at 25°C. with occasional stirring)

	% Sorbed	
Incubation Time	*Soil Q_1*	*Soil$_3$*
1 hour	25	21
1 day	40	. .
3 days	50	28
5 days	64	. .
9 days	. .	36
14 days	. .	27
23 days	71	. .

acid and 0.5 gram of soil were prepared, incubated with periodic agitation for different times, and assayed by the usual method. The sorption
of soil Q_1 with time definitely increased. The possibility that this is
caused by degradation of the chemical is eliminated by the fact that
virtually all the 4-amino-3,5,6-trichloropicolinic acid can be recovered by
extensive extraction, as shown below.

The rapid equilibration of soil 3 is consistent with sorption on a
hydrated metal oxide surface while the slow equilibration in the case
of the organic soil suggests initial surface sorption followed by slow
diffusion of the unionized acid molecules into the interior of a lipid-like
phase. Aqueous sodium hydroxide is more efficient than water in eluting
the sorbed 4-amino-3,5,6-trichloropicolinic acid, which may be caused
partly by its ability to break up and emulsify lipid systems.

The ability of certain soils to sorb the chemical strongly is important
in analyzing residues of the chemical in soil. A procedure must be developed which will recover the chemical quantitatively from any soil.
Table VII compares extraction from two soils, soil 3 which saturates with
4-amino-3,5,6-trichloropicolinic acid quickly and soil B_1 which shows the
slow takeup phenomenon. It is apparent that soil B_1, incubated 2 hours,
holds the chemical more firmly than soil 3, incubated 5 days, but that
hot water will remove most of the chemical from both soils. When soil
B_1 has been incubated for 28 days, removal of chemical was only 78.7%
after three water washes, but further extraction with NaOH increased
the recovery to over 99%. Several mild methods of extraction are compared in Table VIII. The same experimental techniques were used here
but, instead of determining the extracted 4-amino-3,5,6-trichloropicolinic
acid, the washed soil was assayed. A 50-mg. portion of dried, ground
soil was suspended in a silica gel medium for scintillation counting and

Table VII. Extraction of 4-Amino-3,5,6-trichloropicolinic Acid from Two Soils

(0.5 g. soil + 2.0 ml. 1.0 p.p.m. neutral solution washed with
1 ml. for 15 minutes with several agitations)

Incubation	% of Total Found		
	Soil 3, 5 days [a]	Soil B_1, 2 hrs.	Soil B_1, 28 days
Supernatant	66.1 (66.1)	62.9 (62.9)	31.0 (31.0)
Wash H_2O hot	17.1 (83.2)	10.3 (73.2)	20.1 (51.1)
Wash H_2O hot	6.4 (89.6)	5.2 (78.4)	16.9 (68.0)
Wash H_2O hot	2.6 (92.2)	6.5 (84.9)	10.7 (78.7)
10 further H_2O washes		11.4 (96.3)	
			11.0 (89.7)
Three 0.1M NaOH washes, hot			4.4 (94.1)
			3.2 (97.3)
0.5M NaOH washes, hot	1.5 (93.7)		1.8 (99.1)
Soil residue (scintillation counting), %	1.6	1.2	0.5
Total 4-amino-3,5,6-trichloro-picolinic acid recovered	95.3	97.5	99.6

[a] Total 4-amino-3,5,6-trichloropicolinic acid extracted by treatment to the indicated point (in parentheses).

Table VIII. 4-Amino-3,5,6-trichloropicolinic Acid Leached from Soil

(0.5 g. incubated with 2 ml. 0.4 p.p.m. of solution.
All washes 1 ml. for 15 minutes with frequent agitation.
Soil assayed by scintillation counting)

Soil Incubation Treatment	% Left in Soil after Treatment	
	N_1 41 days	B_1 28 days
None	28	25
Cold water washes (6)	2.0	
Hot water washes		
(3)		6.0
(6)	0.63	
Electrodialysis [a] (10 hours)	0.49	3.1

[a] Microdialysis apparatus of Baer (1); chamber flushed once an hour.

compared with a sample of the same soil treated with a known amount of C^{14}-labeled 4-amino-3,5,6-trichloropicolinic acid, dried, and ground.

From these data, it would appear that most soils should yield their residue adequately with thorough hot water extraction or lengthy electrodialysis. Treatment with sodium hydroxide solution should be more effective but will also remove other materials from the soil. These extraction procedures are more exhaustive than many of the procedures recommended for recovery of pesticides from soil. They are mild in the sense that they probably do not extensively disrupt the soil's chemical structure.

Muck soils will probably take more drastic treatment yet to be perfected. This and the question of what happens during long residence times in soil—i.e., a year or more—are under investigation in connection with studies of persistence in soil.

Movement of 4-amino-3,5,6-trichloropicolinic acid and other carboxylic acid herbicides through soil involves sorption and desorption from the percolating solution. Thus, the degree of sorption and rate of desorption as dealt with in this study indicate the rate of movement to be

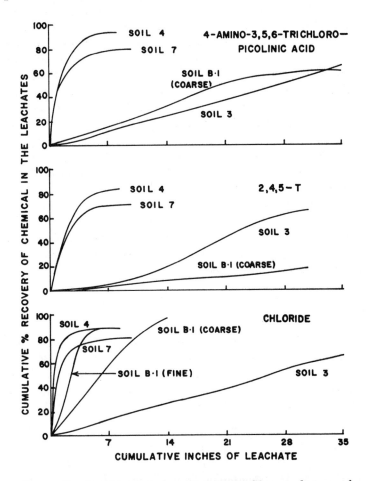

Figure 5. Leaching of 4-amino-3,5,6-trichloropicolinic acid, 2,4,5-T, and chloride through soils 3, 4, 7, and B₁

anticipated. Some idea of this relationship can be deduced from Figure 5. In these experiments, a solution of the chemical was applied to the top of a 6-inch, dry soil column (3 pounds per acre), and after 1-hour equilibration, the water was percolated through the soil under a constant 3-inch head and the effluent collected in 10-ml. portions. Carbon-14-labeled chemicals and Cl^{36} as lithium chloride were used, and aliquots of the effluent were counted to determine the radioactive content. The average percolation rates were 1 hour per inch for soils 7 and 3, 2½ hours per inch for soil B_1, and 41 hours per inch for soil 4. The leaching patterns observed are consistent with the relative sorptions shown in Table I. For example, 2,4,5-T and 4-amino-3,5,6-trichloropicolinic acid, which are strongly sorbed by soils 3 and B_1, are likewise slowly leached. In the case of chloride, soil 3 was the only soil to sorb strongly, and it is the only soil through which chloride is leached slowly. However, Cl^- leaches more slowly from soil B_1 with a coarse granular structure than from the same soil finely powdered. It is believed that this is caused by initial saturation of the dry granules with the "concentrated" Cl^- solution and slow diffusion of Cl^- from the granules into the water streaming past the granules. The sorption of 4-amino-3,5,6-trichloropicolinic acid is higher for B_1 than for soil 3 (35 *vs.* 17%), which appears to be at odds with the equal rate of leaching from the two soils. However, the rate of movement from soil B_1 begins to level off at 21 inches of water while the rate for soil 3 remains the same through the 35th inch. The slower rate by which 4-amino-3,5,6-trichloropicolinic acid is adsorbed into soil B_1 could allow some material to "escape" in the moving front material that would otherwise be sorbed if time were allowed for equilibration. Under natural leaching conditions, where much more time is involved, we could expect the movement in a soil like B_1 to be much slower than for the rapid leaching in column experiments like these.

Conclusions

These experiments have shown some practical implications of sorption of 4-amino-3,5,6-trichloropicolinic acid by soils and some of the factors that may be involved. Suggestions have been made as to possible mechanisms although additional work is needed to elucidate more precisely the nature of the sorption by soils.

Acknowledgment

We thank G. H. Brandt, The Dow Chemical Co., for the samples of Fe_2O_3 and Al_2O_3 used in this work.

Literature Cited

(1) Baer, E., *Kolloid Z.* **46,** 176 (1928).
(2) Bailey, G. W., White, J. L., *J. Agr. Food Chem.* **12,** 324 (1964).
(3) Black, C. A., "Methods of Soil Analysis," American Society of Agronomy, 1965.
(4) Gantz, R. L., Laning, E. R., Jr., *Down to Earth* **19,** 10 (1963).
(5) Hamaker, J. W., Johnston, H., Martin, R. T., Redemann, C. T., *Science* **141,** 363 (1963).
(6) Laning, E. R., Jr., *Down to Earth* **19** 3 (1963).
(7) Sheets, T. J., Crafts, A. S., Drever, H.R., *J. Agr. Food Chem.* **10,** 458 (1962).

RECEIVED December 9, 1965.

3

Biological Effects of Pesticides in the Environment

IRMA WEST

Bureau of Occupational Health, California State Department of Public Health, Berkeley, Calif.

An adequate understanding of the biological effects of pesticides upon people and their living environment requires a synthesis of two important categories of scientific information: (1) the biology, biochemistry, and ecology of the human being and his environment, and (2) the action and effect of each pesticide, over the full course of its influence, as it impinges upon the human being and invades the environment. That we have something less than a full complement of this basic knowledge should be obvious. Undertaking to acquire this information is a monumental and never-ending task. Nevertheless, there is no choice but to pursue it and make much more substantial inroads into it. Introducing new chemicals should be a scientific enterprise based on knowledge and subject to continuous evaluation, criticism, and correction if it is to contribute effectively to human welfare.

There is no question of the great need for effective pest control. There is no question of the immediate efficiency and economic value of modern pesticides in producing food and fiber and in controlling vector-borne disease. There is also no question about the ease of using hindsight to comment on pesticide problems compared with the difficulties of exercising foresight a decade or more ago in predicting these problems. The problems which have arisen with modern pesticides stem from their ability to do much more than is expected or desired of them. The fact that stable pesticides contaminate, accumulate, and move about in the environment has taken time to be realized. Neither the chemical nor the environment in which it is applied is a simple arrangement. Even the successful immediate control of a target pest can be diminished by a chain of events where the pesticide eventually causes an increase in the pest. The pace of application has long ago exceeded our ability to investigate and comprehend the ultimate results. Regardless of whether we do or do not escape various small and large disasters potential to this kind of adventure, proceeding so far ahead of understanding is not in the best traditions of science.

A society which expects to reap the benefits of its technological tools must learn to control the adverse side effects of these tools, whatever they may be. To control adverse side effects arising from pesticides better, the needs are most evident in research, field testing, in monitoring the environment, in human health surveillance, and in limiting the use of pesticides to persons who are competent by knowledge, training, and equipment. Introducing synthetic chemicals into people and their environment before the course of their action and significant effects were adequately understood has resulted in unexpected and undesirable side effects. Furthermore, procedures to control known undesirable side effects have often been deficient, either because of short-term economic influences or because these materials were rushed into the hands of the technically unprepared. These inadequacies have aroused considerable criticism and reservation. Either the standards for research, field testing, and control must be raised and broadened in scope or we must curtail the introduction of new materials. Introducing new chemicals should be a scientific enterprise, based on knowledge and dedicated to the long range benefit of mankind, not short range economic interests. It should be subject to continuous evaluation, criticism, and correction if it is to contribute the most to human welfare.

Technology is not an end in itself but a means to an end, which is public welfare. Scientists tend to forget that it is the public which in the final analysis has the responsibility to decide what it considers to be in its best interest. One of the most important duties of the scientist is to communicate his knowledge to the public. Too often the scientist sees his role as a decision-making one and often even without explanation. Subsequent public protest is then labelled "emotional" or worse. Incidentally, the term "emotional" is, in my opinion, the most misused word in the pesticide controversy. The word which should be substituted for emotional is "irrational," for we must not be irrational about a subject as important as pesticides. At the same time we should be, and cannot escape being, emotional as well.

In using pesticides, I believe the public wants continuing factual evidence that it is proceeding with the greatest care and the widest margin of safety. It does not want to be patted on the head periodically and told that the food supply, or whatever, is perfectly "safe." Public distrust of such pronouncements seems to be obvious to almost everyone but the people making the pronouncements. A primitive state of communication exists between the scientific community and the public, particularly on the subject of pesticides. The scientific community does a lot of communicating, but mostly within itself. Important initial steps toward better communications call for scientists to do more listening to the public and to develop a greater sense of humility. Until the scientists and the public learn to operate in greater understanding and harmony, much valuable effort will be wasted.

I do not believe the scientific community has ever really faced the issue of what would be necessary to prevent the undesirable side effects from using pesticides and still enjoy their benefits. First, it would be necessary to know in advance what these undesirable effects are through research and adequate field tests. Second, their use must be controlled to prevent adverse effects. Third, because methods for predicting adverse effects must be continually evaluated and because they cannot be expected to be perfect, a monitoring system for the environment and for human health must be established with built-in power to stop and revise pesticide uses when they are suspected of producing undesirable effects. This kind of system may seem insurmountably difficult, but only because our administrative thinking has never been big enough for our environmental health problems. A good control program is technically feasible. It has been routine, for example, in developing our space program. However, when it comes to down-to-earth matters involving the general population, too little too late is more often the case. Air pollution is another example of our administrative imagination and machinery not being big enough to catch up and come to grips with the problem.

Some distinguished investigators are less than optimistic about our ability to control unwanted effects arising from our technological tools. Rene Dubos is quoted as follows (13):

Present programs for controlling potential threats to health from new substances and technological innovations are doomed to failure because we lack the scientific knowledge to provide a sound basis for control.

Current testing techniques have been developed almost exclusively for the study of acute, direct toxic effects.

In contrast, most untoward effects of the technological environment are delayed and indirect. . . . Yet little is being done in schools of medicine and public health or in research institutes or government laboratories to develop the kind of knowledge that is needed for evaluating the long-range effects on man of modern ways of life.

The dangers associated with ionizing radiation, or with cigarette smoking, should have sensitized the public as well as scientists to the importance of delayed effects. But, surprisingly, this knowledge has not increased awareness of the fact that most other technological innovations also have delayed effects.

The slow evolution of chronic bronchitis from air pollutants, the late ocular lesions following use of chloroquine, the accumulation of the tetracyclines in the fetus, and of course all the carcinogenic effects, are but a few of the countless objectionable results of new substances or technologies which appeared at first essentially safe.

He elaborates further in another statement (14):

There is no need to belabor the obvious truth that, while modern science has been highly productive of isolated fragments of knowledge, it has been far less successful in dealing with the complexity of natural phenomena, especially those involving life. In order to deal with problems of organized complexity, it is therefore essential to investigate situations in which several interrelated systems function in an integrated manner. Multifactorial investigations will naturally demand entirely new conceptual and experimental methods, very different from those involving only one variable, which have been the stock in trade of experimental science during the past 300 years and to which there is an increasing tendency to limit biological research.

Dubos is saying that our scientific comprehension, imagination, and methodology do not match the problems we face in dealing with complex interrelating biological phenomena. In fact, some of our traditional assumptions and methods may be actual barriers to the kind of new thinking which must be developed.

Let us look at three assumptions which have been accepted in at least some quarters in regard to pesticides.

Threshold Dose Level. The first assumption states that the effects of a chemical upon human beings are in proportion to dose and that there is a threshold dose level below which there is no effect. However, this is not the safe assumption. Even a few exceptions could lead to serious mistakes. No large group of diverse and sometimes multiple chemicals interacting with complex living matter can be expected to add up to such a consistent, simple, and convenient formula. Human experience with chemicals for the past 100 or more years has been in industry and through the use of therapeutic drugs. Here the data do not support such an assumption. Those empowered to make decisions about pesticides often do not take advantage of this wealth of human experience which clearly demonstrates the diversity of human effects from chemicals and how they do not always relate to animal data.

This is not to say that there may not be many chemical effects in proportion to dose and there may not be many "no effect" levels. However, we're hardly in a position to state this is always the case, nor that we necessarily have enough basic knowledge to find whatever "no effect" levels exist.

The possibilities for synergism, antagonism, and potentiation among chemicals, the allergic type responses, and the impaired detoxification and excretion mechanisms in substantial groups of people all call for less rigid assumptions. Data on carcinogenesis alone should give pause for reflection (16, 28). The concept of threshold level may need re-examination and modification with pesticides as it has in the field of ionizing radiation.

Animal Data. The second assumption states that the traditional toxicological tests involving rats and mice consistently reflect human response to chemicals.

Since we must use animal data, three points should be emphasized. First, there are qualitative and quantitative species differences among animals and human beings in reactions to chemicals. We don't necessarily know which we are dealing with when we extrapolate toxicological data from animals to man. Second, we use the most convenient and economically feasible animals—not necessarily those known to reflect best the human biochemistry which is deranged by the chemical being tested. Unfortunately we do not even know the mechanism of action most of the time. (However, when we do know the mechanism of action, specific effects can be determined at lower dose levels than would otherwise be the case—for example, cholinesterase levels for phosphate ester pesticides (21)). Third, we may not know enough about the biochemistry of the experimental animal to recognize variations produced by chemicals.

Relying heavily on animal data and considering them the final rather than the first step in developing toxicological information has not encouraged the necessary human studies and field tests. Careful observations of those persons who are exposed to pesticides in their work, for example, have not been incorporated into a system for careful transition of the chemical from the laboratory into general use.

Sufficient Evidence. The third assumption states that it isn't scientifically proper to state that a chemical is producing harmful effects until all the evidence thoroughly verifies it.

When man is inventing potential sources of human disease and placing them in the general environment, he must be on the alert for adverse effects and be able to withdraw the chemical when he suspects unpredicted serious effects. However, the concept of waiting for proof beyond doubt today in regard to man-made diseases is not tenable. It places the burden of proof on the population and its environment. Furthermore, our lack of basic knowledge severely limits our ability to prove or disprove much in the individual case where new alleged effects may have occurred. Waiting for a sufficient number of dead bodies to provide the proof is crassly immoral and certainly aids and abets the distrust which often exists between the public and the scientific community.

Pesticides in the Environment

There are few places where residues of pesticides have not been found. They are present in water, soil, air, animals, people, food, and many commodities. Although we are adept at detecting and measuring the most minute amounts, we are not as adept at the more difficult task of determining the significance of pesticide residues in the environment. It is only when effects are immediate and substantial that they are likely to be recognized. However, it is a misconception to point only to the known fatal poisonings from pesticides and consider them the extent of the public health problem. Like air pollution and ionizing radiation, pesticide environmental contamination problems must not be considered in such narrow perspective. It is not valid to compare the number of fatal pesticide poisonings with traffic fatalities and conclude that pesticides are therefore a minor problem. Using the same spurious reasoning we could conclude that air pollution and ionizing radiation are much less a hazard than pesticides because there are fewer fatalities attributed to them.

An increasing number of reports in the literature describe the presence of chlorinated hydrocarbon pesticides, particularly DDT (1,1,1,-trichloro-2, 2-bis(p-chlorophenyl) ethane), in surface waters, in well waters, and in marine life in the oceans.

Waters may be contaminated by dumping a large amount of chemical into a water system either by accident or unauthorized disposal. For example, a truck trailer carrying arsenic weed killer was involved in a traffic accident (53). The contents spilled over the highway and were washed subsequently into the river. Pesticides disposed by the manufacturer into the sewer survived the treatment plant and were percolated into the ground water, rendering a city well unfit for use (53). An agricultural aircraft operator placed "used" pesticide containers in an irrigation ditch, which drained into a larger water system where many fish died (99). Another sprayed a city reservoir with a defoliant. He was treating the surrounding fields and didn't shut off his apparatus as he criss-crossed the reservoir. This type of substantial contamination can have both long range and immediate significance depending upon the chemical involved. Acute emergencies arise if water for drinking, recreation, irrigation, commercial use, or water supporting wildlife is contaminated.

Another kind of contamination results when pesticides are applied to water or land for other pest control or agricultural purposes. Runoff from agricultural land is the greatest source of pesticides reaching the waters in California. Immediate effects occur most often from pesticides with a higher degree of acute toxicity and long range effects from pesticides which persist or remain. Some pesticides can produce both types and others, neither. The killing of fish has been a dramatic direct effect. Endrin, (1,2,3,4,10,10-hexachloro-6,7, epoxy-1,4,4a,5,6,7,8,8a, octa-hydro-1-4-endo, endo 5,8-dimethanonaphthalene), a persistent and highly toxic pesticide, will kill fish at 0.5 p.p.b. (parts per billion)(49). Holden (26) noted that fish took up the DDT in water rapidly by virtue of their external mucus coating and that DDT disappears when added to water. His report suggests that measuring water for the water-insoluble pesticides may not necessarily reflect the amount passing into organic matter.

The long range or indirect effects have been most disturbing. The most widely used pesticides, the chlorinated hydrocarbons, are concentrated by living matter in the aquatic environment. An increasing build-up of the pesticide may occur in each link of the food chain. These effects may not be discovered for some time after initial contact, particularly if acute toxicity of the pesticide is low. Multiple contacts may increase the amount of the chemical accumulating in the animal tissues over the years. The amounts tolerated before noticeable effects vary with the particular animal species and the pesticide. Some species can tolerate larger amounts, but sooner or later are affected by decreased fertility, interference with normal food sources, and eventually death (29). The oyster is particularly efficient in its ability to concentrate chlorinated hydrocarbon pesticides. After seven days in water at 10 p.p.b. of DDT, eastern oysters were analyzed and found to contain 151 p.p.m. (parts per million) DDT (52).

There are too many documented instances where food chain build-up of pesticides has occurred to list them all (29, 30, 35, 47). The most minute amounts can be concentrated a thousandfold (30), and there is no predictable safe level for them in waters where food chain build-up can occur. The literature also reports pesticide contamination of waters and aquatic life over the surface of this country into the oceans and Antarctic, (2, 3, 19, 32, 39, 42, 48, 51, 52, 56). Blubber and oil from two whales washed up on the California coast contained DDE (1,1-dichloro-2,2-bis(p-chlorophenyl)ethylene), DDD (1,1-dichloro-2,2-bis (p-chloro-phenyl)ethane)[TDE], and DDT. The highest value in the oil of one whale was 11 p.p.m. DDE, 6 p.p.m. DDT, and 8 p.p.m. DDD (38).

Drinking water has been assayed as extensively as raw water. The levels of pesticides found in raw waters have been considerably below levels considered hazardous to humans. Present knowledge indicates that long before the water becomes hazardous for humans to drink, it is potentially hazardous for aquatic life and fish-eating birds in the area. Biologists tell me that the food chain build-up of these persistent fat-soluble chemicals was predictable. Apparently the biologists were not consulted when the massive applications were initiated. This omission should be carefully noted for it points up an important fact. Knowledge from a much broader base of scientific disciplines must be used to plan and control our technological tools which affect people and their environment. No one group of scientists is capable of encompassing the knowledge vital to this kind of enterprise.

Arsenic and certain chlorinated hydrocarbons may accumulate in the soil and injure plants. Although carrots, potatoes, and leafy plants touching the ground will pick up DDT from the soil, most crops subsequently grown on soil in which DDT has accumulated apparently do not pick up the DDT. The chlorinated hydrocarbons in the soil are reduced by about 30% per year (1) after the last application. Parathion (O,O-diethyl-O-(p-nitrophenyl) phosphorothioate) was found to persist in soils for 9 months in a peach orchard in South Carolina. Rotenone, applied to kill fish in the autumn, unexpectedly weathered a winter's freeze and killed fish the next spring. (Rotenone is an older botanical pesticide extracted from derris root. It usually decomposes rapidly in air and light and is considered a little less toxic to humans than DDT. It is highly toxic to fish.) A child was poisoned almost fatally from parathion which had survived the winter snow and rain after being spilled in the driveway of his home. The child had eaten mud pies made from contaminated soil which was found to contain 1% parathion (43).

Marth, in his summary of the literature (35), states that most of the chlorinated hydrocarbons persist in the soil from several to many years. Temperature, moisture, type of soil, amount, and volatility of the compound influence the duration. Soil microflura are not appreciably altered, but fauna are modified as to kind and number.

Carson has postulated that some of the small particles of pesticides, released as sprays or dusts, when applied to agricultural land may become airborne for some time and distance, eventually producing fall-out (6). Yates and Akkeson point out (60):

There is no known way in which drift of agricultural chemicals can be entirely eliminated, whether applied by ground or aircraft. Drift of tracers used in air pollution studies have been authenticated as far as 22 miles, and further distances could be expected, depending on the accuracy of the means for sensing tracer chemicals. Symptoms of 2,4-D drift have been noted on grapes 8 to 12 miles from the point of application and lawsuits in Texas and Washington have been based on greater drift distance.

A series of exploratory determinations involving air collected from four California cities was made in autumn of 1963. All but two showed measurable amounts of DDT (4). A variety of pesticides has been found in the air in several urban communities in the United States (51).

Pesticides have been found in minute to substantial amounts in several strange and miscellaneous locations in the environment and in people. A leaky drum of Phosdrin concentrate spilled on a bale of blue-jeans during transit by truck. Phosdrin (α-2 carbomethoxy-1—methyl-vinyl dimethyl phosphate), which can be readily absorbed through the skin, is a highly toxic phosphate ester pesticide. Eight months later six boys who wore unwashed jeans from this bale were poisoned (54).

A chemist discovered that his neighborhood dry cleaner had routinely added DDT to the cleaning solvent for mothproofing since 1956. He extracted 30 mg. of DDT from his suit which had been cleaned at this establishment. Additional miscellaneous garments were analyzed, and the DDT extracted varied from 20–565 p.p.m. (50). In one experiment 3.3 mg. dieldrin (1,2,3,4,10,10-hexachloro-exo—6,7, epoxy 1,4,4a,5, 6,7,8,8a-octahydro-1,4—endo, exo, 5,8—dimethanonaphthalene) also used at one time for mothproofing was removed by 1 liter of sweat from treated woolen cloth (35).

Contamination of peach orchards with parathion and possibly its more toxic degradation product, paroxon, sent over 90 poisoned peach pickers to physicians in California in August 1963. Heavy spraying of the orchards in the spring and summer had resulted in a substantial deposit of parathion on the leaves, which were contacted later by the pickers (37). About 400 cases of parathion poisoning have occurred in California in sporadic outbreaks among fruit pickers and others who have worked in heavy foliage which had been sprayed with parathion. Because the crop was considered safe to eat since pesticide residues were below legal tolerance, it was assumed that it was safe to go into the orchard and harvest the crop. This assumption is obviously false.

Home and garden contamination from pesticides have received little attention. An increasing variety of products and applications raises questions. Lindane (γ-benzene hexachloride)-impregnated shelf paper is available for the cupboard. Pesticides in paints and shellac, furnace filters, swimming pool chemicals for algae control, and in an endless variety of sprays, dusts, and pellets for home, for garden, and for pets can be purchased. Dispensers which continuously or intermittently release pesticides into the air are available. Applications of persistent pesticides by pest control operators into living quarters can remain for some time, recirculating and vaporizing through furnaces and ventilating equipment as well as by normal air motion. We know less about environmental contamination from pesticides in the home than we do about pesticides in penguins in the Antarctic (19) despite the fact that the home is the most frequent location from which morbidity and mortality from pesticides is reported.

All samples of human fat tested and reported in the United States show storage of DDT and its metabolite DDE (see Table I). Residue from food, particularly meat (5), is considered the most likely source of stored material. The average fat storage level of DDT plus derived material is about 12 p.p.m. for the approximately 800 samples from the general population which have been reported. For workers with occupational exposure, storage levels over 1000 p.p.m. DDT and DDE are on record. Other chlorinated hydrocarbons have been detected in human fat in Europe as well as in this country (*see* Table I). The significance of this stored material to human health has yet to be determined. There are three possibilities: (1) there are no effects; (2) there are effects we're not yet able to detect; (3) there are effects, but they have yet to manifest themselves.

In 1962 human milk analyzed by the California Department of Public Health ranged from 0 to 0.12 p.p.m. DDT and 0 to 0.25 p.p.m. DDE. The highest total of DDT plus DDE was 0.37 p.p.m. (*56*).

The one by-product of pesticide use which has received the most research attention and regulative control is the residue of pesticide applied to foods. Focusing attention on food residues for so long has led some to assume it is the only problem. This assumption has made it more difficult to see the other compelling problems arising from using pesticides.

Pesticide residue tolerances on food are based upon the maximum level of pesticide in food which has no discernible effect on test animals, usually rats, during their lifetimes. This "no-effect" level is divided by 100 and sometimes less to provide a margin of safety. When good agricultural practices allow a lower tolerance, it may be set accordingly. The contribution to the human diet that a particular food makes is also considered in deciding the amount of pesticide residue allowed. Tolerances are therefore reliable to the degree that the test animal and humans react with no more than a hundredfold quantitative difference to the same level of lifelong feeding exposure to the pesticides in question. When important human effects are not reflected or detected in rats or when other simultaneous chemical exposures alter results, then the safety of the tolerance must rest on the small magnitude characteristic of tolerances. An additional margin of safety arises from the fact that residues actually found on edible crops are about 1% of the legal tolerance (*17*). However, there is considerable room for improvement in the surveillance of animal-derived foods which are the major source of pesticides stored in human fat (*5, 20*). Surveillance of fish and game for pesticide residues also deserves more attention (*56*).

If there is no choice in using pesticides in agriculture, there is also no choice about adequate monitoring of all of our foodstuffs or about setting valid tolerances for pesticides on foods. We cannot afford even one mistake which involves all or most of the population.

Table I. Chlorinated Hydrocarbon

Investigator	Year	Number	Location	Surgical	Autopsy
Hayes et al. (20)	Before 1942	10	U.S.		X
Howell (27)	1948	1	U.S.	X	
Pearce et al. (40)	1948	8	U.S.		
Perry et al. (41)	1950	16	U.S.	X	
Laug et al. (33)	1950	75	U.S. (some Calif.)	X	X
Mattson (36)	1953	50	U.S.		
Mattson (36)	1953	1	U.S.		
Hayes et al. (21)	1953– 1954	51	U.S.	X	
Hayes et al. (21)	1953– 1954	1	U.S. (Ga.)		
Hayes et al. (21)	1953– 1954	49		X	
Hayes et al. (20)	1954– 1956	61	U.S. (Ga., Wash.)	X	X
Hayes et al. (20)	1954– 1956	16	U.S. (Wash.)	X	
Hayes et al. (20)	1954– 1956	110	U.S. (Wash.)	X	X
Hayes et al. (20)	1954– 1956	30	U.S. (Wash.)	X	X
Maier-Bode et al. (34)	1958– 1959	60	West Germany		
Read et al. (45)	1959– 1960	62	Canada	X	X
Denes (10)	1960	50	Hungary		
Durham and Armstrong (11)	1961	20	U.S. (Alaskan Eskimos)	X	
Hayes and Dale (22)	1961	10	France		X
Hunter et al. (31)	1961– 1962	131	England		X
Dale and Quinby (9)	1961– 1962	30	U.S. (Wash., Ky., Ariz.)		
Hoffman et al. (24, 25)	1962– 1963	282 64	U.S. (Chicago) U.S. (Chicago)		X X
Quinby et al. (44)	1961– 1962	130	U.S. (Ariz., Ga., Ky., Wash.)	91%	7%
Quinby et al. (44)	1961– 1962	28	U.S. (Ariz., Ga., Ky., Wash.)	X	X

Pesticide Storage in Human Fat

Exposure			Range of Chlorinated Hydrocarbon in Fat, Average or Mean, p.p.m.				
			DDT (Derived)			Diel-	BHC or
Public	Worker	Other	DDT	DDE	Total	drin	Lindane
X			0	0			
	X				17.0		
					3.6–49.8		
	X	Military	0		0		
X					5.3		
X	X				0–80		
	X		122	127			
		Prisoners fed DDT			270[a]		
	X		648	434			
		Prisoners	7.4	11.2			
X			4.9	6.1			
		Meat abstainers	2.3	3.2			
		Environmental exposure	6.0	8.6			
	X		14.0	19.0			
X			1.01	1.17	2.18		
X			1.6	3.3	4.9		
			5.7	6.7	12.4		
X			0.8	2.0			
X			1.7	3.5	5.2		1.19
X					2.21	0.21	
X			2.44	3.82	6.69	0.15	0.20
X			2.9	7.4	10.3	0.11	0.57
X							
X			4.0	7.8	12.7		
		Heavy environmental exposure	4.3	7.7	12.8		

Table I.

Investigator	Subjects				
	Year	Number	Location	Surgical	Autopsy
Quinby et al. (44)	1961– 1962	6	U.S. (Ariz., Ga.. Ky., Wash.)	X	X
Quinby et al. (44)	1961– 1962	14	U.S. (Ariz., Ga.. Ky., Wash.)	X	X
Wasserman et al. (55)	1963– 1964	254	Israel	142	112
Egan et al. (15)	1963– 1964	66	England		
Zavon et al. (61)	1964	64	U.S.	X	X
Robinson et al. (46)	1964	100	England	X	X
Hayes et al. (23)	1964	25	U.S. (New Orleans)		
Dale et al. (8)	1964	67	India	X	X

[a] Highest average value of subjects eating 35 mg./day for about a year.
[b] Heptachlor epoxide also detected.

The increasing opportunities for accidental contamination of food and other commodities from spills during storage or transit should not be overlooked. In California recently several persons became ill after eating doughnuts made at one bakery. It was only late in the investigation that the true cause was discovered somewhat by chance. A concentrate of diazinon (O,O-diethyl-O-(2-isopropyl-4-methyl-6-pyridimidinyl) phosphorothioate) had been spilled on the doughnut mix through alleged carelessness in pest control operations (57).

One of the delayed effects of exposure to certain chemicals is the production of tumors, some of which are cancerous. Our state of knowledge in this area is growing rapidly but is most difficult to interpret. Chemical carcinogenesis was first reported in 1775 when Sir Percival Pott, an English physician, discovered that the prevalent scrotal cancers of chimney sweeps were caused by the soot. Many additional industrial carcinogens have since been described. It is therefore not surprising that certain pesticides are suspected of producing cancer since it has been demonstrated in animals under certain experimental conditions (16, 18, 28, 59). Arsenic has long been a suspected carcinogen in people, and only recently have arsenic cancers in fish been reported (32). Also suspected are aminotriazole, aramite, dithiocarbamates, DDT, aldrin,

Continued

			Range of Chlorinated Hydrocarbon in Fat, Average or Mean, p.p.m.				
Exposure			DDT (Derived)			Diel-	BHC or
Public	*Worker*	*Other*	*DDT*	*DDE*	*Total*	*drin*	*Lindane*
	X	Pesticide applicators over 1 year ago	6.8	14.0			
	X	Pesticide applicators currently	10.7	21.6			
X			8.5	10.7	19.2		
X			1.1	2.0			
X			2.5	4.6		0.31[b]	
X					3.9		
X			2.3	7.2		0.29[b]	0.60
X			16	9	26		

heptachlor, dieldrin, endrin, 8-hydroxyquinoline, ethylene oxide, propylene oxide, and piperonyl compounds and certain chemosterilants (aziridine derivatives) (9, 14). The evidence which places lindane suspect as a delayed bone marrow toxicant has been reviewed by West (57, 58).

Summary

Widespread substantial contamination of the environment has arisen primarily from the massive use of the persistent chlorinated hydrocarbon pesticides. The extent and significance of this contamination is only partly known. Our limited knowledge is most apparent in two areas. First, there is no organized environmental monitoring and human surveillance system to provide comprehensive and representative data about the locations, amounts, and trends of this contamination; second, we are technically unprepared to predict the significant long term effects of this contamination on animal and human life.

In a few areas of scientific concern, knowledge is developing at a faster pace. The fine program prepared for this symposium presents some excellent examples. It is important that this new knowledge be interpreted, integrated, and organized into information which can be put into practical use. Rather than remaining aloof, scientists should interpret their work more freely, comment candidly on its scientific, social, and ethical implications in language which the public as well as the scientific community understands. Furthermore, controversy among different groups of scientists, the public, and the chemical industry should be welcomed. Only out of such controversy can be generated and synthesized the broad panorama of knowledge, ideas and viewpoints which are capable of developing technology for optimal human welfare.

Literature Cited

(1) Anderson, L. D., Deal, A. S., Gunther, F. A., *Proc. Ann. Conf. Use Agr. Chemicals Calif. 2nd,* Davis, Calif., 1963.
(2) Breidenbach, A. W., *Arch. Environ. Health* **10,** 827 (1965).
(3) Breidenbach, A. W., Lichtenberg, J. J., Report of National Water Quality Network, Division of Water Supply and Pollution Control, Public Health Service (July 17, 1963).
(4) California Department of Public Health, Bureau of Sanitation, unpublished data, preliminary report, January 1964.
(5) Campbell, J. E., *Arch. Environ. Health* **10,** 831 (1965).
(6) Carson, R.: Testimony before U. S. Senate Subcommittee on Reorganization and International Organizations, Part I, p. 214, 1963.
(7) Clayson, D. B., "Chemical Carcinogenesis," p. 114, Little Brown & Company, Boston, 1962.
(8) Dale, W. E. *et al., Bull. World Health Org.* **33,** 471 (1965).
(9) Dale, W. E., Quinby, G., *Science* **142,** 593 (1963).
(10) Denes, A., *Nahrung* **6,** 48 (1962).
(11) Durham, W., Armstrong, J., *Science* **134,** 1880 (1961).
(12) DuBois, K. P., *Arch. Environ. Health* **10,** 847 (1965).
(13) Dubos, R., *Medical Tribune,* October 28, 1964.
(14) Dubos, R., *Bioscience* **14,** 11 (1964).
(15) Egan, H., *Brit. Med. J.* **2,** 66 (1965).
(16) Falk, H. L. *et al., Arch. Environ. Health* **10,** 847 (1965).
(17) Food and Drug Administration, Press release, April 9, 1965.
(18) Food Protection Committee, *Nat. Acad. Sci. Publ.* **749,** (1959).
(19) George, J. L., *San Francisco Chronicle* July 11, 1965.
(20) Hayes, W. J. *et al., Arch. Ind. Health* **18,** 398 (1958).
(21) Hayes, W. J. *et al., J. Am. Med. Assoc.* **162,** 890 (1956).
(22) Hayes, W. J. *et al., Nature* **199,** 1189 (1963).
(23) Hayes, W. J. *et al., Life Sci.* **4,** 1611 (1965).
(24) Hoffman, W. S. *et al., Arch. Environ. Health* **9,** 398 (1964).
(25) Hoffman, W. S. *et al., J. Am. Med. Assoc.* **188,** 819 (1964).
(26) Holden, A. V., *Ann. Appl. Biol.* **50,** 476 (1962).
(27) Howell, D. E., *Proc. Oklahoma Acad. Sci.* **28–32,** 31 (1948).
(28) Heuper, W. E., Conway, W. D., "Chemical Carcinogenesis and Cancers," Charles Thomas, Springfield, Ill. 1964.
(29) Hunt, E. G., Bishoff, A. I., *Calif. Fish Game* **46,** 91 (1960).
(30) Hunt, E. G., Keith, J. O., Proceedings of the Second Annual Conference on Use of Agricultural Chemicals in California, Davis, January 1963, p. 13.
(31) Hunter, C. G. *et al., Brit. Med. J.* **5325,** 221 (1963).
(32) Kraybill, H. F., Presented at Washington State Horticultural Association Meeting, Wenatchee, December 1963.
(33) Laug, E. P. *et al., Arch. Ind. Hyg. Occ. Med.* **3,** 245 (1951).

(34) Maier-Bode, H., *Med. Exptl.* **1**, 146 (1960).
(35) Marth, E. H., "Residue Reviews," Vol. 9, Springer Verlag, New York, 1965.
(36) Mattson, A. M., *Anal. Chem.* **25**, 1065 (1953).
(37) Milby, T. H., Ottoboni, F., Mitchell, H., *J. Am. Med. Assoc.* **189**, 351 (1964).
(38) Navonne, R., California State Health Department Branch Laboratory, Los Angeles, personal communication, 1965.
(39) Paul, R. M., *Am. J. Public Health* **55**, 16 (1965).
(40) Pearce, G. W. *et al.*, *Science* **116**, 254 (1952).
(41) Perry, W. J., Bodenlos, L. J., *Mosquito News* **9–11**, 1 (1950).
(42) President's Science Advisory Committee Report, "Use of Pesticides," White House, Washington, D.C., 1963.
(43) Quinby, G. E., Clappison, G. B., *Arch. Environ. Health* **3**, 538 (1961).
(44) Quinby, G. *et al.*, *J. Am. Med. Assoc.* **191**, 175 (1965).
(45) Read, S., McKinley, W. P., *Arch. Environ. Health* **3**, 209 (1961).
(46) Robinson, J. *et al.*, *Brit. J. Med.* **22**, 220 (1965).
(47) Rudd, R. L., "Pesticides and the Living Landscape," Chap. 20, University of Wisconsin Press, Madison, 1964.
(48) Rudd, R. L., Genelly, R. E., *Calif. Dept. Fish Game, Game Bull.* **7** (1956).
(49) Shannon, W. T., Testimony before California Senate Fact Finding Committee on Agriculture, Sacramento, October 22–23, 1963.
(50) Stanford Research Institute, Pesticide Research Bulletin, Menlo Park, California, November 1963.
(51) Tabor, E. C., *J. Air Pollution Control Assoc.* **15**, 9 (1965).
(52) Udall, S., Testimony before U. S. Senate Subcommittee on Reorganization and International Organizations, Part I, pp. 71–72, May 1963.
(53) Warne, W., Testimony before California Senate Fact Finding Committee on Agriculture, Sacramento, October 22–23, 1963.
(54) Warren, M. C. *et al.*, *J. Am. Med. Assoc.* **184**, 266 (1963).
(55) Wasserman, M. *et al.*, *Arch. Environ. Health* **11**, 375 (1965).
(56) West, I., *Arch. Environ. Health* **9**, 626 (1964).
(57) West, I., *Calif. Health* **23**, 11 (1965).
(58) West, I., submitted for publication, 1966.
(59) World Health Organization Expert Committee on Food Additives, *World Health Org. Tech. Rept. Ser.* **220** (1961).
(60) Yates, W. E., Akesson, N. B., *Proc. Ann. Conf. Use Agr. Chemicals Calif.*, 2nd, Davis, Calif., 1963.
(61) Zavon, M. *et al.*, *J. Am. Med. Assoc.* **193**, 837 (1965).

RECEIVED September 21, 1965.

4

Effect of Pesticides on
Enzyme Systems in Mammals

KINGSLEY KAY

Occupational Health Division,
Department of National Health and Welfare,
Ottawa, Ontario, Canada

At the current state of knowledge, biochemical lesions have been identified for certain pesticides, opening the way to prophylactic, diagnostic, and therapeutic measures. Other pesticides have been found to influence enzyme activity, but the relationship of the effects on the enzyme systems to their toxic action has not yet been established. It may transpire that new enzyme activity changes related to clinical signs of toxicity will come to light for this group of substances. Meanwhile the study of their effects on enzyme systems has directed attention to the adaptive mechanisms of the liver and the possible importance of lysosomal membrane changes in the toxicity of pesticides. It has been revealed that chlorinated hydrocarbon insecticides and smooth-surfaced endoplasmic reticulum (SER)-stimulating drugs can reduce the toxicity of organic phosphates.

There are several possibilities for a relationship between toxic chemicals and enzymes. Some chemicals inhibit enzyme activity and interfere in cellular processes, causing a biochemical lesion and intoxication. This is the basis of pesticidal action. Enzyme activity changes in mammals may also correlate with clinical signs of disease or appear in advance of clinical signs without a biochemical lesion being identifiable. Enzyme activity changes may be observed in organisms subjected to chemical stress, correlating with functional changes in the absence of toxic effects. In recent years these various relationships between chemical stress and enzyme systems have been found to occur in mammals exposed to pesticides. This knowledge has already led to diagnostic, prophylactic, and therapeutic applications capable of reducing the hazard to exposed workers. This paper reviews the present state of knowledge of the field.

Pesticides as Specific Metabolic Inhibitors

The action of several classes of pesticides has now been established in terms of inhibition of specific enzymes and the metabolic processes they mediate.

Organophosphates and Carbamates. The organophosphates and carbamates are specifically active against the esteratic sites by phosphorylation or carbamylation (123), their primary toxicological significance being inhibition of acetylcholinesterase which breaks a metabolic chain and permits acetylcholine to accumulate. Organophosphate inhibition is slowly reversed by hydrolysis of the phosphorylated enzyme, a process which can be speeded up by nucleophilic oximes (73, 74, 122). Carbamate inhibition is competitive and reversible. Dissociation of the enzyme-inhibitor complex is slow and not facilitated by oxime reactivators. Type A carbamates such as eserine have high mammalian toxicity, low insect toxicity appearing to attach to cholinesterase at both anionic and esteratic sites. Type B carbamates such as Sevin have high insect and low mammalian toxicity and do not appear to be ionizable. Last year, Baron et al. (9) noted that some carbamates inhibit esterases in mouse liver but not in the brain. Determination of acetylcholinesterase in erythrocytes or pseudocholinesterase in plasma of persons exposed to these compounds can provide evidence of the biochemical inhibition in advance of clinical signs, though the exact biological function of pseudocholinesterase is not understood (27).

Using the electrometric technique, Kay et al. (79), Callaway et al. (20), and Wolfsie and Winter (124, 125) found individual variation in activity of normal serum cholinesterase (pseudocholinesterase) of around 40%, whereas erythrocyte activity (acetylcholinesterase) varied by 25%. Kay et al. (79) found that a group of parathion-exposed persons reporting minimal symptoms of ill effects such as headaches and nausea had average erythrocyte activity 27% below a matching group of controls ($P=<0.01$). Another exposed group reporting no symptoms had average erythrocyte activity 17% below controls ($P=<0.01$). The difference between the two groups had a significance of $P=>0.05$. It was evident that for diagnosis in individual subclinical cases the activity of the blood of the subject must be measured before and after exposure.

Much more is now known about the factors that may contribute to the wide variation in the individual activities of the cholinesterases. Two variant forms of pseudocholinesterase have been reported, one with

decreased susceptibility to inhibition by dibucaine (76, 78) and the other
to fluoride (66). According to Kalow and Gunn (77) the dibucaine-
resistant enzyme is produced by a gene, for which 3 to 4% of the population is heterozygous. Another gene, described as the "silent gene," is
associated with complete absence of enzyme activity in the homozygote.
Four cases have been described (45, 75, 87) and in one (45) liver biopsy
gave negative results for pseudocholinesterase. Last year, Lee (85)
showed that the rate of hydrolysis of di-(2-chloroethyl) aryl phosphates
by sheep serum was much greater in some sheep than others. The
difference was found to be genetically determined. Malone (90) had
previously found that some sheep on high dosages had a delayed response in the form of an ataxia similar to that produced in pigeons by
TOCP and DFP (8). Lee (85) showed that sheep which hydrolyzed
di-(2-chloroethyl) aryl phosphates rapidly could not be rendered ataxic
even by very high doses, a built-in resistance possessed by a large proportion of a population which has not been exposed to any selection
pressure.

Still other factors are now known to influence pseudocholinesterase
activity. Sawyer and Everett (48, 107) have presented evidence that
activity is higher in female rat serum than in male and that spaying decreased activity whereas estrogens increased it. Leeuwin (86) confirmed
this finding for rat liver, showing also that castration or thyroidectomy
raised the activity of liver pseudocholinesterase in male rats. Thyroidectomy of spayed females also increased activity. Females showed higher
enzyme activity at higher age levels. Male hepatic pseudocholinesterase
decreased in activity with age. Young females and males had some
activity at 3 weeks, but by 16 weeks enzyme activity of the liver of
females was 2½ times higher whereas that of males had decreased in
around 5 weeks by one-third and then remained constant. Clearly
pseudocholinesterase is under hormonal control.

Little is yet known in regard to factors that might cause individual
variation in acetylcholinesterase activity. The activity is greatly reduced
in erythrocytes of persons with paroxysmal nocturnal hemoglobinuria,
but this condition is rare (42). It has been reported that extended
inhibition by organophosphates does not appear to affect adversely the
survival of erythrocytes in the circulation as evidenced by observations
(28, 60, 92) with DFP (diisopropyl fluorophosphonate), OMPA (octamethyl pyrophosphoramide), and malathion (O,O-dimethyl dithiophos-
phate of diethyl mercaptosuccinate).

Role of Drugs. The role of drugs as a factor in the enzyme activity
changes brought about by the organic phosphates and carbamates has
been the subject of several recent papers. Gaines (57) has shown that
phenothiazine derivatives potentiate the toxicity of organophosphate

insecticides. Phenothiazone has been found to inhibit pseudocholinesterase (*30*) and other enzymes (*3, 29, 31–33*).

It has been known for some time that chloroquine and cortisone
stabilize the membranes of the lysosomes and provide protection against
a number of chemically unrelated liver stressors, including quartz; furthermore, release of hydrolytic enzymes from lysosomes occurs in a
number of pathophysiological states including shock. Last year Guth *et al.*
(*62*) indicated that chloropromazine in vivo stabilized rat liver lysosomal
membranes. It was established using *E. coli* endotoxin and vitamin A
that acid phosphatase was prevented from escaping the lysosome. In
light of this work the question arises as to whether the reduction in
pseudocholinesterase activity by phenothiazone (*30*) and the increase
in toxicity of organic phosphates after treatment with chloropromazine
(*57*) in fact represent containment of the esterases in the hepatic microsomes where they mainly exist (*44*).

Cyanide, a Respiratory Poison. Another enzyme inhibition by a
pesticide affects the respiratory group such as the hemoproteins and
the cytochrome oxidase system. This respiratory poison is cyanide, which
inhibits most metalloproteins containing copper or iron by forming stable
complexes with these metals. Among an extensive range of iron- and
copper-containing protein complexes reviewed by Dixon and Webb (*44*),
cytochrome oxidase was listed as having the greatest sensitivity to cyanide, being $10^{-8}M$ for 50% inhibition. Other enzymes not involved in
metal catalysis are also cyanide-sensitive, this chemical combining with
carbonyl groups in enzymes, cofactors, prosthetic group—e.g., pyridoxal
—or substrate, or acting as a reducing agent to break disulfide links.

The toxicological implications in the effect of the respiratory poisons
on the enzyme systems of mammals are not fully comprehended, even at
this stage of knowledge. For instance, Dixon and Webb (*44*) point out
that the respiration of most animal tissues is insensitive to carbon mon-
oxide which, in the blood, competes with oxygen for the reduced hemoproteins whereas cyanide has a broad inhibitory spectrum which includes
various oxidative systems at cellular level and, most importantly, the oxidized forms of the hemoproteins, especially methemoglobin. In this latter
connection, phenazine methosulfate has recently been found effective as
an experimental therapeutic in cyanide poisoning of mice (*13*). The
respiratory poisons have just been reviewed by Hewitt and Nicholas (*72*).

Pesticidal Mercury Compounds. Owens (*98*) established in 1953
that mercury produced in vitro inhibition of amino-dependent, sulfhydryl-
dependent, iron-dependent, and copper-dependent enzymes. It is well
known that mercury in high concentrations acts as a protein denaturant.
For example, Sohler *et al.* (*109*) have shown that mercury compounds
inhibit catalase activity at high concentrations. The inhibition of enzymes

containing thiol groups by organic mercury and trivalent arsenic compounds in low concentrations and by inorganic mercury in higher concentrations has been demonstrated on such fundamental enzymes as succinic dehydrogenase of the citric acid cycle and pyruvate oxidase involved in mitochondrial oxidation in the brain. The inhibition of the thiol enzymes results from the formation of mercaptides with the thiol groups. The reaction is reversible. For instance, the inhibition may be reversed in vitro by adding excess of cysteine or other monothiol compounds. This leads to an equilibrium in which the agent is partitioned in relation to affinities and concentration (44).

Thompson and Williams (112) found that arsenicals form stable ring structures with dithiol compounds like reduced lipoic acid. Monothiols such as cysteine will not reverse this reaction. For instance, pyruvate oxidase has a lipoate factor and is inhibited by arsenicals. Cysteine does not reverse this inhibition, but other dithiols do—notably dimercaprol (BAL) developed in England (110). Using BAL, Barron and Kalnitsky (10) were able partially to reverse succinoxidase inhibition produced by p-chloromercuribenzoate. BAL has also been found effective in mercury poisoning (12, 63, 88). The full picture on the biochemical lesions created by mercury has not been developed, but existing evidence points particularly to its effect on the thiol enzymes in mitochondrial oxidation in the brain. This is possibly reflected in the neurological sequelae often occurring from exposure of workers to low concentrations of organic mercurials used for seed treatment.

Fluoroacetate. Another metabolic inhibitor is fluoroacetic acid, a compound of high mammalian toxicity which has been widely used as a rodenticide. In 1952 Peters (99) discovered that fluoroacetic acid is converted in the body to fluorocitrate by acetyl CoA and oxaloacetate transacetase. The fluorocitrate proved by competition to be powerfully inhibiting to the metabolism of citric acid by aconitase. Thus the natural cycle is blocked and citrate accumulates in the tissues. Treatment with glycerol monoacetate has been used (24).

Enzyme Changes without Identification of a Prime Biochemical Event

Enzyme changes without identification of a prime biochemical event have also proved meaningful, particularly since 1957 when Wieland and Pfleiderer (120) reported the existence of electrophoretically distinct isoenzymes of lactic dehydrogenase (LDH). It became possible from this work to distinguish heart muscle and liver tissue enzymatically, the former being rich in fast-moving isoenzymes and the latter in the slow-moving type (121). Certain organs have been found to be rich in particular enzymes—for instance, esterase in liver and aldolase in muscle—thus permitting tissue damage to be identified from the released enzyme. Along with other developments in this field (71) early diagnosis of myocardial infarction, differential diagnosis of liver diseases, and diagnosis of certain types of malignancy have been greatly advanced. In the case of the chlorinated hydrocarbon pesticides some study of enzymes not identifiable with a biochemical lesion has been made in relation to associated pathophysiological signs (5) and their antagonism of organic phosphates (7).

Chlorinated Hydrocarbon Insecticides. It was shown in our laboratory (40) that a rise in rat serum aliesterase activity which was largely B type (89) occurred within a few days after acute doses of aldrin. The rise reached 150% of normal in 60 days when 100 p.p.m. were ingested in the diet. No change in serum pseudocholinesterase activity or in erythrocyte acetylcholinesterase occurred. Chlordan, DDT, and heptachlor, not very chemically related, also stimulated serum esterase activity at acute levels. Dieldrin was active at both acute and chronic levels of administration. A change occurring with the serum esterase activity rise was a reduction in oxygen consumption of aldrin-treated rats ranging from 25 to 40% depending on dosage. Apart from these changes, dietary aldrin at 20 p.p.m. or dieldrin at 50 p.p.m. accelerated weight gain around 20%, and there was estrus interruption. When sacrificed at 14 months, livers were found enlarged, and there was mild cloudy swelling on histological examination.

In our subsequent experiments (7) it was shown that aldrin pretreatment reduced the toxicity of parathion for rats as much as 7 times and TEPP by 5 times. There was no toxicity reduction for eserine, which inhibits cholinesterase but not the aliesterases. Thus it may be supposed that the protective action was caused by the provision of enzyme capable of replacing that inhibited by the organic phosphate and did not result from a damaged liver unable to convert parathion to toxic paraoxon according to the metabolic pattern established by Gage (56). Aldridge (2) demonstrated that aliesterase, A-type, could hydrolyze paraoxon. Subsequently one of us showed (89) that the activity of A-esterase was greatly increased in the liver by aldrin pretreatment, that paraoxon's toxicity was reduced by aldrin pretreatment, and finally that the toxicity of paraoxon was reduced by preinjection of an A-esterase concentrate.

Adaptive Enzyme Theory. The aliesterases are largely found in the microsomes of rat liver cells (44). Recently Hart and Fouts (51, 52, 67–69) have presented evidence that in vivo administration of chlordan or chemically related DDT stimulates the activity of hepatic microsomal drug-metabolizing enzymes, as evidenced by proliferation of smooth-surfaced endoplasmic reticulum (SER) which was first noted with phenobarbital. Several reviews of hepatic drug metabolism

(35, 59, 97, 102) have considered that the stimulatory effects may be adaptive. One reason is that chlordan is nonspecific in the variety of drug pathways that it stimulates. Metabolism of estradiol and other endogenous substrates is accelerated by chlordan (36) as well as by phenobarbital (34). Taken with observed increases in SER (smooth-surfaced endoplasmic reticulum), available evidence suggests that the action is caused by an increase in the amount of enzyme protein. In fact, Welch and Coon (118) showed last year that phenobarbital and other SER-stimulating drugs increased plasma aliesterase and protected against organic phosphates, as we had originally found with aldrin and chlordan.

Enzyme Changes with Carbon Tetrachloride. In 1952, Popper *et al.* (100) noted an initial increase and subsequent decrease in serum esterase activity of laboratory animals after injection of carbon tetrachloride (CCl_4). These workers suggested that loss of enzyme from liver cells accounted for the increase. Christie and Judah (25) and Dianzani (43) thought that administration of CCl_4 might lead to mitochondrial changes in liver cells that result in leakage of necessary enzymes, with a consequent failure of the oxidative system of the cells. There were a number of subsequent investigations of the pattern of change in esterase activity (16–19, 47), but results were conflicting. We then studied the serum esterase response of rats dosed with carbon tetrachloride by inhalation (6). The response was shown to be largely B-esterase (89). It was found (6) that exposures of 100, 500, and 1000 p.p.m. in the air breathed 6 hours per day produced a marked drop in serum esterase activity which, after 4 to 6 days, rose and fell in cycles of longer and longer duration, an average recovery taking place. For 100 p.p.m. in the air breathed, recovery was complete by the 55th day. On termination of exposure, serum esterase activity rose to 160% of normal. At 500 p.p.m. exposure it rose to 253% of normal, but this did not modify the toxicity of injected parathion.

Other workers have subsequently studied esterase changes with CCl_4 (14, 37, 38, 53) to determine the mechanisms involved. No esterase change in brain, adrenal, or fat of rats was found by Cornish (39), but he (37) found variations in the pattern of esterase change in rat serum by electrophoresis. Beatty *et al.* (11) demonstrated similar pattern changes in the serum of a human case of CCl_4 poisoning. Despite these extensive studies it has not been possible to explain the mechanism of the esterase response to CCl_4, which appears to be adaptive but different from the response of the chlorinated hydrocarbon insecticides and the SER-stimulating drugs, at least to the extent that CCl_4 is not protective against organic phosphates.

New data from our experiments on enzyme changes with other chemicals now show that in rats, not only carbon tetrachloride but also ethylene dichloride, benzene, and methanol bring about a reduction in serum B-esterase during 4 days after a single oral dose at the acute level. These findings seem to indicate that the serum esterase activity response is considerably independent of the chemical structure and the molecular configuration of the stressing chemical, except that the stimulation of esterase activity occurs later than with the chlorinated hydrocarbon pesticides.

In view of the observations of Guth *et al.* (*62*) on the reduction of the lysosomal membrane leakage by chloropromazine and the work of Hart and Fouts and others (*34–36, 51, 52, 67–69*) on adaptive changes in hepatic microsomal drug metabolizing enzymes, it ultimately may be possible to demonstrate some division of esterase-stimulating stressors in terms of these fundamental aspects of liver metabolism and their ability to antagonize organic phosphates.

Transaminases and Other CCl₄-Induced Enzyme Activity Changes. One more aspect of adaptation is hormonal and may be considered in terms of the elevations in the activity of various enzymes including serum xanthine oxidase (*1, 14, 38, 100*), glutamic oxaloacetic transaminase (*14, 38, 41, 55, 93, 126*), fumarase (*55*), glutamic pyruvic transaminase (*41, 91*), and other enzymes (*30, 41, 82*) which have been observed after intake of CCl₄ by laboratory animals. Glucose-6-phosphate dehydrogenase was found unchanged (*91*). Molander and Friedman (*93*) found serum glutamic oxalic transaminase elevated in rats, but hepatic levels were unaffected. Rees and Sinha (*101*) failed to establish a correlation between activity of blood enzymes and degree of liver injury in terms of the number of necrotized cells. The significance of all these enzyme activity changes is not understood, but there is some evidence that the transaminase system adapts to chemical stressors with hormonal mediation (*95, 96*). Casula *et al.* (*22, 23*) have found an increase in serum aldolase (ALD), glutamic oxaloacetic (GOT) and glutamic pyruvic transaminase (GPT), and malic and lactic dehydrogenase activities owing to organic phosphates, though Grech (*61*) reported reduction in aldolase and the activities of the transaminases in malathion exposures.

Apart from hormonal aspects of pseudocholinesterase activity previously dealt with (*48, 86, 107*), there have been a number of studies since 1954 showing that cortisone may act on the transaminase activity of various organs (*46, 49, 103*), particularly liver, heart, and kidneys, which have the highest activity (*4, 21*). In 1957 Gavosto *et al.* (*58*) suggested that the hormone may enhance gluconeogenesis by activating the transamination process in the liver. Rosen *et al.* (*104–106*) found alanine transaminase activity markedly increased in the liver of rats treated with glucocorticoids or corticotropins, whereas deoxycorticos- terone (106) or adrenalectomy (64) caused a reduction in activity level. Subsequently, Harding et al. (65) found that the inhibitory action of desoxycorticosterone appeared to be due to suppression of ACTH release by the pituitary. Recently glucocorticoids such as cortisol have been found in vitro to reduce leakage of transaminases and glucose-6-phos- phatase from liver cells, whereas sex hormones have the reverse effect (111). The de novo synthesis of enzymes involved in gluconeogenesis —for instance, glucose-6-phosphatase—may be induced by adrenocorti- costeroids (115, 116), notably triamcinolone (117). However, DDT reduces glucose-6-phosphate activity (113). There is, in fact, extensive evidence for the influence of age and sex, both under hormonal control, on the activity of many enzymes occurring in mammals (26, 48, 50, 54, 70, 80, 81, 84, 86, 94, 107, 114–117, 119, 127, 128). Hence it is not sur- prising to find that stress as hypothermia increases GPT and GOT activity in liver, heart, brain, and plasma of rats (15). On the other hand, Schapiro (108) induced secretion of adrenocortical hormone in rats by 30 minutes' stress on a reciprocating shaker but failed to influence the enzyme activity of tyrosine and tryptophan transaminases, previously shown to respond dramatically to adrenal cortical hormone (83). Nor was it increased after subsequent injection of cortisol, suggesting that the stress blocked the effect. However, Murphy (95, 96) has now shown with organic phosphates and other chemical stressors that adrenal-medi- ated induction of hepatic tyrosine transaminases occurs in rats. It seems to be well established that there is hormonal mediation of at least transaminases and pseudocholinesterase activity owing to chemical stressors.

Conclusions

Specific Metabolic Inhibitors. The organic phosphates and carba- mates interfere with the synaptic chemistry through inhibition of acetyl- cholinesterase.

Cyanide interferes with respiration by forming stable compounds with respiratory enzymes notably the oxidized hemoproteins.

Mercury interferes with mitochondrial oxidation in the brain through mercaptide formation with thiol groups in pyruvate oxidase. Succinic dehydrogenase of the citric acid cycle is also inhibited.

Fluoroacetate interferes with the citric acid cycle by conversion to fluorocitrate, which by competition inhibits the metabolism of citric acid by aconitase.

Biochemically Nonspecific Group. Organic phosphates and carbamates inhibit pseudocholinesterase and other esterases. Toxicity and enzymatic inhibitory power are augmented by phenothiazine derivatives but reduced by chemicals which are SER- and esterase-stimulating but not by carbon tetrachloride.

Chlorinated hydrocarbon pesticides are esterase- and SER-stimulating, like phenobarbital, chlorcyclizine, and certain other drugs, and antagonistic to organic phosphates, presumably by reinforcing available esterase supply.

Carbon tetrachloride is esterase-stimulating but not antagonistic organic phosphates, and transaminases-stimulating, presumably by adrenocortical mediation, like the organic phosphates and other chemicals.

These phenomena may be explained in terms of hepatic lysosomal membrane change induced by the chemicals (suggested by recent work with phenothiazine derivatives), or in terms of stress and adrenocortical intervention, or of adaptive enzyme power of the liver.

Even though biochemical lesions have not been identified for this group, one class of insecticides (aldrin, DDT, etc.) can reduce the toxicity of another class (parathion, etc.) in rats, suggesting a possible reason why some exposed workers seem able to withstand high exposures to these toxic substances without apparent ill effects.

Literature Cited

(1) Affonso, O. R., Mitidieri, E., Ribeiro, L., Villelo, G., *Proc. Soc. Exptl. Biol. Med.* **90**, 527 (1955).
(2) Aldridge, W. N., *Biochem. J.* **53**, 110 (1953).
(3) Allenby, G. M., Collier, H. B., *Can. J. Med. Sci.* **30**, 549 (1952).
(4) Awapara, J., Seale, B., *J. Biol. Chem.* **194**, 497 (1952).
(5) Ball, W. L., Kay, K., *A.M.A. Arch. Ind. Health* **14**, 319 (1956).
(6) *Ibid.,* p. 450.
(7) Ball, W. L., Sinclair, J. W., Crevier, M., Kay, K., *Can. J. Biochem. Physiol.* **32**, 440 (1954).
(8) Baron, R. L., Bennett, D. R., Casida, J. E., *Brit. J. Pharmacol.* **18**, 465 (1962).
(9) Baron, R. L., Casterline, J. L., Jr., Fitzhugh, O. G., *Toxicol. Appl. Pharmacol.* **6**, 402 (1964).
(10) Barron, E. S. G., Kalnitsky, G., *Biochem. J.* **41**, 346 (1947).
(11) Beatty, L. D., Dodson, V. N., Cornish, H. H., *Toxicol. Appl. Pharmacol.* **7**, 480 (May 1965).
(12) Bell, R. F., Gilliland, J. C., Dunn, W. S., *A.M.A. Arch. Ind. Health* **11**, 231 (1955).
(13) Bhide, N. K., Keswani, A. N., Mishra, R. K., *Nature* **205**, 915 (1965).
(14) Block, W. D., Cornish, H. H., *Proc. Soc. Exptl. Biol. Med.* **97**, 178 (1958).
(15) Blyuger, A. F., Belen'kii, M. L., Shuster, Ya. Ya., *Federation Proc.* **24**, T93 (1965).
(16) Brauer, R. W., Root, M. A., *Am. J. Physiol.* **149**, 611 (1947).
(17) Brauer, R. W., Root, M. A. *Federation Proc.* (Pt. 2), **5**, 168 (1946).

(18) Brauer, R. W., Root, M. A., *J. Pharmacol. Exptl. Therap.* **188**, 109 (1946).
(19) Brown, L. M., Harrison, M. F., *Nature* **168**, 83 (1951).
(20) Callaway, S., Davies, D. R., Rutland, J. P., *Brit. Med. J.* **2**, 812 (1951).
(21) Cammarata, P. S., Cohen, P. P., *J. Biol. Chem.* **187**, 439 (1950).
(22) Casula, D., Cherchi, P., Spinazzola, A., *Boll. Soc. Ital. Biol. Sper.* **35**, 1480 (1959).
(23) *Ibid.*, p. 1482.
(24) Chenoweth, M. G., Kandel, A., Johnson, L. B., Bennett, D. R., *J. Pharmacol. Exptl. Therap.* **102**, 31 (1951).
(25) Christie, G. S., Judah, J. D., *Proc. Roy. Soc.* **142B**, 241 (1954).
(26) Cleland, K. W., Slater, E. C., *Biochem. J.* **53**, 547 (1953).
(27) Clitherow, J. W., Mitchard, M., Harper, N. J., *Nature* **199**, 1000 (1963).
(28) Cohen, J. A., Warringa, M. G. P. J., *J. Clin. Invest.* **33**, 459 (1954).
(29) Collier, H. B., *Can. J. Med. Sci.* **31**, 195 (1953).
(30) Collier, H. B., Allen, D. E., *Can. J. Res.* (**B**) **20**, 189 (1942).
(31) Collier, H. B., Allenby, G. M., *Can. J. Med. Sci.* **30**, 443 (1952).
(32) Collier, H. B., Gray, M. W., *Can. J. Biochem.* **43**, 105 (1965).
(33) Collier, H. B., McRae, S. C., *Can. J. Biochem.* **33**, 773 (1955).
(34) Conney, A. H., in "Metabolic Factors Controlling Drug Action," p. 250, B B. Brodié, E. G. Erdös, eds., Pergamon Press, London, 1962.
(35) Conney, A. H., Burns, J. J., *Advan. Pharmacol.* **1**, 31 (1962).
(36) Conney, A. H., Schneidman, K., Jacobson, M., Kuntzman, R., *Ann. N.Y. Acad. Sci.* **123**, 98 (1965).
(37) Cornish, H. H., *Toxicol. Appl. Pharmacol.* **4**, 468 (1962).
(38) Cornish, H. H., Block, W. D., *Arch. Environ. Health* **1**, 96 (1960).
(39) Cornish, H. H., Dambrauskas, T., *Ind. Med. Surg.* **30**, 323 (1961).
(40) Crevier, M., Ball, W. L., Kay, K., *A.M.A. Arch. Ind. Hyg. Occup. Med.* **9**, 306 (1954).
(41) Cristol, P., Macabies, J., Ayavou, T., *Compt. Rend. Soc. Biol.* **158**, 1703 (1965).
(42) De Gruchy, G. C., Clinical Haematology in Medical Practice," Blackwell Scientific Publications, Oxford, 1964.
(43) Dianzani, M. U., *Biochem. Biophys. Acta* **14**, 514 (1954).
(44) Dixon, M., Webb, E. C. "Enzymes," Spottiswoode Ballantyne, London, 1960.
(45) Doenicke, A., Gürtner, T., Kreutzberg, G., Remes, I., Speiss, W., Steinbereithner, K., *Acta Anaesthesiol. Scand.* **7**, 59 (1963).
(46) Eischeid, A. M., Kochakian, C. D., *Proc. Soc. Exptl. Biol. Med.* **85**, 339 (1954).
(47) Ellis, S., Sanders, S., Bodansky, O., *J. Pharmacol. Exptl. Therap.* **91**, 255 (1947).
(48) Everett, J. W., Sawyer, C. H., *Endocrinol.* **39**, 323 (1946).
(49) Ferrari, V., Tenconi, L. T. *Acta Vitaminol.* **10**, 99 (1956).
(50) Fitch, C. D., *Proc. Soc. Exptl. Biol. Med.* **112**, 636 (1963).
(51) Fouts, J. R., *Ann. N.Y. Acad. Sci.* **104**, 875 (1963).
(52) Fouts, J. R., Rogers, L. A., *J. Pharmacol.* **147**, 112 (1965).
(53) Frankl, H., Gaertner, P., Kossuth, L., Milch, L., *Texas Rept. Biol. Med.* **15**, 868 (1957).
(54) Freedland, R. A., Krakowski, M. C., Walesman, H. A., *Amer J. Physiol.* **202**, 145 (1962).
(55) Friedman, M. M., Lapan, B., *Clin. Chem.* **10**, 335 (1964).
(56) Gage, J. C., *Biochem. J.* **54**, 426 (1953).
(57) Gaines, T. B., *Science* **138**, 1260 (1962).
(58) Gavosto, F., Pileri, A., Brusca, A., *Biochim. Biophys. Acta* **24**, 250 (1957).

(59) Gillette, J. R., *Progr. Drug Res.* **6**, 11 (1963).
(60) Goldin, A. R., Rubenstein, A. H., Bradlow, B. A., Elliot, G. A., *N.E. J. Med.* **271**, 1289 (1964).
(61) Grech, J. L., *Brit. J. Ind. Med.* **22**, 67 (1965).
(62) Guth, P. S., Amaro, J., Sellinger, O. Z., Elmer, L., *Biochem. Pharmacol.* **14**, 769 (1965).
(63) Hadenque, A., Barre, Y., Manson, J., LeBreton, R., Charlier, J., *Arch. Mal. Prof. Med. Travail Sécurité Sociale* **18**, 561 (1957).
(64) Harding, H. R., Rosen, F., Nichol, C. A., *Am. J. Physiol.* **201**, 271 (1961).
(65) Harding, H. R., Rosen, F., Nichol, C. A., *Proc. Soc. Exptl. Biol. Med.* **108**, 96 (1961).
(66) Harris, H., Whittaker, M., *Nature* **191**, 496 (1961).
(67) Hart, L. G., Fouts, J. R., *Biochem. Pharmacol.* **14**, 263 (1965).
(68) Hart, L. G., Fouts, J. R., *Proc. Soc. Exptl. Biol. Med.* **114**, 388 (1963).
(69) Hart, L. G., Shultice, R. W., Fouts, J. R., *Toxicol. Appl. Pharmacol.* **5**, 371 (1963).
(70) Hawkins, R. D., Nishikawara, M., Mendel, B., *Endocrinology* **43**, 167 (1948).
(71) Hayaishi, O., *Current Therapeut. Res.* **7**, 66 (1965).
(72) Hewitt, E. J., Nicholas, D. J. D., "Cations and Anions. Inhibitions and Interactions in Metabolism and in Enzyme Activity," Chap. 29, Vol. II, Inhibitors," R. M. Hochster and J. H. Quastel, eds., Academic Press, New York, London, 1963.
(73) Hobbiger, F., O'Sullivan, D. G., Sadler, P. W., *Nature* **182**, 1498 (1958).
(74) Hobbiger, F., Pitman, M., Sadler, P. W., *Biochem. J.* **75**, 363 (1960).
(75) Hodgkin, W. E., Giblett, E. R., Levine, H., Bauer, W., Motulsky, A. G., *J. Clin. Invest.* **44**, 486 (1965).
(76) Kalow, W., Genest, K., *Can. J. Biochem.* **35**, 339 (1957).
(77) Kalow, W., Gunn, D. R., *Ann. Hum. Genetica* **23**, 239 (1959).
(78) Kalow, W., Staron, N., *Can. J. Biochem.* **35**, 1305 (1957).
(79) Kay, K., Monkman, J. L., Windish, J. P. Doherty, T., Pare, J., Racicot, C., *A.M.A. Arch. Ind. Hyg.* **6**, 252 (1952).
(80) Kiessling, K. H., Pilström, L., *Acta Chem. Scand.* **18**, 1307 (1964).
(81) Kiessling, K. H., Tilander, K., *Exptl. Cell. Res.* **30**, 476 (1963).
(82) Knights, E. M., Jr., Whitehouse, J. L., Hue, A. C., Santos, C. L., *J. Lab. Clin. Med.* **65**, 355 (1965).
(83) Knox, E. W., *Trans. N.Y. Acad. Sci.* **25**, 503 (1963).
(84) Lacuara, J. L., Gerschenson, L., Moguipevsky, H. C., Malinow, M. R., *J. Atherosclerosis Res.* **2**, 496 (1962).
(85) Lee, R. M., *Biochem. Pharmacol.* **13**, 1551 (1964).
(86) Leeuwin, R. S., *Acta Physiol. Pharmacol. Neerland.* **12**, 295 (1963).
(87) Liddell, J., Lehmann, H., Silk, E., *Nature* **193**, 561 (1962).
(88) Longcope, W. T., *Bull. Ayer Clin. Lab. Penn. Hosp.* **4**, 61 (1952).
(89) Main, A. R., *Can. J. Biochem. Physiol.* **34**, 197 (1956).
(90) Malone, J. C., *Res. Vet. Sci.* **5**, 17 (1964).
(91) Maximchuk, A. J., Rubinstein, D., *Ann. Occup. Hyg.* **4**, 49 (1961).
(92) Metz, J., Bradlow, B. A., Lewis, S. M., Dacie, J. V., *Brit. J. Haematol.* **6**, 372 (1960).
(93) Molander, D. W., Friedman, M.M., *Clin. Res. Proc.* **4**, 39 (1956).
(94) Muhlbock, O., Kaufmann, C., *Biochem. Z.* **283**, 377 (1931).
(95) Murphy, S. D., *Toxicol. Appl. Pharmacol.* **6**, 355 (1964).
(96) Murphy, S. D., *Toxicol. Appl. Pharmacol.* **7**, 492 (May 1965).

(97) Netter, K. J., in "Metabolic Factors Controlling Duration of Drug Action," B. B. Brodie and E. G. Erdös, eds., Vol. 6, p. 213, Proceedings of First International Pharmacological Meeting, Stockholm, Pergamon Press, New York, 1962.
(98) Owens, R. G., *Contrib. Boyce Thompson Inst.* **17**, 221 (1953).
(99) Peters, R. A., *Proc. Roy. Soc.* **B139**, 143 (1952).
(100) Popper, H., Koch-Weser, D., de la Huerga, J., *J. Mt. Sinai Hosp. New York* **19**, 256 (1952).
(101) Rees, K. R., Sinha, K. P., *J. Pathol. Bacteriol.* **80**, 297 (1960).
(102) Remmer, H., in "Metabolic Factors Controlling Duration of Drug Action, B. B. Brodie and E. G. Erdös, eds., Vol. 6, p. 235, Proceedings of First International Pharmacological Meetings, Stockholm, Pergamon Press, New York, 1962.
(103) Rindi, G., *Arch. Sci. Biol. (Italy)* **38**, 155 (1954).
(104) Rosen, F., Roberts, N. R., Budnick, L. E., Nichol, C. A., *Endocrinology* **65**, 256 (1959).
(105) Rosen, F., Roberts, N. R., Budnick, L. R., Nichol, C. A., *Science* **127**, 287 (1958).
(106) Rosen, F., Roberts, N. R., Nichol, C. A., *J. Biol. Chem.* **234**, 476 (1959).
(107) Sawyer, C. H., Everett, J. W., *Endocrinology* **39**, 307 (1946).
(108) Schapiro, S., Yuwiler, A., Geller, E., *Life Sci.* **3**, 1221 (1964).
(109) Sohler, M. R., Seibert, M. A., Kreke, C. W., Cook, E. S., *J. Biol. Chem.* **198**, 281 (1952).
(110) Stockens, L. A., Thompson, R. H. S *Physiol. Rev.* **29**, 168 (1949).
(111) Takeda, Y., Ichihara, A., Tanioka, H., Inoue, H., *J. Biol. Chem.* **239**, 3590 (1964).
(112) Thompson, R. H. S., Symposium on the Biochemical Reactions of Chemical Warfare Agents (Biochemical Society Symposium No. 2), in R. T. Williams, ed., p. 28, Cambridge University Press, Cambridge, 1948.
(113) Tinsely, I. J., *Nature* **202**, 1113 (1964).
(114) Tomkins, G. M., Yielding, K. L., *Cold Spring Harbor Symp. Quan. Biol.* **26**, 331 (1961).
(115) Weber, G., Allard, C., De Lamirande, G., Cantero, A., *Biochim. Biophys. Acta* **16**, 618 (1955).
(116) Weber, G., Allard, C., De Lamirande, G., Cantero, A., *Endocrinology* **58**, 40 (1956).
(117) Weber, G., Singhal, R. L., *Biochem. Pharmacol.* **13**, 1173 (1964).
(118) Welch, R. M., Coon, J. M., *J. Pharmacol. Exptl. Therap.* **144**, 192 (1964).
(119) Westling, H., Wettergvist, H., *Brit. J. Pharmacol.* **19**, 64 (1962).
(120) Wieland, T., Pfleiderer, G., *Biochem. Z.* **329**, 112 (1957).
(121) Wilkinson, J. H., *Clin. Chem.* **11**, 239 (1965).
(122) Wilson, I. B., Ginsburg, S., Quan, C., *Arch. Biochem.* **77**, 286 (1958).
(123) Wilson, I. B., Hatch, M. A., Ginsburg, S., *J. Biol. Chem.* **235**, 2312 (1960).
(124) Wolfsie, J. H., Winter, G. D., *Arch. Ind. Hyg. Occup. Med.* **6**, 43 (1952).
(125) *Ibid.,* **9**, 396 (1954).
(126) Wroblewski, F., Jervis, G., LaDue, J., *Ann. Intern. Med.* **45**, 782 (1956).
(127) Yielding, K. L., Tomkins, G. M., Bitensky, M. W., *Clin. Chem.* **11**, 213 (1965).
(128) Yielding, K. L., Tomkins, G. M., Munday, J. S., Curran, J., *Biochem. Biophys. Res. Commun.* **2**, 303 (1960).

RECEIVED October 27, 1965.

Urinary *p*-Nitrophenol Concentrations in Acute and Chronic Parathion Exposures

JOHN E. DAVIES

Community Studies on Pesticides–Dade County, Miami, Fla.

JOSEPH H. DAVIS

Dade County Medical Examiner's Office, Miami, Fla.

DWIGHT E. FRAZIER

Miami Regional Laboratories, Florida State Board of Health, Miami, Fla.

JOEL B. MANN

Section of Metabolism, School of Medicine, University of Miami, Miami, Fla.

JOHN O. WELKE

Florida State Board of Health, Miami, Fla.

p-Nitrophenol, the metabolite of parathion, methylpara-thion, EPN, and chlorthion, is excreted in the sweat and urine of exposed persons. The urinary concentrations when measured by the Elliott and thin layer chromatography methods were so close as to be inconsequential in interpreting pesticide exposures. The urinary metabolite was stable at room temperatures for 5 days with formaldehyde added, making it an ideal surveillance tool. Average concentrations of 40.3 and 10.8 p.p.m. were observed in acute fatal and nonfatal poisonings, respectively. Average concentrations of less than 1 p.p.m. were observed in the careful operator, in contrast to 4.3 p.p.m. in seven careless operators with high absenteeism.

Parathion, methylparathion, EPN (*O*-ethyl-*O*-*p*-nitrophenyl phenyl-phosphonothioate), and chlorthion all contain the *p*-nitrophenol radical (abbreviated PNP), which is excreted in the urine and sweat of persons exposed to these pesticides. Conventionally, the diagnosis of acute organophosphate intoxication and the occupational surveillance of the organophosphate handler are confirmed by measuring the erythrocyte and plasma cholinesterase enzymes. Elliott *et al.* (3) were the first to point out the need for a more sensitive measure of exposure and urged the greater use of this urinary metabolite, as it was a true measure of exposure and obviated the need for repeated venipuncture. Arterberry *et al.* (1) were able to demonstrate that significant urinary concentrations could be detected before cholinesterase decline was noted. In contrast, other workers (5, 6, 7) have shown that after short exposures larger quantities of PNP can be recovered from the urine without simultaneous enzyme decline. In these human volunteer studies, however, the exposure was very different from the type and duration of the exposures usually encountered under normal working conditions and in an occupational surveillance situation.

It occurred to us that if the specificity of the analytical methods could be assured and if serious degradation of this metabolite could be prevented when stored at room temperatures for as long as a week, regular monitoring of the urinary PNP might provide a means of occupational surveillance of the parathion-exposed worker. This paper presents the results of our studies in this field and reports on the concentrations of PNP observed in acute parathion poisonings occurring in Dade County and under conditions of chronic exposure during a surveillance program of the occupationally exposed worker.

Materials and Methods

Urinary *p*-nitrophenol concentrations were obtained by the Elliott (3) method and a thin layer chromatography method. To compare these two methods, duplicate analyses were run on 45 urine samples with levels of PNP (measured by Elliott) ranging from 0.10 to 11.3 p.p.m. In both methods the urine was hydrolyzed with concentrated hydrochloric acid and heated. The benzene–ethyl ether extracts were made and either tested as described by Elliott (3) or evaporated, resuspended in ether, and applied to silica gel plates for chromatographic separation. Kidney concentrations were obtained from a weighed, hydrolyzed, benzene–ethyl ether extract of homogenized kidney (5 to 10 grams) and treated by the Elliott procedure (3) for urinary assay.

Comparative tests were run from a specimen of urine from a lawn sprayman containing 2.4 p.p.m. of PNP initially, which was treated with different preservatives and stored at room temperature and at 5°C. for 5 days. This experiment was conducted to establish the stability of this metabolite when left to stand at room temperature for as long as 5 days, conditions which were essential for a surveillance program.

Urine samples were obtained from acute parathion intoxications and from persons occupationally exposed. All fatal organophosphate intoxications were autopsied by the Dade County Medical Examiner's Office and urine and kidney specimens saved from such cases.

Since the inception of these community studies, more of the nonfatal acute poisonings have been reported, and hospital, home, and field visits made to 41 cases occurring during the study period. The diagnosis of organophosphate poisoning has been confirmed by clinical, epidemiological, and laboratory (4) means and the demonstration of cholinesterase inhibition as measured by the Michel method (8), and in nine cases (9) the diagnosis has been further substantiated by measurement of PNP in the urine.

The surveillance of the occupationally exposed workers was developed with groups of pesticide formulators and lawn and agricultural spraymen, all continuously handling parathion. The period of urinary surveillance ranged from 2 to 12 weeks and the cholinesterase surveillance from 1 to 9 months. The working conditions and degree of protection of each subject were observed by a senior sanitarian, and these persons were arbitrarily classified as being well or poorly protected against pesticide exposure. Data on the amount of parathion handled daily were obtained from the employers and expressed as pounds of 100% parathion. A sample of 10 ml. of heparinized blood was collected monthly, and the plasma and erythrocyte cholinesterase levels were measured by the Michel method (8). At the end of each working day and within 1 hour of completion of his day's work, each subject was requested to void into a 100-ml. wide-mouthed glass bottle containing 6 to 7 drops of 37% formaldehyde added as a preservative. These daily specimens were stored at room temperature (29°C.) and collected for laboratory analysis at the end of each week. At the laboratory, the specimens were refrigerated at 5°C. and analyzed for PNP within 3 or 4 days. For the most part, measurements were made by thin layer chromatography, although in a few cases the Elliott method (3) was used.

Determination of p-Nitrophenol

Pipet a 10-ml. sample of urine and 10 ml. of distilled water into a flask. Add 2 ml. of concentrated hydrochloric acid and reflux 4 hours. Extract urine with 15 ml. of benzene–ethyl ether (80 to 20) mixed solvent. Shake by machine 5 minutes. Allow separation of phases. Save the organic layer in a 50-ml. beaker. Pour the water layer into a second separatory funnel containing 15 ml. more benzene–ethyl ether. Shake 5 minutes by machine. Pour off the water layer and save the organic layer in the beaker that has the first organic layer. Add to the combined organic layer about 3 to 5 grams of Na_2SO_4 to dry and pour into a clean 50-ml. beaker. Rinse the separatory funnel and beaker with 10 ml. of benzene–ether solvent and combine the rinsing with combined extract. Evaporate the extract to dryness in a 50-ml. beaker on a hot plate with a gentle stream of air blowing on the surface. Dissolve the residue in a small amount of ether.

Preheat the silica gel plate for ½ hour at 110°C. Allow to cool. Spot the ether solution as a narrow band on the bottom of the silica gel plate. Rinse the beaker with a small amount of ether and spot the rinse also. Continue this rinsing process until all traces of residue are gone from the beaker. Spot a standard solution at the same level of sample. Place the silica gel plate in a tank containing 150 ml. of solvent mixture of petroleum ether–acetone (4 to 1). Allow the solvent line to ascend to the top of the plate and wait until the standard line ascends with a definitive line aspect (about 2½ hours). Air-dry the plate and spray carefully with a 5% ethyl alcohol solution of potassium hydroxide. Heat the plate in an oven. Scrape the light greenish-yellow portions having the same R_f as the standard into a 15-ml. centrifuge tube. Add exactly 5 ml. of 0.05N KOH; shake and centrifuge at high speed for 3 to 5 minutes. Decant into a 5-ml. colorimetric cell and centrifuge 2 minutes. Read without delay on a Coleman Junior spectrophotometer at 400 mm., using a water blank at 0. Read density on the equipment. From the observed density read the concentration in parts per million from calibration curve.

Results

The results of the duplicate analysis of urines by thin layer chromatography and the Elliott method (3) run on 45 samples with levels of PNP (as measured by Elliott) are shown in Figure 1. These two methods were compared because it was felt that thin layer chromatography would better separate interfering compounds found, especially in the urine of pesticide formulators whose multiple exposures created analytical problems not encountered in other high-risk groups. The results of the Elliott test (3) are shown on the abscissa and of the thin layer chromatography on the ordinate. The interrupted line indicates the line on which results should fall if these results were identical for both tests. The continuous line is the line obtained from least squares regression analysis. The equation for this line is $Y = 0.37 + 0.96\ X$, indicating that the slope of this regression is 0.96, which for all practical purposes indicates that the methods are comparable. Experience suggested that for volume testing, the Elliott method (3) was the method of choice whereas thin layer chromatography was of most value where interfering compounds were a problem.

The effects of storage of a known concentrate of PNP under different degrees of temperature and with different preservatives added are shown in Table I. With formaldehyde added at room temperature the specimen degraded from 2.4 to 2.2 p.p.m. of PNP in 5 days, a decline that would not have seriously influenced the conclusions drawn in a surveillance program. This metabolite stability was subsequently confirmed in other urine samples.

Acute exposure to parathion is a not infrequent occurrence in Dade County. Thus, of 68 deaths attributed to pesticides occurring since 1959, 40 have been caused by organophosphate insecticides and 77% have been

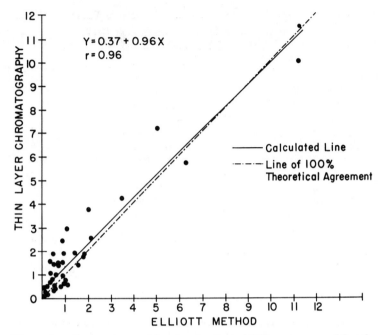

Figure 1.   Comparisons of levels of urinary PNP, as measured by the Elliott Method and a thin layer chromatography method

caused by parathion (31). The diagnoses of these phosphatic insecticide deaths have been confirmed by the demonstration of significant cholinesterase inhibition at all times, and in 14 of these fatalities specific confirmation of parathion intoxication has been obtained by the identification of PNP in the urine and/or kidney of the deceased (other PNP-containing organophosphates have not been encountered in Dade County). These bladder and kidney concentrations are shown in Tables II and III. Simi-

Table I. *p*-Nitrophenol Levels of Refrigerated Urine and Urine Stored at Room Temperature (23°C) with Different Preservatives Added

[Initial concentration of urinary *p*-nitrophenol 2.4 p.p.m.
Volume of urine 120 ml.]

Duration of Storage (Days)	No Preservatives Added		18 Mg. NaFl Added		6 Drops 37% Formaldehyde Added	
	Refrig.	Room Temp.	Refrig.	Room Temp.	Refrig.	Room Temp.
3	2.4	1.3	2.4	1.6	2.4	2.2
5	2.4	0.7	2.3	0.9	2.4	2.2
7	2.2	0.5	2.3	0.6	2.2	2.2
14	2.2	0.4	2.3	0.1	2.1	2.1

Table II. Urinary *p*-Nitrophenol of 14 Patients Fatally Poisoned by Parathion in Dade County, 1962–1965
(Medical Examiner's data)

Year	Age, Years	Race	Sex	Manner of Death	p-Nitrophenol, p.p.m.
1962	1.5	N	F	Accidental	12.9
1962	53	W	M	Homicide	12.0
1963	78	N	M	Accidental	9.7
1963	1.25	N	M	Accidental	19.2
1963	2	N	F	Accidental	21.3
1963	3	N	M	Accidental	100.0
1963	43	N	M	Suicide	17.4
1963	1	N	M	Accidental	25.0
1964	1.5	N	F	Accidental	33.3
1964	2	N	M	Accidental	56.0
1964	36	W	F	Suicide	122.0
1965	51	N	F	Suicide	2.4
1965	1.5	N	M	Accidental	80.0
1965	20	W	M	Suicide	54.0

$$\overline{X} \; PNP = 40.3 \; p.p.m$$

Table III. Kidney and Urine Concentrations of *p*-Nitrophenol from Fatal Cases of Parathion Poisonings in Dade County, 1963–1965

Year	In Kidney [a]	In Urine [a]	Kidney-Urine Ratio
1963	0.4	19.2	1:48
1965	2.0	2.4	1:1.2
1965	0.8	80.0	1:100
1965	4.2	54.0	1:13

[a] Parts per million.

larly, urine concentrations have been obtained from nine nonfatal poisonings (Table IV). The mean PNP observed in 14 fatalities was 40.3 p.p.m. with a range varying from 2.4 to 122.0 p.p.m. In ·the nonfatal series the mean PNP was 10.8 p.p.m. with a range of 0.7 to 22.0 p.p.m. Simultaneous bladder and kidney concentrations of PNP were available in four cases. The mean kidney PNP concentration was found to be 1.9 and the bladder concentration approximately 10 to 100 times greater than the kidney level, except in one case where the kidney-bladder PNP ratio was only 1 to 1.2. This was in a patient who was intensively treated with diuretics and intensive intravenous fluid infusions, procedures which could be expected to produce a dilution effect on the bladder concentration of PNP.

Next, several groups of persons occupationally exposed to parathion and, therefore, typical of a more chronic exposure to parathion, were observed and the average weekly urinary PNP concentration was evaluated and correlated with the average monthly cholinesterase levels, the total pesticide induced absenteeism record, and the over-all pesticide exposure as judged by the amount of pesticide handled and the general care with which the pesticide was handled. The average PNP is compared with these other parameters of exposure in Table V.

Table IV. Urinary p-Nitrophenol Levels in 9 Hospitalized Nonfatal Parathion Poisonings in Dade County, 1964–1965

					Admission Cholinesterase		Admission
Case No.	Age, Years	Sex	Race	Occupation	RBC, ΔpH/hr.	Plasma, ΔpH/hr.	Urinary PNP Levels, P.P.M.
1	50	M	N	Sprayman	0.0	0.0	14.2
2	22	M	W	Sprayman	0.0	0.0	22.0
3	1	M	N	Infant	0.08	0.10	16.0
4	47	M	N	Sprayman	0.1	0.1	6.6
5	19	M	N	Sprayman	0.1	0.15	0.7
6	12	M	N	Child	0.18	0.19	13.3
7	1.5	M	N	Infant	0.13	0.16	5.2
8	18	M	N	Sprayman	0.15	0.05	16.5
9	1	M	N	Infant	0.100	0.36	2.6

$\overline{X}$ PNP = 10.8 p.p.m

Persons who were assessed as being careful and well protected spraymen, handling 11.02 pounds of 100% parathion daily, had an average daily concentration of PNP of 0.8. The absenteeism rate in this group during a 6-month period of observation was 20% and their mean

Table V. Average Monthly RBC Cholinesterase and Urinary p-Nitrophenol Levels of Persons Occupationally Exposed to Parathion in Dade County, 1965

Occupational Types	No.	Av. amt. 100% Parathion Handled daily Lb.	% Absenteeism	ChE Level, ΔpH/Hr.	No. of Samples	PNP, P.P.M.	No. of Samples
A. Careful and protected spraymen	5	11.02	20	0.69	31	0.8	140
B. Well protected formulators	4	65.5	0	0.69	26	0.9	95
C. Careless spraymen	7	10.3	71	0.59	39	4.3	171

erythrocyte cholinesterase level was 0.69 ΔpH per hour. This was the same level noted for a group of formulators whose very creditable work record was further substantiated by having no absenteeism rate and a mean urinary PNP of 0.9 p.p.m. in spite of handling 65 pounds of 100% parathion a day! These favorable indices of safe pesticide handling were in marked contrast to those found in a group of careless spraymen. Here, though handling only 10.3 pounds of 100% parathion a day, the group exhibited a 71% absenteeism rate, an erythrocyte cholinesterase level of 0.59 ΔpH per hour, and a mean urinary PNP of 4.3 p.p.m.

The understandable correlation among careless technique, absenteeism, cholinesterase inhibition, and elevated average urinary PNP levels suggested that the latter was a highly reliable biological index of chronic parathion exposure and one that could ultimately predict chronic parathion toxicity.

Discussion

Once it became apparent that the urinary PNP was a specific and stable urinary metabolite, capable of reflecting parathion exposure, especially dermal, it was obvious that its measurement would provide useful information both in the acute poisoning and in the daily surveillance of the chronically exposed occupational worker.

In the acute situation the measurement of the urinary PNP was of value not only because the magnitude of the concentration provided in part some index of the extent of this acute exposure, but also because its measurement added specificity to the diagnosis of organophosphate poisonings, especially when there was a history of multiple pesticide exposure. In the 14 fatalities, estimations of the duration of life following acute exposure varied from 20 minutes to 4 hours. In only two was any treatment provided before death, the other cases being either dead on arrival or not diagnosed before death. The urinary PNP level, therefore, in these circumstances was only a grab sample, and this fact would explain the wide range of concentrations observed in the 14 fatalities. In the nine nonfatal cases the interval between acute exposure and hospitalization was not ascertainable in industrial exposures, but in accidental ingestions the interval ranged from 15 minutes to 12 hours. The subsequent excretion of PNP following hospitalization is shown in Figure 2. The sequential urinary concentrations observed in a group of three children and four adult spraymen are presented. The three children exhibited excretion patterns similar to the one shown in this figure, the essential characteristic of which was the total excretion of metabolite within 24 hours. This was in striking contrast to the pattern observed in the spraymen, one of whom was excreting PNP 96 hours following his acute exposure. This differing excretion pattern might be explained on the basis

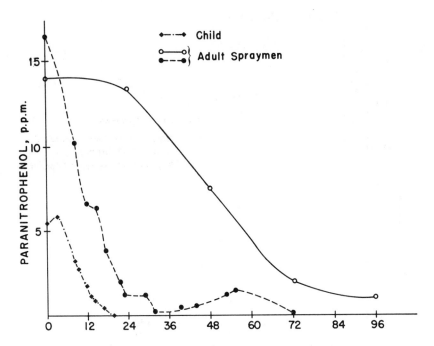

Figure 2. Urinary PNP levels following acute parathion poisoning Dade county, 1964–65.

of one or more of the following possibilities: age, routes of absorption, continued absorption of pesticides from the skin and hair reservoirs in the occupationally exposed group, and impaired renal excretion of metabolite in the occupational group.

Recently, a 6-year-old child, acutely poisoned by sitting in a pool of parathion, was studied and found to be excreting PNP for 72 hours, suggesting that the prolonged excretion pattern is more a manifestation of dermal exposure and is in contrast to the shorter excretion pattern observed following accidental ingestion.

In one instance, the sequential PNP excretion levels and the simultaneous cholinesterase change observed following 2-PAM therapy were documented (Figure 3). Another pitfall encountered in the interpretation of acute PNP concentrations related to the problem of mixed exposures; thus, a 22-year-old sprayman who was handling a variety of pesticides including parathion and guthion was studied. His acute intoxication was a result of an excessive exposure to guthion rather than parathion, since this was the material handled on the day of hospitalization. However, his PNP concentration was found to be 0.7 p.p.m., a figure well below the level observed in other acute intoxications and representing no more

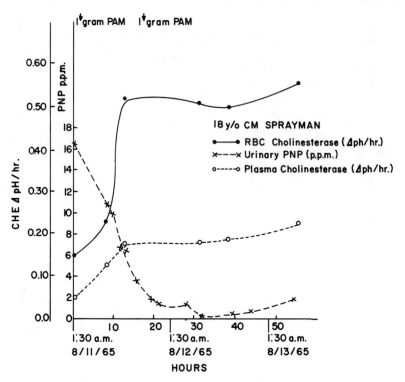

Figure 3. Cholinesterase and urinary PNP levels following acute parathion poisoning. Dade county, 1965.

than the carryover of the metabolite from the previous day's parathion exposure.

Equally informative has been the study of the pesticide metabolite under conditions of chronic exposure. Nowadays, strenuous efforts are being made to promote the safe handling of pesticides through educational programs. Essential though such programs are, there are significant pointers which suggest that education alone may not be enough. Thus, the more favorable insurance rates available to industries sponsoring cholinesterase programs, the continued occurrence of occupational poisonings in spite of these educational efforts, and lastly, the enormous problem of the illiterate worker suggest that education may well have to be combined with surveillance. A successful surveillance program must protect against excessive exposure and, in the pesticide field, several investigators (2, 5, 7, 9) have emphasized the importance of dermal exposure. This is where PNP monitoring is of most value. Arterberry (1) showed that cholinesterase decline occurred with exposures producing urinary concentrations of PNP of 2 p.p.m. or greater. Our experience suggested that weekly averages of between 3 or 4 p.p.m. were indicative of excessive exposure and usually the hallmark of a careless operator. Thus, one excessively exposed sprayman presented average concentrations for a 5-day-week period in one month of 3.5, 2.5, 2.4, 3.6, and 2.8 p.p.m. of PNP. These weekly averages were sufficient to produce a 50% decline in his erythrocyte cholinesterase level and drew attention to the occurrence of a large tear in his glove. When this defect was corrected, subsequent levels were 0.7 and 0.6 p.p.m. of PNP for the 2 subsequent week periods of study, even though the same amount of material was being handled.

Obviously, ambient temperature will influence the absorption of parathion and the rapidity with which cholinesterase enzyme decline will occur. Funckes *et al.* (5) showed the temperature dependence of urinary PNP in volunteers dermally exposed to parathion. In our study, while temperature recordings were not documented, the impression was gained that in the month of August, the hottest and most humid month, higher weekly PNP levels were obtained and more cholinesterase declines observed.

Conclusions

Certain pitfalls were encountered in the surveillance program whereby elevated PNP levels were observed but did not relate to poor spray techniques. These pitfalls are best illustrated by two case studies. The first was a 28-year-old sprayman, whose persistently elevated PNP levels could not be explained on the basis of a careless technique. It was not until the operator himself was examined and the extensive atopic eczema identified that the cause became apparent. There were deep fissures on the dorsum of his hands and in the interdigital clefts. Later, when his skin condition improved, lower concentrations of urinary PNP were observed, suggesting that the mechanism of this exposure was a breakdown of the natural protection provided by the intact skin barrier.

The other case history was an example of the complete opposite. Here, low urine concentrations were observed in spite of obvious excessive exposure and moderate cholinesterase decline. This was a 49-year-old agricultural sprayman whose techniques were atrocious and protection was minimal. In spite of these practices, however, urine concentrations were always below the 1-p.p.m. level of PNP. It was also noted that, although not drinking excessively, over an 80-day period he failed to concentrate his urine above isotonic levels, suggesting some underlying urinary concentration defect. Correction of his urine to osmotic levels observed in other spraymen would have raised his PNP level to 5 p.p.m. Subsequent evaluation confirmed the presence of proximal and distal renal tubular dysfunction.

These two cases indicate the need for evaluating each situation on its own merits, having regard to both the method of the spray operation and the general health of the operator. In spite of the aforementioned limitations, it has been our experience that pesticide surveillance by metabolite measurement is favored by employer and employee alike—the former, because slipshod practices can be detected and safety measures more readily accepted by staff personnel when related to a concentration figure, and the latter, because the frequency of cholinesterase venipuncture can be reduced and the value of protection rendered more meaningful when related quantitatively.

Literature Cited

(1) Arterberry, J. D., Durham, W. F., Elliott, J. W., Wolfe, H. R., *Arch. Environ. Health* **3**, 476 (1961).
(2) Davies, J. E., *et al., J. Occupational Med.* **7**, 612 (1965).
(3) Elliott, J. W., Walker, K. C., Penick, A. E., Durham, W. F., *J. Agr. Food Chem.* **8**, 111 (1960).
(4) Fish, A. J., *et al., J. Forensic Sci.* **10**, 473 (1965).
(5) Funckes, A. J., Hayes, G. R., Jr., Hartwell, W. V., *J. Agr. Food Chem.* **11**, 455 (1963).
(6) Hartwell, W. V., Hayes, G. R., Funckes, A. J., *Arch. Environ. Health* **8**, 820 (1964).
(7) Hayes, G. R., Jr., Funckes, A. J., Hartwell, W. V., *Ibid.*, **8**, 829 (1964).
(8) Michel, H. O., *J. Lab. Clin Med.* **34**, 1564 (1949).
(9) Simpson, G. R., Beck, A., *Arch. Environ. Health* **11**, 784 (1965).

RECEIVED September 23, 1965. Views expressed herein are those of the investigators and do not necessarily reflect official viewpoint of the Public Health Service. Contract project supported by the Office of Pesticides, Bureau of State Services (EH), Public Health Service, Washington, D. C., under Contract Number 86-65-26.

Effects of Chronic Poisoning by an Organophosphorus Cholinesterase Inhibitor on Acetylcholine and Norepinephrine Content of the Brain

W. B. STAVINOHA, J. A. RIEGER, Jr., L. C. RYAN, and P. W. SMITH

Civil Aeromedical Institute, Federal Aviation Agency, Oklahoma City, Okla.

In animals receiving daily doses of an organophosphorus cholinesterase inhibitor for 24 days, symptoms of poisoning became maximal at about the third day, declined thereafter, and became mild after 8 to 10 days. Acetylcholine content of brain tissue rose to a high level at the third day, had returned to the control level at the tenth day, and remained at this level thereafter, although brain cholinesterase activity was only 20% of the normal value from the tenth through the 24th day. It is concluded that compensatory changes in the acetylcholine content of brain tissue occur during symptomatic adaptation to low cholinesterase activity. No significant changes in brain norepinephrine content were observed.

The experiments described constitute one portion of an investigation of the mechanism by which animals become adapted to the persistent depression of cholinesterase activity which can be produced by organophosphorus pesticides.

The more prominent signs and symptoms of acute organophosphorus poisoning are generally well known. They consist of a complex of the actions of acetylcholine, which persists at the sites of its release when the rate of its destruction is reduced. Thus, there are effects which can be attributed to the actions of acetylcholine at autonomic ganglia, at cholinergic postganglionic autonomic nerve endings, at somatic motor nerve terminations, and within the central nervous system in the case of those inhibitors which can traverse the blood-brain barrier. Although it is possible that the commercially useful organophosphorus pesticides affect other enzyme systems or have other intrinsic pharmacological actions, these have not been adequately explored.

The order of appearance and the eventual pattern and severity of the signs and symptoms depend upon the specific organophosphorus compound involved, the route of entry into the body, the size of a single dose, or the size, number, and spacing of multiple doses.

In 1952, Rider, Ellinwood, and Coon (7) demonstrated that rats can become tolerant to octamethyl pyrophosphoramide (OMPA). Since then it has been shown that rats can acquire tolerance to a variety of organophosphorus cholinesterase inhibitors. Typical of such reports is that of Bombinski and DuBois (2), who administered O,O-diethyl S-2-ethyl-2-mercaptoethyl phosphorodithioate (Di-Syston) to rats each day for periods as long as 60 days. Signs of poisoning appeared after 2 days, but began to subside after 7–10 days, even though the activity of brain cholinesterase remained at or about 20% of its normal value from the 5th day onward.

It is now apparent from evidence which has been accumulating since the 1950's when large-scale use of cholinesterase inhibitors as pest-control agents began, that man can become tolerant to most, if not all, of the commercially important organophosphorus pesticides. It is not unusual for a person who has become acutely ill from a single large dose or a series of smaller doses of a persistent cholinesterase inhibitor to recover within days or weeks to an apparently asymptomatic state. At this time the cholinesterases of blood plasma and erythrocytes will usually exhibit only a small fraction of their normal activity. From knowledge of the relationship between the activity of the enzymes in blood and central nervous system and the recovery rate of the latter in experimental animals, it is safe to assume that cholinesterase activity in nerve tissue of these human subjects is also low after the acute symptoms have subsided.

In contrast with the picture of acute poisoning, it is possible for persons who are continuously exposed to organophosphorus pesticides to absorb the material so slowly and at such a uniform rate that acute symptoms are minimal or absent, even though cholinesterase activity in the blood, measured by accepted methods, is markedly depressed. Ganelin (5) has assembled an impressive number of such cases among persons occupationally exposed to organophosphorus compounds. Summerford et al. (11) have pointed out that the rate of change of enzyme activity appears to be as important as the degree of depression in determining whether an acute phase of the poisoning syndrome occurs.

There has been much speculation concerning the mechanisms responsible for adaptation, and numerous suggestions have emerged. One of these, which proposes that excitable tissues can acquire tolerance to abnormally high levels of acetylcholine, has recently received experimental support. Brodeur and DuBois (3) have reported that the free acetylcholine content of the brain of rats remained above control levels throughout a 60-day period of daily Di-Syston injections although the acute symptoms which followed each dose became progressively less severe after 8 to 12 days. Animals thus resistant to the pesticide were reported to be less susceptible to the cholinergic drug, carbachol.

Our study was initiated because the mechanism of adaptation is still obscure, and much additional information is needed concerning the relationship between cholinesterase activity and the acetylcholine content of the central nervous system during the adaptation process. We also desired to investigate the possibility that adaptation might involve compensatory changes in the production or release of neural mediators, other than acetylcholine, capable of modifying the effects of high levels of the latter within the central nervous system. Norepinephrine was the first such mediator selected for study.

Materials and Methods

Female white rats obtained from Holtzman (Madison, Wisc.) were used. The animals were held in our animal quarters for 2 weeks after their arrival. They were maintained on a diet of Purina Micro-mixed Laboratory Chow, fed *ad libitum*, and weighed approximately 190 grams each at the beginning of an experiment.

The experimental animals received daily injections of Di-Syston, 1 mg. per kg., given intraperitoneally. The pesticide was dissolved in a solvent mixture consisting of 10 parts of ethanol and 90 parts of propylene glycol, in a concentration of 1 mg. per ml. Control animals received daily injections of an appropriate volume of the solvent mixture, at approximately the same time each day.

Di-Syston was selected as the cholinesterase inhibitor for use in this study because of a suitable duration of action and because the acutely toxic but nonlethal dose has been established (2, 3). Preliminary tests proved that its ethyl groups do not interfere with the gas-chromatographic estimation of acetylcholine.

One or more animals was taken from the experimental group for brain acetylcholine measurement after 3, 10, 17, and 24 Di-Syston injections. In each instance, 24 hours had elapsed after the respective injection had been given. Cholinesterase activity of blood plasma, erythrocytes, and brain, and the norepinephrine content of brain were measured 24 hours after the third, tenth, and 24th injections. All of these measurements were repeated on the 38th day, 14 days after the last administration of Di-Syston. Animals were taken from the control group at each of the sampling times for the measurement of normal values. Each constituent was measured in the whole brain of an individual animal. All animals, control and experimental, were weighed daily through the injection period, and again at the 38th day.

The entire experiment was repeated three times, consecutively, each time on a newly purchased group of animals. In each instance the starting ages and weights were nearly identical.

Animals taken from experimental or control groups for the analytical procedures were decapitated by guillotine. The brain of each animal was then removed as rapidly as possible, the total elapsed time seldom exceeding 20 seconds. Further processing of the tissue depended upon the constituent to be measured.

Acetylcholine. Acetylcholine was measured by a new gas chromatographic method developed in this laboratory (10). Use of this method in the measurement of tissue levels of acetylcholine has been described in detail (9). Briefly, the tissue is frozen in a dry ice–ether bath immediately after excision, weighed, crushed, and extracted by a modification of the method of Crossland (4) with an acetic acid–alcohol mixture. After centrifugation and washing of the residue, the supernates are combined and evaporated to dryness under reduced pressure. The residue from the evaporation is taken up in water acidified with acetic acid and the product is centrifuged. Again, the supernate is evaporated to dryness. The residue is dissolved in a small volume of water, and solid potassium borohydride and calcium chloride are added. The subsequent reaction converts the acetate moiety of acetylcholine to ethanol, which is then assayed by means of a gas chromatograph.

The method is essentially specific for alcohol esters of choline and measures the total acetylcholine (free plus bound) content of the brain tissue. There is no interference from other substances which might have acetylcholine-like effects in biological assay. The results are expressed as micrograms of acetylcholine per gram of wet tissue.

Cholinesterase Activity. Cholinesterase activity was assayed by automatic, continuous, alkali titration of acid released from the substrate, a method previously utilized by Wilson (12), Main and Dauterman (6), Shellenberger et al. (8), and others.

Our procedure employed the Metrohm pH-Stat system in which the reaction proceeds at constant temperature and pH in an unbuffered, balanced-ion medium calculated to afford optimal conditions for enzyme activity. The closed reaction vessel is preflushed with nitrogen. In this inert atmosphere there is no interference from atmospheric CO_2, and because there is no spontaneous hydrolysis of the substrates during the short reaction period, blank runs are unnecessary. Only enough substrate is added to allow a linear reaction for a maximum of 10 minutes at the highest activities encountered, so that substrate inhibition is minimal. A description of our final version of this method, which is now being standardized on human subjects, will be published elsewhere.

Cholinesterase activity of blood and brain was measured in the same animals. Blood was collected in heparinized tubes at the time of decapitation. Plasma and cells from 2 ml. of blood were separated immediately by centrifugation. The hematocrit value was obtained on a separate sample.

Butyrylcholine iodide monohydrate (Calbiochem grade B) was used as the substrate for plasma assay, and the results are expressed as micromoles of butyric acid produced per milliliter of plasma per minute.

Acetylcholine perchlorate was used as the substrate for erythrocyte and brain cholinesterase. The washed erythrocytes from 2 ml. of blood were diluted with the solution mentioned above, to which saponin was added to lake the cells, and an aliquot was taken for assay. The results are expressed as micromoles of acetic acid produced per minute per milliliter of whole blood. Because we preferred to express erythrocyte activity in terms of whole blood, we adjusted each final value to its equivalent at a hematocrit of 50%. This calculation, involving the hematocrit obtained on each blood sample, serves to differentiate enzyme inhibition from the variability in activity associated with abnormal plasma-erythrocyte volume ratios.

The brain was homogenized in the saline diluent which is used in the assay procedure, and an aliquot of uniformly suspended homogenate was transferred directly to the reaction vessel. The results are expressed as micromoles of acetic acid produced per minute per gram of wet tissue.

Norepinephrine. The norepinephrine content of the whole brain was measured by the method of Anton and Sayre (1).

Results

After the second injection of Di-Syston, the animals began to lose weight and continued to do so for 7 days. After the 7th day they began to gain weight, and for the remainder of the injection period their growth curve roughly paralleled that of the control group. When the administration of Di-Syston was discontinued, the gain in weight accelerated, and at the 38th day, 14 days after the last injection, the animals remaining in the two groups weighed approximately the same. These weight relationships are illustrated in Figure 1.

Signs of poisoning reached their peak at about the 3rd day. They consisted of diarrhea, tremor, hyperexcitability, and excessive secretions from eyes, nose, and mouth. After the 3rd day the severity of the objective signs began to diminish, and by the 10th day they had subsided to a mild tremor and a slight but clearly apparent muscular weakness. Although these latter signs persisted until the injections were discontinued, the daily injections failed to elicit the acute phase seen earlier.

Table I shows that the cholinesterase activity in the brain 24 hours after the third Di-Syston injection was approximately one third of the control value. Erythrocyte cholinesterase activity at the same time was inhibited to about the same degree, but the activity of the plasma esterase was only 25% of the control level. During the succeeding 21 days of the injection period the brain cholinesterase activity declined further and remained at the 20% level while the activity of the plasma enzyme in-

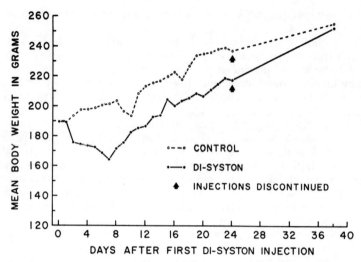

Figure 1. Effect of chronic Di-Syston administration on body weight

creased slightly and paralleled erythrocyte activity at about one third of the normal value.

Fourteen days after the last Di-Syston injection of the series, brain and erythrocyte cholinesterase activities had returned to 66 and 60% of normal, respectively, and the activity of the plasma enzyme exceeded the control level.

Figure 2, A, shows the response of brain cholinesterase to the daily Di-Syston injections, expressed as percent of the activity measured in control animals sacrificed on the same days. The curve was derived from

Table I. Cholinesterase Activity of Rat Tissues

Days after First Di-Syston Injection	Brain, μmoles Acetic Acid/G./Min. ± SE		Erythrocytes, μmoles Acetic Acid/Ml./Min. ± SE [a]		Plasma, μmoles Butyric Acid/Ml./Min. ± SE	
	Di-Syston	Control	Di-Syston	Control	Di-Syston	Control
	(6) [b]	(3)	(6)	(3)	(5)	(3)
3	2.50 ±0.14	7.30 ±0.05	0.38 ±0.03	1.05 ±0.05	0.20 ±0.02	0.80 ±0.03
	(4)	(2)	(4)	(2)	(4)	(2)
10	1.50 ±0.27	7.35 ±0.07	0.38 ±0.02	1.30 ±0.03	0.30 ±0.03	1.00 ±0.33
	(5)	(2)	(5)	(2)	(5)	(2)
24	1.40 ±0.19	6.80 ±0.04	0.58 ±0.05	1.88 ±0.00	0.30 ±0.00	0.90 ±0.00
	(5)	(2)	(5)	(2)	(5)	(2)
38 [c]	4.25 ±0.12	6.40 ±0.02	1:03 ±0.09	1.73 ±0.20	1.35 ±0.05	1.10 ±0.30

[a] Per ml. whole blood adjusted to 50% hematocrit.
[b] Numbers in parentheses represent number of animals used.
[c] Estimations made 14 days after last injection of Di-Syston.

data given in the first column of Table I, in which the standard error of each mean value is indicated. It is presented adjacent to the acetylcholine curves to show more clearly the quantitative relationships between the two sets of measurements. Although there was appreciable variability in the cholinesterase activity of the brain from animal to animal, we are confident that the percentages shown are reliable and that the form of the curve is accurate.

Figure 2, *B*, presents the most significant results of this study in graphic form. It shows that the acetylcholine content of the brain rose from a control level of 3.5 μg. per gram of tissue to 4.67 μg. per gram 24 hours after the third Di-Syston injection. It had returned to 3.57 μg. per gram after the tenth injection and remained at or near the control level thereafter.

Table II shows that the norepinephrine content of the whole brain of animals receiving Di-Syston did not vary significantly from that found in control animals at any time during the injection period, and was precisely at the control level 14 days after administration of the pesticide had been discontinued.

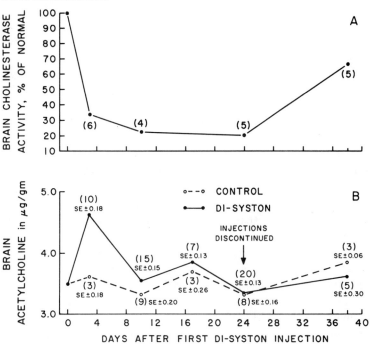

Figure 2. Effect of chronic Di-Syston administration
A. Brain cholinesterase activity as % of normal. Numbers in parentheses indicate number of animals receiving Di-Syston.
B. Acetylcholine content of the brain. Numbers in parentheses indicate number of animals used. Standard error of mean indicated at each point.

Table II. Norepinephrine Concentration in Brain Tissue
Norepinephrine, μg./G. $\pm$ SE

Days after First Di-Syston Injection	Controls		Di-Syston	
3	(6)[a]	0.291 ±0.012	(10)	0.304 ±0.008
10	(6)	0.310 ±0.011	(10)	0.346 ±0.008
24	(6)	0.329 ±0.011	(10)	0.354 ±0.016
38 [b]	(2)	0.306 ±0.006	(6)	0.305 ±0.010

[a] Numbers in parentheses represent number of animals.
[b] Estimations made 14 days after last injection.

Discussion and Summary

Our data show that the acetylcholine content of the brain of rats chronically poisoned by daily injections of Di-Syston was high during the first few days of the injection period when the acute signs of poisoning were prominent, and that it had returned to control levels when the acute phase of poisoning had subsided.

We have shown that this pattern can be reproduced readily, in that the data were collected from a series of consecutive experiments. In the later experiments the number of animals was increased to improve the reliability of the mean acetylcholine values at certain critical sampling times, primarily after the 10th and 24th Di-Syston injections. Thus, we can state with assurance that brain acetylcholine remained at control levels from the 10th day onward while the administration of the insecticide was continued.

These observations suggest that adaptation within the central nervous system involves an adjustment of the acetylcholine level downward to compensate for the persistent depression of cholinesterase activity.

Although this conclusion is opposed to that of Brodeur and Du-Bois (3), closer examination reveals that the experimental differences may be more apparent than real. There were, of course, certain differences between their experimental plan and ours. They employed a slightly higher dosage level of Di-Syston and made measurements at 1, 3, 6, 12, and 24 hours on small groups of animals after the latter had received the last injection of a series. Free and bound acetylcholine were measured by biological assay on pooled brain tissue of the animals in the small groups. Although this procedure does not reveal variability between animals, we do not question the validity of the average values so obtained.

Brodeur and DuBois observed that the free acetylcholine content of the brain rose to high levels in the poisoned animals, particularly at the 3rd and 6th hours after the last Di-Syston injection, and this phenomenon persisted throughout the injection period. It is noteworthy that the highest free acetylcholine values coincided with the lowest levels of brain cholinesterase activity within the 24-hour period. The latter measurements indicate the extent to which spontaneous reactivation of the enzyme can occur within 24 hours with this particular organophosphorus inhibitor.

However, there are certain similarities between the results of the two studies. Brain cholinesterase, measured 24 hours post-injection, declined steadily throughout the period of chronic Di-Syston administration in both studies. Although Brodeur and DuBois found that free acetylcholine remained high at the 3- and 6-hour post-injection periods, there was a return toward normal at the 24th hour, and this tendency appears slightly more marked at the 20th day of the experiment. Bound acetylcholine also tended to fall after its initial rise on the 3rd day, and on numerous occasions thereafter it was below normal levels. If one looks, therefore, at their values for total acetylcholine (free plus bound) 24 hours post-injection through the first 30 days of their study, the results resemble our own. We have no basis for speculation about events beyond 30 days.

It is our opinion that our measurements of total acetylcholine at the 24-hour post-injection interval have revealed an essential trend in the adaptation process. We consider it to be especially significant that the highest acetylcholine level occurred when the cholinesterase activity was 35% of the normal value, and that normal acetylcholine levels were observed after the cholinesterase activity had decreased further to 20% of the control value.

Because it is possible that free acetylcholine may constitute the predominant fraction of the reduced total which is observed after adaptation has occurred, our experiments do not rule out the possibility that cholinergic receptors may acquire tolerance to acetylcholine, as Brodeur and DuBois suggest. We are not prepared to evaluate the importance of increased resistance to carbachol which they present in support of their hypothesis, in view of the strong nicotinic component of the action of that drug.

We found no evidence that norepinephrine is involved in the adaptation process within the central nervous system since its concentration in the brain of Di-Syston-poisoned animals did not vary significantly from control levels at any time during the entire experimental period.

Acknowledgment

The Di-Syston used in this study was supplied by the Chemagro Corp., Kansas City, Mo.

Literature Cited

(1) Anton, A. H., Sayre, D. F., *J. Pharmacol. Exptl. Therap.* **138**, 360 (1962).
(2) Bombinski, T. J., DuBois, K. P., *A.M.A. Arch. Ind. Health* **17**, 192 (1958).
(3) Brodeur, J., DuBois, K. P., *Arch. Intern. Pharmacodyn.* **149**, 560 (1964).
(4) Crossland, J., *Methods Med. Res.* **9**, 125 (1961).
(5) Ganelin, R. S., *Arizona Med.* **21**, 710 (1964).
(6) Main, A. R., Dauterman, W. C., *Nature* **198**, 551 (1963).
(7) Rider, J. A., Ellinwood, L. E., Coon, J. M., *Proc. Soc. Exptl. Biol. Med.* **81**, 455 (1952).
(8) Shellenberger, T. E., Newell, G. W., Okamoto, S. S., Sarros, A., *Biochem. Pharmacol.* **14**, 943 (1965).
(9) Stavinoha, W. B., Ryan, L. C., *J. Pharmacol. Exptl. Therap.* **150**, 231 (1965).
(10) Stavinoha, W. B., Ryan, L. C., Treat, E. L., *Life Sci.* **3**, 689 (1964).
(11) Summerford, W. T., Hayes, W. J., Jr., Johnston, J. M., Spillane, J., *A.M.A. Arch. Ind. Hyg.* **7**, 383 (1953).
(12) Wilson, I. B., *J. Biol. Chem.* **208**, 123 (1954).

RECEIVED April 25, 1966.

Distribution of Pesticide Residues in Human Body Tissues from Montgomery County, Ohio

MARY L. SCHAFER and JEPTHA E. CAMPBELL

Milk and Food Research, Robert A. Taft Sanitary Engineering Center, Public Health Service, U.S. Department of Health, Education, and Welfare, Cincinnati, Ohio

Blood, omental fat, and organs of 19 cadavers, resulting from accidental deaths during 1964–65 in Montgomery County, Southern Ohio, were assayed for chlorinated hydrocarbons using gas chromatographs equipped with electron capture detectors. All samples contained DDT plus DDE. The total body burden of these two compounds was estimated to range from 22 to 300 mg. Over 95% was present in the fat. Eighteen of the cadavers contained blood concentrations ranging from 2 to 58 p.p.b. and fat concentrations ranging from 2 to 31 p.p.m.. A correlation index, R^2, of 0.77 was observed between fat and blood assays. One cadaver with a blood assay of 94 p.p.b. and fat assay of 5.4 p.p.m. was rejected as a member of the population represented by the other 18 cadavers.

In our laboratory studies on catfish (*4*), measurable concentrations of endrin were observed in the blood of those exposed to endrin. With exposure levels sufficiently high to cause death, there was a significant increase in blood endrin concentrations. In 1964 Brown, Hunter, and Richardson (*1*) reported a correlation between the levels of dieldrin in blood and clinical signs of poisoning in humans and suggested the usefulness of the blood test to diagnose marginal exposure. The present investigation was undertaken to determine the relationship between the levels of DDT in blood and the total body burden of humans, so that the total body burden for this pesticide may be estimated from analysis of blood. In an attempt to study this relationship in persons subjected to normal environmental exposures, cadavers resulting from accidental deaths were used.

A total of 19 cadavers from Montgomery County, Southern Ohio, was studied. They included six females and 13 males ranging between 18 and 76 years of age. The tissues and body fluids that were assayed included blood, omental fat, liver, kidney, brain, heart, and gut.

All samples were assayed according to the method developed in our laboratories (6). After saponification of the fat, the pesticides were extracted into hexane. Since DDT is quantitatively dehydrohalogenated to DDE during alkaline hydrolysis, all results reported as DDE are the sum of DDT plus DDE. The hexane extracts were resolved and assayed in gas chromatographs equipped with electron capture detectors. In addition to columns packed with Dow 11 plus Epon coated on Fluoropak 80, at least one replicate from each sample was assayed on a column packed with 3% QF-1 on anakrom ABS. This latter column showed excellent resolution for dieldrin and DDE, as shown in Figure 1.

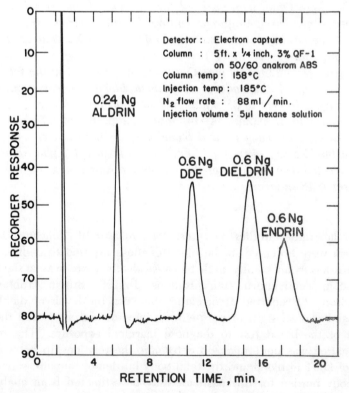

Figure 1. Chromatograph of standard solution of pesticides

Duplicate 10-gram blood samples for each cadaver were saponified and assayed. The concentrations of DDE ranged from 2 to 94 p.p.b. Chromatographs of the two extreme values are shown in Figure 2. Addi-

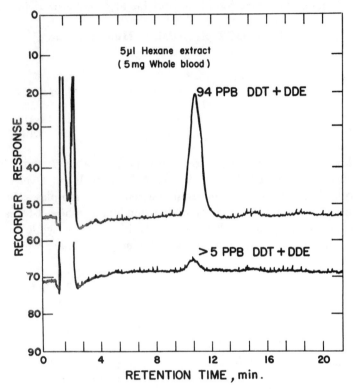

Figure 2.   Chromatograph of hexane extracts of whole blood

tional studies to confirm the identity of the DDE peak included the use of a thin layer chromatographic technique (7) and the comparison of the retention times for the hexane extracts of the blood sample and a standard solution of DDE on two additional column packings in which Apiezon L and a mixture of QF-1 plus XE 60 were used as liquid phases. For recovery studies, one of the duplicate samples from each of two cadavers was contaminated with sufficient DDT to produce a concentration of 40 p.p.b. Assuming 100% recovery of the added DDT, the duplicates agreed within the standard deviation observed for replicates of samples. This was less than 350/1000.

Portions of omental fat were rendered on a steam bath and 0.5- to 1.0-gram portions of the rendered fat were assayed. For recovery studies, two of the four replicate fat samples from one cadaver were contaminated with sufficient DDT to produce a concentration of 2 p.p.m. Assuming

100% recovery of the added DDT, the four replicates agreed within the standard deviation for replicates of samples, which was less than 100/1000. The concentrations of DDE found in these samples ranged from 2 to 31 p.p.m. The data for blood and fat are summarized in Table I.

Table I. DDT plus DDE in Human Tissue

No. of Persons	Blood, p.p.b.	Fat, p.p.m.
5	< 5	2.2– 4.7
9	5–20	3.3–13.8
4	28–58	9.4–31.0
1	94	5.4

Data for individual cadavers, along with the available personal history, are given in Table II. Cadaver 19, with the high blood level and low fat level, obviously is different from the remaining samples. He was a supervisor or a foreman at a manufacturing plant, white, 64 years old, and weighed 200 pounds. He apparently blacked out while driving a car, ran off the roadway, and struck a power pole. There were no skid

Table II. Personal

Occupation	Cause of Death	Coroner's Statement
Teacher	Suicide	Gun shot
Bank teller	Suicide	Gun shot
Retired	Natural causes	Heart condition
Unknown	Homicide	
Unknown	Accidental	Carbon monoxide
Dentist	Unknown	
Retired	Natural causes	Multiple degenerative diseases
Teacher	Natural causes	Influenza
Unknown	Homicide	
Housewife	Traffic accident [a]	
Housewife	Traffic accident [b]	
Housewife	Homicide	
Construction worker	Suicide	Carbon monoxide
Foundry employee	Traffic accident [a]	
Unknown	Homicide	
Unknown	Traffic accident [b]	
Garbage collector	Natural causes	Heart condition
Cement worker	Homicide	
Factory foreman	Traffic accident [a, c]	

[a] Driver of car that caused accident.
[b] Passenger in car involved in accident.
[c] Lived 3 days after accident.

marks. He lived 3 days after the accident. The pathological findings referred to small bowel hemorrhage.

During the early spring of 1964, blood samples from 25 employees at Taft Center were assayed using the procedure described above. Blood samples from 20 employees of the Lower Mississippi River Project, PHS, DHEW, 16 located in Baton Rouge, La., and four in Memphis, Tenn., were assayed in 1965–6. All samples contained detectable concentrations of DDT plus DDE. A comparison of the data for these groups with those from Montgomery County is shown in Table III. Fortunately, blood assays were obtained on five of the individuals from Baton Rouge in May 1965 and again in January 1966. For four of these individuals with assays in the range of 21 to 30 p.p.m. DDT plus DDE, the samples taken 7 months apart agreed within the precision of the method. One individual with a blood concentration of 40 p.p.b. in May 1965 showed a significant decrease to 19 p.p.b. in January 1966.

The mean concentrations of DDT plus DDE in the omental fat, 5.1 p.p.m., and the average value, 9.0 p.p.m., are less than the mean storage level of 12.7 p.p.m. reported for the U.S. population in 1961–2 by Quinby

History of Subjects

Cadaver No.	Blood, p.p.b.	Fat, p.p.m.	Age	Sex	Ht., In.	Wt., Lb.	Race
1	2	2.4	40	F	68	140	W
2	2	2.9	18	F	63	110	W
3	3	2.3	76	F	58	145	W
4	3	4.7	34	M	73	180	N
5	4	2.2	56	M	70	170	W
6	8	3.3	32	M	72	180	W
7	8	4.6	72	M	70	150	W
8	9	3.5	25	M	70	260	W
9	11	7.1	35	M	75	190	N
10	13	5.0	41	F	63	130	W
11	13	5.5	52	F	62	135	W
12	15	5.3	31	F	63	95	N
13	17	13.8	47	M	68	145	W
14	20	6.0	40	M	72	180	W
15	28	23.4	28	M	Unk.	Unk.	N
16	34	9.4	21	M	70	205	W
17	44	31.0	38	M	68	150	N
18	58	30.2	48	M	72	150	N
19	94	5.4	64	M	73	200	W

et al. (5). However, these workers reported data of samples assayed by a colorimetric procedure which according to Dale and Quinby (2) shows incorrectly high values as compared to those obtained with gas chromatographic procedures.

Table III. Frequency Distribution of DDT Concentration in
Human Blood from Four Geographic Locations

Blood, (P.P.B.)	Montgomery County, Ohio	Cincinnati, Ohio	Baton Rouge, La.	Memphis, Tenn.
< 8	5	6	0	0
8–10	3	3	1	0
11–20	6	10	10	2
21–30	1	5	3	1
31–40	1	1	1	0
41–50	1	0	1	1
51–60	1	0	0	0
61–70	0	0	0	0
71–80	0	0	0	0
81–100	1	0	0	0

The available sample size for kidney, brain, liver, and gut varied from 20 to 100 grams. Replicate assays of these samples did not agree and recovery studies indicated that these assays were not quantitative. Assays of one whole kidney showed significant differences between the concentrations of DDT plus DDE in the cortex and the medulla. The precision and the accuracy, as measured by recovery studies of replicate samples from homogenized portions of either the cortex or the medulla, were within the limits considered acceptable for this method. With the realization that it was impossible to obtain reliable data on the samples as they had been collected, an arithmetic average of all replicate assays for the organs from four cadavers was used to estimate the total body burden. Cadavers 3, 10, 14, and 18 were studied.

Table IV. DDT Plus DDE in Human Tissue
(Mg.)

Age	Sex	Blood	Brain	Kidney	Liver	Protein	Fat	Total
48	M	0.230	0.30	0.05	2.0	4.0	290	300
40	M	0.079	0.06	0.05	1.0	2.0	69	72
41	F	0.053	0.04	0.03	0.2	0.4	41	42
76	F	0.012	0.02	0.02	0.2	0.7	21	22

For estimation of the total body burden the following assumptions were used: The total volume of blood was 6% of the body weight. Protein was estimated as 15% of the body weight and then adjusted for the known weights of the liver, kidney, and brain. The DDT plus DDE content of the heart tissue and omental fat was considered representative of the remainder of the protein tissue and total fat, respectively. Fat was estimated as 14% of the body weight.

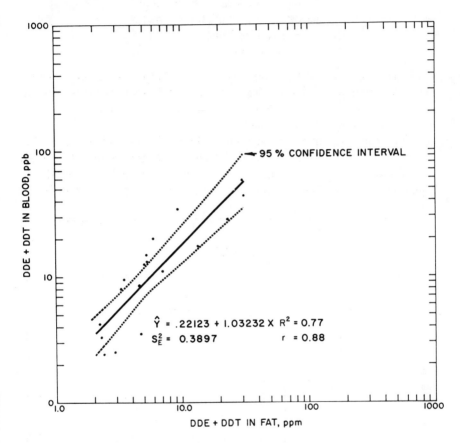

Figure 3.   Comparison of DDE + DDT in human blood and fat

The results, as shown in Table IV, estimate total body burdens of DDT plus DDE ranging from 22 to 300 mg. Over 95% of this was accounted for in the fat, indicating that analysis of the organs is relatively unimportant in computing the total body burden and the relationship between blood levels and the total body burden is essentially that between blood and fat levels.

Since one of the main purposes of this investigation was to find the relationship between the levels of DDT plus DDE in blood and the total body burden, the data for blood and fat for 18 cadavers were statistically analyzed. The following equation was fitted to the data:

$$y = b_0 + b_1 x \qquad\qquad (1)$$

where

$$
\begin{aligned}
y &= \log_{10} y' = \log_{10} \,(\text{blood, p.p.b.}) \\
x &= \log_{10} x' = \log_{10} \,(\text{fat, p.p.m.}) \\
b_0 &= \text{intercept of line} \\
b_1 &= \text{slope of line}
\end{aligned}
$$

In recognition that both variables were subject to error in measurement, the method (3) for $\lambda = \sigma_d{}^2/\sigma_e{}^2$, where λ is assumed to be known, was used to fit the data and estimate a confidence interval. The value of λ was assumed to be about 0.09.

The resulting equation, correlation index R^2, and error about the regression line are shown in Figure 3. The correlation index, $R^2 = 0.77$, indicates that 77% of the sum of squares is explained by the model in Equation 1. Two other possible variables that might have contributed

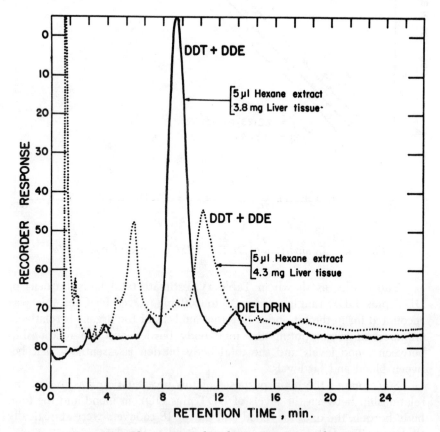

Figure 4. Chromatograph of hexane extracts of liver tissue

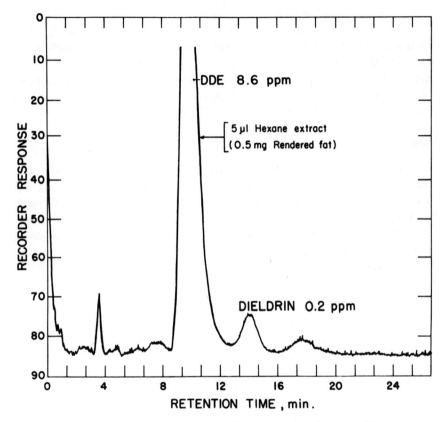

Figure 5.   Chromatograph of hexane extract of omental fat

to the error associated with fitting the data to this model are sex and occupation.

Just as sex differences are recognized in estimating average weights, it seems reasonable that both sexes should be considered separately in the development of a model to show the relationship between levels of DDT plus DDE in the blood and body fat. The information in Table II indicates a possible relationship also between occupation and total body burden. Unfortunately, it is impossible to evaluate the significance of these variables with the number of cadavers studied in this report.

Under the assumption that these data are normally distributed about a linear regression, as shown in Figure 3, the data for the 19th cadaver (5.4 p.p.m. of DDT plus DDE in fat and 94 p.p.b. in blood) were rejected as a member of this population. This pair of assays would have occurred much less than one time in a million by chance alone.

All of the organs contained additional compounds with sufficient electronegativity values to be detected with an electron capture detector.

Two typical chromatographs of hexane extracts of liver tissues are shown in Figure 4. Dieldrin is the only other chlorinated hydrocarbon that has been identified. It was found in most of the samples, but in such small concentrations that quantitative assays were not attempted. All fat samples except cadaver 19 contained detectable concentrations of dieldrin ranging from 2 to 800 p.p.b. A chromatograph of fat tissue containing 200 p.p.b. of dieldrin and 8.6 p.p.m. of DDE is shown in Figure 5.

Conclusions

Our studies indicate the presence of dieldrin in some samples and DDT plus DDE in all samples of human tissues that were assayed. Total body burdens of DDT ranging from 22 to 300 mg. were estimated. Greater than 95% of the total body burden of DDT plus DDE was found in the fat. Although the actual concentration of DDT plus DDE in the blood is small, the correlation index, $R^2 = 0.77$, indicates a positive correlation between the fat and blood assays.

Acknowledgment

The authors gratefully acknowledge the assistance of Cleo H. Hamilton in running most of the assays. They express their thanks to Linda Vigor and J. E. Gilchrist for their assistance with the assays, to G. K. Murthy and L. A. Richardson for their interest and helpful suggestions, to James T. Peeler and Jeanetta Brown for the statistical analyses, and to George Putnicki and staff of the Lower Mississippi River Project, PHS, DHEW, for graciously permitting us to use the data on their blood samples.

Literature Cited

(1) Brown, V. K. H., Hunter, C. G., Richardson, A., Brit. J. Ind. Med. 21, 283 (1964).
(2) Dale, W. E., Quinby, G. E., Science 142, 593 (1963).
(3) Graybill, F. A., "Introduction to Linear Statistical Models," Vol. 1, McGraw-Hill, New York, 1961.
(4) Mount, D., Vigor, L., Schafer, M., Science 152, 1388 (1966).
(5) Quinby, G. E., Hayes, W. J., Jr., Armstrong, J. F., Durham, W. F., J. Am. Med. Assoc. 191, 175 (1965).
(6) Schafer, M. L., Busch, K. A., Campbell, J. E., J. Dairy Sci. 46, 1025 (1963).
(7) Smith, D., Eichelberger, J., J. Water Pollution Control Federation 37, 77 (1965).

RECEIVED November 17, 1965.

Respiratory Exposure of Dairy Animals to Pesticides

J. M. WITT, F. M. WHITING, and W. H. BROWN

Departments of Entomology and Dairy Science,
The University of Arizona, Tucson, Ariz.

In the Arizona milkshed the level of pesticide in milk fluctuated on a seasonal cycle with a low of about 1.0 p.p.m. of pesticide in the milk fat in the spring and early summer months and a high of 3.0 to 3.5 p.p.m. in the late fall and early winter months. The rise during the fall and winter was eliminated by a moratorium on the use of DDT. Careful checking of all conceivable sources of DDT on a dairy farm with a high pesticide level did not account for the high level of pesticide secreted in the milk. Respiratory exposure studies showed that pulmonary tissues are not uniquely efficient in their absorption of DDT and thus should not contribute appreciably to the over-all secretory picture.

A critical pesticide residue problem today is that of chlorinated hydrocarbon pesticides in milk. The easiest solution to this problem is an across-the-board restriction on the use of chlorinated hydrocarbon pesticides in any environment which might contaminate dairy animals or feeds. This type of restriction would doubtless create hardships on other agricultural enterprises in those areas and may in fact be unnecessary. Detailed examination of the possible sources may well point to solutions which will not sweepingly encompass all chlorinated hydrocarbon insecticides or all uses of them.

Published data on the extent and nature of pesticide residues in milk are scant. The Dairy Industry Committee published an interim report (3) on the incidence and levels of pesticide residues in milk and milk products according to both individual states and geographic areas. Heineman (7) also published a survey of pesticides in milk according to wide geographic areas. Both of these studies covered a 12-month period in

1960–1961. Although there has been a great deal of work on the nature of the pesticide milk problem at various locations in the United States, only these two early reports have presented their data in a way which defines the problem. Any study of the sources of pesticides in milk must be preceded by a study defining the extent and nature of the problem.

A study showed that the level of pesticide contamination of milk produced in the Arizona milkshed was somewhat higher than in most other states. It fluctuated on a seasonal cycle with a low of about 1.0 p.p.m. of pesticide in the milk fat in the late spring and early summer months and a high of 3.0 to 3.5 p.p.m. in the late fall and early winter months. The pesticides found in the milk were predominantly DDT [2,2-bis-(p-chlorophenyl)-1,1,1-trichloroethane] and its metabolites DDD [2,2-bis-(p-chlorophenyl)-1,1-dichloroethane] and DDE [2,2-bis-(p-chlorophenyl)-1,1-dichloroethylene]. The metabolite DDE was generally present in 5–10 times greater amounts than DDT or DDD. The insecticide β-BHC was encountered occasionally at very low levels (< 0.2 p.p.m. in milk fat), and other insecticides were encountered sporadically when related to a particular instance of misuse.

DDT and Metabolites

DDT and its metabolites were the constant problem. Their peak incidence occurred 2–3 months after the peak use of DDT on agricultural crops which were grown in fields intermingled with other fields used to produce forage. This lag fell within the normal length of time for forage to be harvested and consumed. Measurements showed that insecticide drift during aerial application of spray and dust insecticide was an important source of contamination of feed and that the dust formulations provided about four times as much deposit on forage crops from drift as sprays. Following a moratorium on the use of DDT dust formulations, the level of DDT (and its metabolites) contamination of milk decreased. The most striking feature of the decrease was the failure of the pesticide level in the milk to rise spectacularly in the fall months; it remained between 1.5 and 1.8 p.p.m. in the milk fat throughout the year.

The continuing presence of DDT (and its metabolites) in milk prompted detailed studies on the epidemiology of DDT on several dairy farms. All conceivable sources and reservoirs for DDT on a dairy farm, including all the feed, bedding, water, corral environment, and soil, were sampled and analyzed for DDT and its metabolites. The DDT (and its metabolites) in the milk fat was also determined for 6 to 18 consecutive months at the end of the month during which the feed sampled was fed. If the DDT input is known, it should be possible to predict the level of DDT appearing in the milk fat on the basis of the numerous feeding studies on dairy cows carried out with DDT (2, 4, 5, 6, 12, 14, 17).

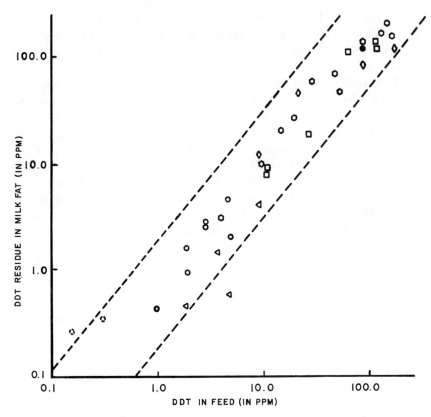

Figure 1.   DDT residue in milk fat in relation to DDT residue in feed

Bruce *et al.* (2)   Shepherd *et al.* (12)
Ely *et al.* (4)   Williams *et al.* (14)
Gannon *et al.* (5)   Zweig *et al.* (17)
Gyrisco *et al.* (6)

    The data from these authors are summarized and plotted in Figure 1 in a form which should permit one to predict DDT levels in the milk fat from DDT levels in the feed. Although there is a range of response from the different experiments, there is a reasonably good homogeneity for experiments of this type. The 1 to 1 ratio of the amount of DDT in the feed to the amount in the milk fat, which is sometimes used as a rule of thumb for predictions, fits within the limits shown in Figure 1. The 1.25-p.p.m. level of DDT in milk fat, which is the *ad hoc* "analytical zero" at the present time, may be expected to arise from about 0.5 to 5.0 p.p.m. of DDT in the feed. A deficiency in the available data is that very few are available below 2.0 p.p.m., and although the dose-response relationship is linear from 200 to 2 p.p.m. in the feed, linearity must be assumed for the lower values. Lehman (9) has summarized data to show that the ratio of DDT in the feed to DDT stored in the body fat of rats changes from 1 to 15 at 10 p.p.m. (in the feed) to 1 to 25 at 1 p.p.m., and to 1 to 60 at 0.1 p.p.m. This extreme change in the storage ratio has not been noted in dairy animals as yet.

Most studies on the epidemiology of DDT on dairy farms are concerned with the region below 1.0 p.p.m. in the feed. These data must be used at present to guide dairy farmers as to the acceptable levels of pesticide in feed for producing milk below the "zero tolerance" level. The validity of such predictions from these data was tested by using them to interpret the results received from the dairy farms on which pesticide inputs were studied. An example of one of these studies which was conducted for 12 months is shown in Figure 2. The level of DDT in the feed ranged from 0.01 to 0.3 p.p.m. for the hay and concentrate and from 0.2 to 5.0 p.p.m. for the silage over the period of the study. When the

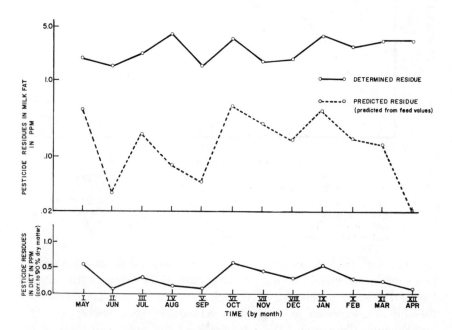

Figure 2.   Pesticide residue in milk fat
Actual values from a dairy farm vs. predicted values of DDT and its metabolites.

pesticide level for the diet was calculated, based on the proportion of each type of feed used, it was from 0.1 to 0.5 p.p.m. According to the data in Figure 1, the residue level in the milk fat should have been from a maximum of 0.1 to 0.8 p.p.m. The results (Figure 2) show that the actual response exceeds the predicted response consistently and by a factor of 5- to 40-fold. These DDT-epidemiology studies have shown that this is often the case when low pesticide values are involved, but when large pesticide inputs are involved the response is predictable.

These predictions could be in error for several reasons. The data from which they are made could be inadequate because of the low number of values at the low levels of pesticide input; because the dosing experiments were not carried out for a long enough time to establish a true equilibrium between input and storage; because the method of exposure used (dosing of the grain concentrate with an acetone solution of DDT) was not comparable to exposure by way of a normally aged residue; because the type of diet may affect accumulation; or because the analytical method used to detect the stored DDT did not detect all of the metabolites such as DDE and therefore gave a low result. The results obtained in the DDT-epidemiology study could be in error because of inadequate sampling, although care was taken to ensure accurate sampling, or because of some incident of exposure to pesticide prior to the study which is still affecting the degree of storage, although the length of term of the epidemiology study should have resolved such interference. Another possible source of error is the existence of an unmonitored source of pesticide input, such as direct respiratory exposure of the cow to drifting pesticides. Although such exposures would be less frequent than exposure to feed contaminated by drifting pesticides, they may be more significant if a higher degree of absorption and storage results from pulmonary exposure than from alimentary exposure.

Experiments with Lactating Cows

To test whether or not respiratory exposure may have been a major source of contamination not accounted for in earlier studies, we studied the effect of respiratory exposure of lactating cows on excretion of pesticides in the milk. Holstein cows from the University of Arizona dairy herd were used as experimental animals. The animals were fed normally, with care to assure feed intake of less than 0.1 p.p.m. of chlorinated hydrocarbon pesticide.

Because the percentage of the dose excreted in the milk is a method of measuring efficiency of pesticide absorption and storage, four routes for administering DDT were compared (intratracheal or respiratory, intravenous, rumen capsule, and aged residue), with three cows being assigned to each route. The dose was administered only once to each cow during the first phase of the experiment. During the second phase, the dose was administered once a day for 6 consecutive days, except in the case of the aged residue, where the cows refused to eat the entire dose. In all cases, the dose was based on the weight of feed consumed (which in turn was based on production) and was calculated to be equivalent to 4.0 p.p.m. of the feed. Several pretreatment samples were taken to establish the base line excretion of pesticides. Following exposure, samples were taken at each milking (twice daily) and analyzed separately until excretion had leveled off; then samples were collected at one milking each day for 6 days per week (three morning and three evening milkings) and three contiguous samples were composited to form a single sample for analysis.

In the intratracheal administration a polyethylene tube previously filled with DDT powder was inserted through a large needle directly into the trachea. The powder was expelled by blowing air through the tube with a large syringe. The other methods of administration were: an oil solution in a capsule direct into the rumen, an oil solution direct into the jugular vein, or pelleted alfalfa hay which was exposed before harvest.

The milk samples were extracted by ether-pentane, cleaned up on activated Florisil, and detected by electron capture gas chromatography using a 5% Dow-11 column at 175°C.

Preliminary results of these experiments are summarized in Table I, and an example of response of each type of dose is given in Figures 3–6. The figures show that the level of unavoidable contamination before exposure produced a low base line level of pesticide in the milk, which was quite uniform for each cow.

Table I. Effect of Method of Administration on Appearance of DDT and Its Metabolites in Milk

Method of Administration	Consecutive Days Dosed	Mean Max. Response [a] p.p.m. in Milk Fat			
		DDT	DDE	DDD	Total
Intratracheal	1	0.68	0.06	0.0	0.74
	6	1.54	0.01	0.08	1.64
Rumen-capsular	1	0.59	0.0	0.28	0.87
	6	0.49	0.08	1.18	1.75
Rumen-aged residue	1	0.38	0.90	0.56	1.84
Intravenous	1	3.00	0.12	0.12	3.24
	6	7.60	0.25	0.68	8.53

[a] Average of three cows. Net gain over base line.

All four dosing methods produced definite accumulations of DDT and its metabolites in the milk. This was of major importance since one of the questions involved in such low rates of exposure was whether there would be a measurable response. This was of special concern in the case of the single dose. A comparison showed that the intratracheal exposure resulted in slightly less total excretion of DDT and its metabolites in milk than either of the two alimentary modes of exposure. As expected, the intravenous infusion produced considerably higher pesticide levels in the milk than any of the other three exposures (see Table I). The intravenous method was included on the assumption that any administered dose of insecticide must first be absorbed into the blood, and direct administration into the blood would provide the maximum response possible.

On the single dosing phase, slightly over twice as much chlorinated hydrocarbon from aged residue appears in the milk as from the same dose given in an oil solution in a capsule. This type of response has been reported by Ely *et al.* (*4*). A possible explanation of this phenomenon may be that the pesticide that is thoroughly incorporated into the feed remains longer in the rumen while the feed is being digested than does the pesticide in oil, which may be washed out into the lower alimentary tract, giving less time for absorption into the blood. From the results of this experiment no claims are made as to whether or not this explanation is valid; however, further work should be undertaken to establish the validity of pipetting a solution of DDT in acetone onto the feed prior to feeding and then assuming that this is identical to an aged residue.

Depletion rates of the pesticide varied markedly for the different modes and durations of the experiment. The rate of depletion from the 1-day exposure was rather uniform; however, all the 6-day exposures appeared to present two rates of decline—one taking less than· a week on the average and a second taking up to 90 days.

Variations in rate of loss may perhaps be explained or understood by using the percentage of the dose which is secreted. Some workers (*10, 17*) found anywhere from 3 to 30% of the dose excreted in the milk. Our study had a variation in the recovered dose in the milk of from 0.78% in one of the intratracheal one-dose exposures to 32.2% in one of the intravenous six-dose exposures. No correlation was noted between recovered dose and milk fat production, lactation number, stage of lactation, or weight of the cow. There was, of course, a correlation between level of residue in the milk and length of time the residue can be followed in the milk.

One of the most significant findings of this experiment is the differences in the ratios of the metabolic products of DDT detected in the milk resulting from the different modes of exposure. Earlier work (*1, 4, 8, 13, 15, 17*) by Ely, Zweig, and others could perhaps have also shown this phenomenon, but detection methods used at that time were not sophisticated enough to distinguish between the various metabolites and thus may not have detected the metabolites in some instances. In this study almost the entire amount of pesticide appearing in the milk was unchanged DDT when the exposure was intratracheal or intravenous, which bypassed the rumen. When the dose was rumen-capsular, a major

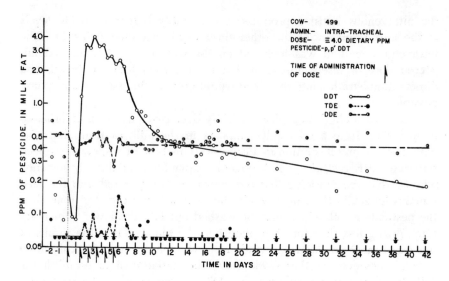

Figure 3. Secretion of DDT in milk fat in response to a 6-day intratracheal
dose of DDT

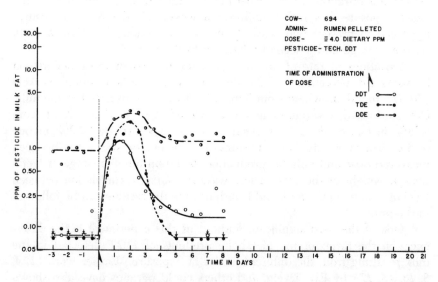

Figure 4. Secretion of DDT in milk fat in response to a one-day aged-residue
dose of DDT

portion of the secreted pesticide was DDD while in the case of aged
residue exposure nearly 50% of the secreted pesticide was DDE, most
of the remaining portion being DDD.

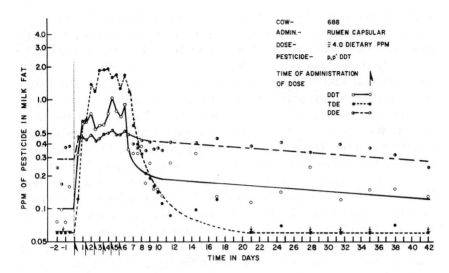

Figure 5.   Secretion of DDT in milk fat in response to a 6-day rumen-capsule
dose of DDT

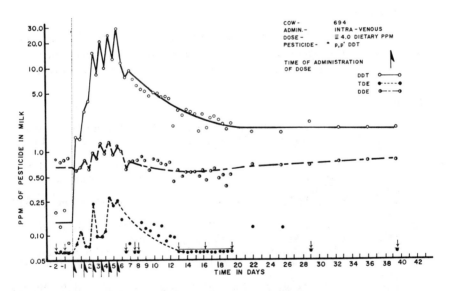

Figure 6.   Secretion of DDT in milk fat in response to a 6-day intravenous
dose of DDT

It is obvious from these results that dosing by way of the rumen and
thus exposing the DDT to metabolism by the rumen microorganisms
causes a much greater metabolism of the pesticide than routes of

administration which bypass the rumen. The six-dose intravenous exposure does, however, show that the cow herself (as distinct from symbiotic microorganisms) can produce DDE and probably DDD from DDT. The increase in the level of DDE in the milk resulting from the aged residue administration and the lack of this metabolic step when the dosing used an oil solution is difficult to explain, and further study of this phenomenon must be undertaken before an explanation can be given. Various surveys (7, 11, 16) have shown considerable DDE in milk in relation to DDT. This transformation is presumed to be accomplished by the metabolic processes of the cow. This is not supported by the relatively short-term exposures presented here. Longer-term exposures may, however, shed new light on the subject. The intratracheal or respiratory exposure studies show that the pulmonary tissues are not uniquely efficient in their absorption of DDT, and therefore this route of exposure probably does not contribute a sufficient amount of DDT intake to account for the discrepancy found between the levels of pesticide detected in the milk of a dairy herd and the level which was predicted on the basis of measuring the input through the feed.

Acknowledgment

The assistance of the late Nancy Lord and of Mary Milbrath and Gail Shaw in processing the samples is appreciated. Appreciation is expressed to the Geigy Chemical Co. for supplying the DDT for this study.

Literature Cited

(1) Allen, N. N., Lardy, H. A., Wilsòn, H. F., *J. Dairy Sci.* **29**, 530 (1946).
(2) Bruce, W. N., Link, R. P., Decker, G. C., *J. Agr. Food Chem.* **13**, 63 (1965).
(3) Dairy Industry Committee, Washington, D.C., interim report (June 1961).
(4) Ely, R. E., Moore, L. A., Carter, R. H., App, B. A., *J. Econ. Entomol.* **50**, 348 (1957).
(5) Gannon, N., Link, R. P., Decker, G. C., *J. Agr. Food Chem.* **7**, 829 (1959).
(6) Gyrisco, G. G., Norton, L. B., Trimberger, G. W., Holland, R. F., McEnerney, P. J., Muka, A. A., *Ibid.*, **7**, 707 (1959).
(7) Heineman, H. E. O., Miller, C. B., *J. Dairy Sci.* **44**, 1775 (1961).
(8) Laben, R. C., Archer, T. E., Crosby, D. G., Peoples, S. A., *Ibid.*, **48**, 701 (1965).
(9) Lehman, A. J., *Assoc. Food Drug Officials U.S. Quart. Bull.* **20**, 95 (1956).
(10) Marth, E. H., *J. Milk Food Technol.* **25**, 72 (1962).
(11) Paul, C., Merrill, M. H., Petition to Food and Drug Administration (March 1, 1965).
(12) Shepherd, J. B., Moore, L. A., Carter, R. H., Poos, F. W., *J. Dairy Sci.* **32**, 549 (1949).
(13) Smith, R. F., Hoskins, W. M., Fullmer, O. H., *J. Econ. Entomol.* **41**, 759 (1948).

(14) Williams, S., Mills, P. A., McDowell, R. E., *J. Assoc. Agr. Chemists* **47**, 1124 (1964).
(15) Wingo, C. W., Crisler, O. S., *J. Econ. Entomol.* **41**, 105 (1948).
(16) Witt, J. M., Whiting, F. M., Brown, W. H., unpublished data, 1966.
(17) Zweig, G., Smith, L. M., Peoples, S. A., Cox, R., *J. Agr. Food Chem.* **9**, 481 (1961).

RECEIVED February 7, 1966. Arizona Agricultural Experiment Station Technical Paper 1088. Work supported in part by Grant EF-00627-01 from the U. S. Public Health Service and a grant from the United Dairymen of Arizona.

9

Occurrence and Mode of Introduction of Pesticides in the Environment

WILLIAM E. WESTLAKE and FRANCIS A. GUNTHER

Department of Entomology, University of California, Riverside, Calif.

Pesticides occur in detectable amounts throughout the environment in virtually all inhabited areas of the world and in some, if not all, of the uninhabited portions. If our methods of detection were sufficiently sensitive and definitive, there is no part of the earth where we could not now find at least a few molecules of many pesticides in plants, man, animals, soil, water, and air. Pesticides are introduced into the environment in ‡ variety of ways, including direct application in agriculture, in forest pest control, and for control of pests affecting human health. Comparatively small areas of the world are so treated, but transport by wind, water, and movement of food and feed in commerce results in universal distribution of minute amounts of these compounds.

The best approach to this subject appears to be a consideration of the source—or mode of introduction—of pesticides in our environment, followed by a discussion of their occurrence. We direct our attention, then, to a general survey of the sources of pesticide contamination.

Sources of Pesticide Contamination

Over 125 major organic insecticides are registered for use and covered by legal tolerances or exemptions in the United States. Federal registrations cover over 2500 crop items. A like number of fungicides and about 50 herbicides are also available. About 20 insecticides, 15 fungicides, and 10 herbicides account for most of the sales, however. Some conception of the amount of material involved is shown in Figure 1, showing the total yearly U.S. sales of organic pesticides since 1954. In

1964 this amounted to about 3 pounds per person in the United States. Table I shows the U.S. production of some of the major pesticide chemicals from 1961 through 1964. These data give us some conception of the amount of pesticide chemicals available for potential contamination of the environment in the United States. The total amount sold is increasing. Substantial amounts are also used throughout the rest of the world, particularly in Canada, Great Britain, Japan, the U.S.S.R., and Western Europe, and pesticide use is increasing rapidly in Asia, Africa, and South America. Although the amounts of pesticides involved are small when compared with contaminants from other sources such as industrial and household wastes and automobile exhausts, nonetheless they constitute an impressive total. Table II lists some of the other worrisome contaminants of our environment.

In order that we may keep our perspective, let us consider the all-time world production of DDT in another way. As quoted by Gunther and Jeppson (9), the total arable land area in about 90 counties in the world is 2,287,000,000 acres. The total land area is probably about 10 times this amount. DDT production in the United States since 1952 has been about 1,801,000,000 pounds. Estimating U.S. production prior to 1952 at 500,000,000 pounds and production in the rest of the world at 1,150,000,000 pounds to date, we arrive at a total of about 3,500,000,000

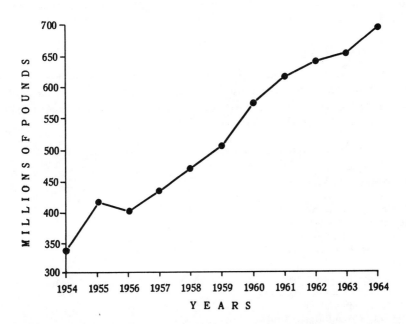

Figure 1. Annual production of pesticide chemicals in the United States

Table I. U.S. Production of Some Major Pesticide Chemicals,
1961–1964

(1000 pounds)

Chemicals	1961	1962	1963	1964
DDT	171,438	167,032	178,913	123,709
BHC, gross	25,080	12,022	6,778	N.A.
Other chlorinated				
hydrocarbons [a]	103,763	106,226	105,986	105,296
2,4-D, 2,4,5-T [b]	94,876	98,975	109,901	136,157
Parathion, methyl parathion				
Other organophosphorus	26,960	24,942		29,467
insecticides	.....	......	75,992	......

[a] Aldrin, dieldrin, endrin, chlordan, toxaphene.
[b] Acid, esters, acid salts.

pounds. This is about 1.5 pounds of DDT per arable acre or less than 20 mg. per square foot of arable land surface over the 13-year period involved. On the basis of total land area of the world this is less than 2 mg. per square foot of land surface. This is not a large amount and is calculated on the basis of total production, with no allowance for losses owing to alterations or to deposition on water surfaces. We know that the time required for degradation of 50% of the DDT present in most soils is not longer than 10 years; the actual amount of unchanged DDT now remaining would, therefore, be much less than the amount produced and distributed as assumed above.

Introduction of Pesticides into the Environment

The means of introducing pesticides into our environment may be divided into two broad categories: intentional application for pest control as contrasted with the unintentional, or accidental, contamination that often occurs. Table III lists some of these sources.

Table II. Some Residues Contaminating Our Environment

Boron (certain fuels, washing aids)
Detergents (nonbiodegradable)
Fluorides (naturally occurring and from industry)
Household and farm wastes
Industrial wastes (immense quantity and variety)
Lead (from gasoline, plumbing, solder in tin cans)
Peroxyacetyl nitrites (in smog)
Pesticides
Polynuclears (auto exhaust, burning, asphalt, some food-grade waxes, petroleum
     oil sprays, and many other sources)
Strontium –89 and –90
SO_2, SO_3 (from industry and in smog)
Tin from cans, concrete, glass, aluminum, and plastic wrapping materials
Yttrium –90

Almost all of this pesticide production is introduced into the environment by direct application to agricultural crops, livestock, soil, forests, water sources, homes, gardens, and to all types of environment for controlling parasites and vectors of disease to protect the public health. While—as commonly claimed—only about 5% of the arable area of the world has been so treated, these limited areas may be heavily treated. For example, in 1962 in California alone, 12,000,000 acres were sprayed or dusted. Over 1,800,000 pounds of 14 different pesticides were applied in 1963 to 700,000 of these acres, planted in cotton in the San Joaquin Valley, resulting in 2.6 pounds per acre in one year or 25 mg. per square foot per year. Over the past 20 years, therefore, many millions of pounds of DDT alone have been used there. Although few agricultural areas in the world are so intensively treated, substantial amounts of pesticide chemicals are always used wherever modern agriculture is practiced.

Table III. Some Sources of Environmental Contamination by Pesticides

A. Intentional (Direct) Application
1. Animals
2. Crops
3. Soil
4. Water (mosquito control, water weed control, trash fish control, etc.)
5. Household and garden use
6. Mothproofed fabrics for human and household use

B. Unintentional (Indirect) Contamination
1. Industrial wastes—Water, soil, air
   a. Pesticide manufacturers
   b. Mothproofing plants and others
   c. Food industry wastes
2. Drift (air currents), snowout, and rainout—water, soil, air
3. Animal dipping vats—water, soil
4. Dumping and cleaning spray tanks—water, soil
5. Home use (sewers)—water
6. Dumped milk and other products containing residues higher than tolerances—water, soil
7. Dead animals and animal excreta—water, soil
8. Decaying plant tissues (refuse, soil conditioners)—water, soil
9. Garbage disposals (sewers)—water
10. Pest control operations—air (volatilization, wind)

Smaller but still significant amounts of pesticides are used for forest and rangeland insect and disease control and to protect the public against insect-borne disease. The areas covered by these programs are large, but the rates of application are usually low. For example, the highly publicized programs to control the spruce budworm and the gypsy moth were carried out using application rates of 1 pound per acre, or less, of DDT. Although millions of acres were treated in these programs, the total amount of insecticide was small when compared with more direct agricultural uses. The major use in the public health field is in the malaria eradication program; thus, the World Health Organization and the U.S. Agency for International Development used 75,000,000 pounds of DDT in Asia in 1962 and 65,000,000 pounds in 1963. Other uses of various pesticides include the treatment of marshes and water sources for the control of nuisance pests such as mosquitoes, gnats, and other biting arthropods, the treatment of ponds, canals, and streams for water weed control, treatment of lakes and ponds for trash fish control, and a variety of home and garden uses. This last item should not be overlooked as a major source of direct contamination in and around our homes, since shipments of household insecticides and repellants in the United States in 1963 were valued at over $110,000,000. About 5% of the United States pesticide production goes into these products (1). Another use, often overlooked, is the mothproofing of clothing, furniture, and rugs with pesticide chemicals.

There are many unintentional or accidental ways to introduce pesticides into the environment. One overly publicized example is the recent Mississippi River fish kill, the cause for which has been variously attributed to waste from a pesticide manufacturing plant, runoff from insecticide-treated agricultural land, and "natural" causes such as oxygen deficiency, disease, and the like. Whatever the cause of this particular fish kill, we face the fact that industrial wastes containing pesticides or related compounds do escape into waterways or ground waters. This danger is well illustrated by two incidents involving 2,4-D and related compounds. In 1945 a company began to manufacture 2,4-D in California, emptying wastes containing 2,4-D and 2,4-DCP into the local sewage system. Within 17 days phenolic tastes and odors were reported downstream in shallow wells, and they persisted for 3 years (20). In Colorado, at the Rocky Mountain Arsenal, 2,4-D was manufactured, and wastes were discharged into lagoons from 1943 to 1957. Ground water contamination was first reported in 1951 (22) when crops were damaged by irrigation well water. It had taken 7–8 years for the contaminant to migrate 3.5 miles and eventually to affect an area of 6.5 square miles.

Industrial wastes from pesticide and other manufacturing processes merit particular attention. While we know a great deal about the fates of many registered pesticide chemicals, we know very little about the natures and fates of the many products in the immense tonnages of wastes in the dumps of pesticide manufacturers. These compounds will slowly leach from already existing "dumps" into our waters and soils for hundreds of years.

Agricultural by-products and wastes also constitute a major source from which pesticides are introduced into our total environment. As expected, apple and tomato pomace, citrus rind, bean and peanut vines, alfalfa threshings, cottonseed and soybean meal, and various other products incorporated into cattle feeds contain pesticides. Except for citrus products, in some instances levels have been so high that this use of these products could not be permitted. Bovard *et al.* (3), for example, found that some apple pomace, used as beef cattle feed, contained 103 p.p.m. of DDT. Beef animals fed this pomace for 104 days stored an average of about 70 p.p.m. in their fat. This is an extreme case but illustrates the possibilities if we become careless or remain indifferent to this source. Almost all agricultural by-products and wastes contain small amounts of pesticides, the levels usually being low enough to permit their use without fear of violating the law and certainly at present without danger to public health. All by-products and wastes from any crop treated with a pesticide will contain some residue of the compound and its metabolites or other alteration products; it only requires a sufficiently sensitive method, properly used, for their detection.

Accidental contamination of the environment occurs during and after application of pesticides to crops and forest lands by several routes. Inadvertent application to streams and ponds or to land areas not intended to be treated has been common. This source of contamination can be minimized but not completely eliminated. Drift, owing to air currents, often occurs, particularly when application is by aircraft, although drift from other types of application, even under the most favorable meteorological conditions, must not be underestimated. While this undesirable situation can be minimized by careful application, a certain amount of drift is unavoidable.

Erosion resulting from heavy rains or from irrigation is a source of pesticide movement from treated to untreated areas and into ponds and into both surface and underground waterways. Sorbed pesticides are carried with the soil particles, sometimes for considerable distances, and deposited in the beds of streams, in ponds and lakes, and on land areas subject to flooding. In addition, minute amounts are carried in solution in the water and particularly in soil water, according to some investigators. Nicholson *et al.* (18) made a detailed study of the runoff from a peach orchard into a farm pond, finding as much as 1.9 p.p.m. of parathion in the pond bottom mud and 0.01 to 1.22 p.p.b. in the water. Young and Nicholson (27) reported on a particularly heavy fish kill in northern Alabama following several heavy rains. Fish kills followed each rain, suggesting that toxic materials were carried into the streams, either with soil particles or in solution, from adjacent heavily treated cotton-growing areas. Tarzwell and Henderson (21) determined the dieldrin content of runoff water from a grassy area treated with 4.66 pounds of dieldrin per acre. The first runoff contained 0.13 p.p.m. of dieldrin, the third 0.01, and the fourth none detectable. Hindin, May, and Dunstan (10) give data obtained from the analysis of samples of irrigation waste water and river water in the Columbia Basin in the State of Washington. They conclude that the amounts found were far below any known toxicity level but could be important because of concentration by aquatic zooplankton and microfauna.

Marth (15) gives an excellent review on residues and effects of organochlorine insecticides in biological material that should be of interest to all workers in this field.

Movement by air currents is a potential source of contamination that is not well understood and needs careful study. Drift of sprays and dusts over relatively short distances, previously mentioned, is recognized. The transport of herbicides for a considerable distance in dust clouds during high winds has been reported in several areas. It is not definitely known, however, whether pesticides are dispersed in this manner in the form of fine particles or as aerosols. Certainly the potential is present, for it is well known that particulate matter is carried to high altitudes and for great distances by air currents, as abundantly confirmed by high-flying aircraft equipped with air sampling devices.

Evidence of pesticide dispersal in air remote from treated areas is given by West (23). Exploratory determinations were made on 18 samples of ambient air collected over four California cities in 1963. All but two contained measurable amounts of DDT. Air samples from nine different stations in the national air sampling network contained from 0.0002 to 0.34 μg. of DDT per 1000 cubic meters of air filtered over a 24-hour period.

Cohen and Pinkerton (5) report on the analysis of rainwater which contained two pesticides applied 3 weeks previously in an area one mile away from the sampling site. Organic chlorine- and sulfur-containing pesticides were detected in Cincinnati in precipitated dust deposited by a trace of rain, that was thought to have originated in the southwestern United States where a dust cloud was generated by high winds that moved it in a northeasterly direction. In Washington State, Bamesberger and Adams (2) sampled ambient air in two field sites for 100 days in 1964, finding measurable amounts of aerosol and gaseous 2,4-D compounds.

The heavy contamination of areas on which livestock dipping vats are located is recognized, as is the contamination of streams and ponds from careless dumping and cleaning of spray tanks. Pesticides used in homes and gardens may be partially disposed of in the sewer, ultimately reaching streams, lakes, and oceans. Milk and other products not suitable for human consumption because of excessive pesticide content must be disposed of some way and thus are potential environmental contaminants. Dead animals and excreta from treated animals are also minor sources for introducing pesticides into our environment, as are the immense volumes of kitchen vegetable trimmings and other wastes placed in garbage disposals.

Occurrence of Pesticides in Environment

Turning now to the occurrence of pesticides, it can be said again with no fear of contradiction that pesticides are present in all types of environment in all parts of the world. The levels may be too low to detect by methods now at our disposal and may have no immediate significance in many areas, particularly those remote from civilization. It is not the purpose of this paper, however, to evaluate the significance of the amounts present but rather to discuss the occurrence, regardless of amount.

In our immediate environment, we know that pesticides occur in our food supply as a direct result of agricultural uses. The market basket surveys conducted by the U.S. Food and Drug Administration are a potential means of keeping us informed of the amounts and kinds present. Unfortunately, though, they are not comprehensive enough to be completely reassuring, nor are the surveys conducted in accord with any acceptable sampling procedure.

Briedenbach and Lichtenberg (4) have reported, in a preliminary way, on findings of the national water quality network. In 1962 DDT and dieldrin were detected in 14 of 101 locations in 10 streams in the United States. The levels were estimated at 1 to 2 p.p.b. These were samples of water only and do not indicate how much, if any, was present in the silt carried by these streams. Metcalf (16) cites unpublished data of the U.S. Public Health Service, resulting from the analysis of water at 100 locations throughout the U.S. The range of values measured was (p.p.b.):

Endrin	0.0000 to 0.094
Dieldrin	0.0000 to 0.118
DDT	0.0000 to 0.087
DDE	0.0000 to 0.018

He further states that such pesticidal contamination represents 0.0001 to 0.001% of the total organic pollution of water and would be insignificant if it were not for the biological magnification of residues in living organisms by 1000- to 10,000-fold. Nicholson (17) reported on sampling of a water supply in Alabama in a heavily treated cotton-growing area. Maximum concentrations of 0.4 p.p.b. of toxaphene and 0.75 p.p.b. of BHC were found. It is not known how far downstream these compounds persisted. He concluded that the pesticides detected were in solution rather than carried by soil particles since filtration did not lower the concentrations. The possibility that the pesticides were sorbed on colloidal material that was not removed in the filters should also be investigated.

Forage crops have been shown to contain small amounts of pesticides, not only as a result of direct application but from being grown in soil previously treated. The amounts, admittedly ofteñ very small, may appear in the milk of dairy cattle receiving such feed. In fact, because of the concentration of fat-soluble pesticides in the butterfat, it may be possible to detect some of them in the milk when the levels in the feed are too low to determine by the methods now available. For example, Westlake et al. (25) have reported the presence of heptachlor epoxide in the milk of cows grazed on chlordan-treated pasture when the amount of this compound present on the forage was too small to detect. The heptachlor epoxide probably originated from a small amount of heptachlor present as an impurity in the chlordan. While this is unimportant from a public health standpoint, it does present a problem for milk producers and law enforcement personnel.

The occurrence of pesticides in wildlife has been the subject of some study and much controversy in recent years. A number of reports have been issued on studies made on wildlife in areas treated with pesticides, usually DDT, and, as would be expected, accumulations similar to those found in domestic animals under like conditions were found. Occasional reports of residues of DDT and related compounds in animals from remote areas are of exceptional interest, however. Where aquatic life is concerned, an entirely different situation may exist. Certain lower forms in the aquatic food chain are able to accumulate organochlorine pesticides that may be present in the water in almost infinitesimal amounts. Fish that use these microfauna and microflora as a major source of food may then accumulate very high levels of pesticide in their fat. An outstanding example was found in Clear Lake, Calif., where DDE (TDE) was applied to the water in 1949, 1954, and 1957 at a dosage of 14 p.p.b. to control gnats. It was later found that plankton accumulated residues of 5 p.p.m., and subsequent analysis of fish in the lake showed from 40 to 2500 p.p.m. of the insecticide to be present in the fat—a level high enough to cause a high rate of mortality in western grebes feeding on the fish (11). Similar situations have been found in Tule Lake and the Salton Sea, also in California.

Of even greater interest are recent reports of the presence of organochlorine pesticides (again principally DDT and its metabolites) in sharks, tuna, and other salt water fish (19). Studies are now under way to determine pesticide levels in fish from all salt water areas of the world to learn more about their distribution in ocean life. The aquatic food chain must be involved in the build-up to high levels, but to trace the compounds back to their sources may be an exceedingly difficult task and is perhaps pointless in terms of solving the over-all problem of water pollution. The occurrence of pesticides in shrimp and oysters is now well recognized, and the source is reasonably assumed to be contaminated fresh water entering the sea. Oysters are particularly efficient in extracting DDT from the water and are reported to have stored as much as 151 p.p.m. during a 7-day exposure to water containing 0.01 p.p.m. (*24*). Many smaller organisms in addition to plankton, shrimp, and oysters, possess this same ability for the biological magnification of many chemicals and thus efficiently act as the initial carriers in a world-wide undersea distribution system.

The reported efficiency of oysters in extracting DDT from water is worthy of additional comment. According to biologists, oysters will filter from 1 to 4 liters of water per hour. Assuming an average of 2 liters per hour, the daily throughput would be 48 liters. A 20-gram oyster containing 150 p.p.m. of DDT would contain a total of 3000 μg. of this pesticide, this being the amount in 300 liters of water containing 0.01 p.p.m. For a 7-day exposure period, this is 43 liters per day or about 90% of the volume of water estimated as the total throughput for an oyster. This is an extraordinarily high degree of efficiency of extraction from such dilute solutions and leads us to recommend that similar studies on other shellfish and fishes should be made. If fish are capable of extracting organochlorine pesticides from water as efficiently as oysters, the theoretical biological magnification through lower organisms may not be required to explain high levels in these fish.

The ability of certain plants to absorb and store organochlorine pesticides has also been observed, the most notable examples being certain varieties of carrots, soybeans (*6*), and roots of forage crops (*26*). With carrots, for example, in a series of papers Lichtenstein and coworkers (*12, 13, 14*) have reported many conclusive experiments conducted under both controlled and field conditions. Marth (*15*) gives a comprehensive review of this type of work on numerous vegetables.

DDT has been reported in the fat of Eskimos in the Arctic and in fish according to Durham (*7*), and in Weddell seals and Adelie penguins in the Antarctic according to George (*8*). In these remote areas any form of direct contamination is out of the question and we must turn to the sea and air for the source. Certainly the sea, or the life dwelling in it, is a prime suspect. We cannot, however, rule out air-borne contamination. Ice laid down in 1964 on Mt. Olympus, in the state of Washington, has been found to contain 0.3 p.p.b. of DDT [cited by Metcalf

(*16*)] but none in ice laid down before 1944. The only conceivable way the insecticide could have reached this altitude was from the air, probably being carried down by precipitation as "rain out" or "snow out."

This occurrence of pesticides in the atmosphere, referred to earlier, warrants some elaboration. The fact that fine particulate matter may be carried to great heights by air currents, and around the world, is well known. Why, then, should not pesticide particles be rather generously distributed in this fashion and carried to earth again by rain and snow or by gravity? Chemists have long been plagued by the fact that they could usually account for only a fraction of the amount of pesticide applied by analyzing the plants and soil that were treated. It is not unusual to find 50% or more of the applied material unaccounted for in the materials balance in the treated area immediately after application, at least when organochlorine pesticides are used. Most of the missing part is dispersed in the air as fine particles, or aerosols, and carried to an adjacent area, the next county, or the next continent. Some of this missing material, depending on many factors, may be quickly altered by sunlight, oxygen, etc., into other persisting compounds perhaps of unknown pharmacology and toxicology.

Conclusions

What conclusions can be drawn from all of this? Perhaps the most obvious is that a tremendous tonnage of pesticides is used throughout the world and that this will most certainly increase, particularly in the less-developed countries. We have then a continuing and increasing source of pesticide contamination with which we must be prepared to live during the foreseeable future. We know now with analytical certainty that pesticides are present and will continue to be present not only in the areas where they are applied but on land, in the sea, and in the air in areas remote from the sites of application. From the standpoint of public health safety there appears to be little cause for alarm. The levels in water and air, for example, are so far below our levels of exposure from many other sources that they must be individually insignificant. Thus, if we should inhale 7000 liters of air per day, containing 0.3 μg. of any pesticide in 1000 cubic meters, we will inhale about 2×10^{-6} mg. per day. If we drink 2 liters of water per day, containing 10 p.p.b. of pesticide, we will ingest 0.02 mg. per day. Actually, our water supplies contain from 0 to about 2 p.p.b., according to the National Water Quality Network reports, and our intake of pesticides from this source is something less than 0.004 mg. per day. Our food supplies probably contain not more than about 0.5 p.p.m. of total organochloride pesticides, and the average resident of the United

States could ingest about 0.85 mg. from this source. The one area in which there is cause for justifiable concern is in aquatic environments where concentration occurs in food chains, ultimately resulting in damage to some member of the chain and perhaps exposure of human beings to high pesticide levels through consumption of the accumulator species or of a subsequent predator species as food.

Literature Cited

(1) Agricultural Stabilization and Conservation Service, U.S. Dept. Agriculture, "The Pesticide Situation for 1963-1964."
(2) Bamesberger, L. L., Adams, D. F. ADVAN. CHEM. SER., **60**, 219 (1966).
(3) Bovard, K. P., Priode, B. M., Whitmore, G. E., Ackerman, A. J., *J. Animal Sci.* **20**, 824 (1961).
(4) Briedenbach, A. W., Lichtenberg, J. J., *Science* **141**, 899 (1963).
(5) Cohen, J. M., Pinkerton, C., ADVAN. CHEM. SER., **60**, 163 (1966).
(6) Decker, G. C., Bruce, W. N., "Abstracts of Papers," 150th Meeting, ACS, September 1965, p. 18A.
(7) Durham, W. F., *Residue Revs.* **4**, 33 (1963).
(8) George, J. L., Symposium on Pesticides and the Environment, Monks Wood Experiment Sta., Abbots Ripton, Huntington, England, 1965; *Chem. Eng. News* **43**, 92 (July 19, 1965).
(9) Gunther, F. A., Jeppson, L. R., "Modern Insecticides and World Food Production," Chapman and Hall, London, 1960.
(10) Hindin, Ervin, May, D. S., Dunstan, G. H., *Residue Revs.* **7**, 130 (1964).
(11) Hunt, E. G., Bishoff, I. G., *Calif. Fish Game* **46**, 91 (1960).
(12) Lichtenstein, E. P., *J. Agr. Food Chem.* **7**, 430 (1959).
(13) *Ibid.*, **8**, 448 (1960).
(14) Lichtenstein, E. P., Myrdal, G. R., Schulz, K. R., *Ibid.*, **13**, 126 (1965).
(15) Marth, C. H., *Residue Revs.* **9**, 1 (1965).
(16) Metcalf, R. L., Report on National Academy of Science Traveling Symposium on Pesticides, Nov. 15-21, 1964.
(17) Nicholson, H. P., Proceedings of Third Seminar on Biological Problems in Water Pollution, Robert A. Taft Sanitary Engineering Center, Cincinnati, Ohio, 1962.
(18) Nicholson, H. P., Webb, H. J., Lauer, G. J., O'Brien, R. E., Grzenda, A. R., Shanklin, D. W., *Trans. Am. Fisheries Soc.* **91**, 213 (1962).
(19) *President's Science Advisory Committee*, Report on Use of Pesticides, White House, Washington, D. C., 1963; *Residue Revs.* **6**, 1 (1964).
(20) Swenson, H. A., *Proc. Soc. Water Treatment* **11**, 84 (1962).
(21) Tarzwell, C. M., Henderson, C., *Trans. Am. Fisheries Soc.* **86**, 245 (1956).
(22) Walker, T. R., *Geol. Soc. Am., Bull.* **72** (1961).
(23) West, Irma, *Arch. Environ. Health* **9**, 626 (1964).
(24) West, Irma, Milby, T. H., *Residue Revs.* **11**, 141 (1965).
(25) Westlake, W. E., Corley, C., Murphy, R. T., Barthel, W. F., Bryant, H., Schutzmann, R. L., *J. Agr. Food Chem.* **11**, 244 (1963).
(26) Wheeler, W. B., Mumma, R. O., Frear, D. E. H., Symposium on Detection, Fate, and Effects of Organic Pesticides in the Environment, 150th Meeting, ACS, Atlantic City, N. J., 1965.
(27) Young, L. A., Nicholson, H. P., *Progressive Fish Culturist* **13**, 193 (1951).

RECEIVED October 12, 1965. Paper No. 1727, University of California Citrus Research Center and Agricultural Experiment Station, Riverside, Calif.

10

Mathematical Prediction of Cumulative Levels of Pesticides in Soil

JOHN W. HAMAKER

Bioproducts Research Laboratory, The Dow Chemical Co.,
Walnut Creek, Calif.

Rate laws are needed to predict mathematically the accumulation of residues in soil. The pattern of accumulation under a program of periodic additions was computed for rate laws ranging from zero order to second order. For the higher orders, lower equilibrium residues were obtained. In Michaelis-Menton kinetics, the order varies between first and zero with increasing concentration, and the equilibrium accumulation of residue increases rapidly as the annual rate of addition approaches the maximum decomposition rate for the soil. Other factors such as volatility, side reactions, etc., may lead to complex kinetics, and it is suggested that usable rate law expressions could be obtained empirically.

Any residue which accumulates in soil is part of the problem of general contamination of our environment. We are all aware of the concern of the public and the authorities about this problem. It is possible that in the future estimates of expected contribution to environmental contamination will be required before large-scale use of new pesticides is permitted. Reliable prediction of accumulation in soil residue would be a necessary part of this knowledge.

Pesticide accumulation in soil is determined by the difference between the rate at which the pesticide is added and the rate at which it disappears. The rate of addition is determined by the application schedule and is discontinuous, while the rate of disappearance is continuous and is controlled by the concentration of pesticide residue plus other factors. It is as if we had a reservoir into which fluid were being dumped by the bucket and out of which it escaped steadily through a small pipe, with the rate of flow determined by the height of fluid in the reservoir plus other factors.

If other factors are, for the moment, considered constant, the rate of disappearance will depend upon some continuous function of the concentration of residue in the soil. When this rate is integrated with regular periodic additions of pesticide, the result is a sawtooth pattern like that shown in Figure 1. If there is a concentration of residue at which the loss in between applications becomes exactly equal to the addition rate, the maximum residue will approach a limiting value which is the number 2 in Figure 1. It is possible, of course, that this condition cannot be achieved, and in such a case, the residue will increase without limit.

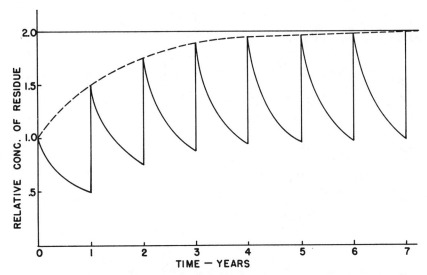

Figure 1.   Residue pattern for single annual addition and first-order half life of 1 year

The magnitude of the limiting value for maximum residue will depend upon the slope and curvature of the decay curves and upon the magnitude and frequency of pesticide addition. If the decay curve can be generalized—i.e., expressed as a mathematical function—it should be possible, in principle, to calculate for any desired pattern or magnitude of pesticide addition, whether or not there is a limiting value for residue concentration and what it is. This should be true whether the mathematical function is arrived at through theory or empirically—i.e., by curve fitting experimental results. The requirement is that it be valid over the range of concentrations and conditions to be expected in practice. This is no small requirement.

The curve in Figure 1 was calculated by assuming first-order kinetics, which is probably the simplest way mathematically. Also, it is probably the most simple kinetics likely to be encountered under practical conditions.

Two commonly used properties of first-order kinetics are: A plot of logarithm of concentration *vs.* time is a straight line; and there is a constant half life. Thus, each time half life is treated as a constant or a straight line is drawn on semilog paper, one is assuming that first-order kinetics apply. The mathematical expressions appropriate to this rate law are given below:

$$\text{Log}_{10} \frac{C_o}{C} = \frac{0.30103 \, t}{t_{1/2}}$$

$$f = C/C_o$$

After N annual additions:

$$\frac{r}{C_o} = 1 + f_1 + f_1^2 + f_1^3 + \cdots f_1^{n-1}$$

$$\left(\frac{r}{C_o}\right)_\infty = \frac{1}{1-f_1}$$

where:

C_o = initial concentration
C = concentration at time t
f_1 = fraction left after one year
$t_{1/2}$ = half life of decomposition
r = accumulated residue, immediately after addition of annual increment

The limit of the maximum amount of residue $\left(\dfrac{r}{C_o}\right)_\infty$ —is given by a relatively simple expression, $\dfrac{1}{1-f_1}$. In Table I, this limit is computed for a number of different half lives and for two cases—single addition annually and the same dose split into four parts applied quarterly.

It shows that for half lives of up to 1 year the residue obtained is not over twice the annual addition, whether added once a year or four times a year. If the half life is as much as 10 years, the expected accumulation of pesticide will approach 15 times the annual addition. Adding the same annual dose in four equally distributed, equal portions will produce a significantly smaller accumulated residue than annual addition for half lives of 1 year and less but will gradually approach the cumulative levels for the single annual additions with longer half lives. End points for other patterns of application, if regular, can be worked out if needed but will, of course, be mathematically more complex and difficult to handle.

**Table I. Maximum Accumulated Pesticide Residue in Soil
Calculated for First-Order Kinetics**

Half Life for Residue Disappearance, Months	Ratio of Maximum Accumulated Residue in Soil, r, to Total Annual Dosage, C_0	
	Single annual additions	*Quarterly additions of one-fourth the annual rate*
1	1.00	0.29
2	1.02	0.40
3	1.07	0.50
6	1.33	0.85
12	2.00	1.57
24	3.40	3.04
36	4.84	4.44
48	6.29	5.90
120	14.9	13.7

Decker, Bruce, and Bigger (2) have successfully used first-order kinetics to calculate the long term residues from aldrin soil treatments in 35 locations in Illinois. They found that for this group of soils the values obtained for accumulated residue were bracketed by calculated values based on a fairly rapid loss of 80–90% of the aldrin, a 10–20% conversion of aldrin to dieldrin, and first-order half lives of between 2 and 4 years for the loss of dieldrin.

Lichtenstein and Schulz (5) studied the disappearance of aldrin over a 5-year period from a Wisconsin soil, both for a single application of 25 pounds per acre and for five annual applications of 5 pounds per acre. Soil was analyzed for dieldrin and aldrin. The data for the single application indicated that dieldrin decomposition is first-order with a half life of 4.2 years, which is similar to the results found by Decker *et al.* for Illinois soils. If the dieldrin first-order decomposition curve is extrapolated to zero time, a value of 24% is obtained to "represent" the efficiency of conversion of aldrin to dieldrin—again similar to Illinois results. Assuming that the addition of 24% as much dieldrin is an approximately equivalent situation to the addition of aldrin, the accumulated residue for the case of five annual additions can be calculated according to the equation:

$$r_n = (f_1 + f_1^2 + f_1^3 + \cdots f_1^n) \, E \times C_o$$

where n = number of annual pesticide additions, 5 pounds per acre

C_o = concentration of annual addition of aldrin, 3.2 p.p.m.

E = efficiency of aldrin-dieldrin conversion, 0.24

f_1 = fraction left after 1-year decay, 0.8479, corresponding to a half life of 4.2 years for dieldrin

This differs from the relationship given above because the residue being calculated is the residue immediately before rather than after an annual increment. The results of the calculations are shown in Table II and are probably reasonably close, considering the simplifying approximations. The maximum possible accumulated residue of dieldrin for this case is calculated as 1.6 times the annual addition rate of aldrin, or 5.1 p.p.m.—i.e., 8 pounds per acre. The values found for dieldrin tend to be lower than those calculated.

Table II. Accumulated Residue of Dieldrin According to Data of Lichtenstein and Schulz

Residue, p.p.m.	Time Elapsed, Years				
	1	2	3	4	5
Dieldrin					
Calculated	0.66	1.22	1.67	2.10	2.45
Found	0.76	1.2	1.4	1.8	2.0

The first-order rate law is but one of many possibilities, and an interesting comparison can be made between several of the simpler rate laws using a pseudo half life. Consider the case where two measurements of pesticide residue in soil are made 1 year apart and assume, further, that one half of the added pesticide has disappeared during that year—that is, the pesticide shows a half life of 1 year for this specific concentration. In Figure 2, the path of disappearance of one concentration unit is plotted on semilog paper according to a pseudo half life of 1 year and four possible rate laws: first-order, second-order, one-half-order, and zero-order—that is, whether the rate of decomposition is proportional to the concentration, the square of the concentration, the square root of the concentration, or independent of the concentration.

A graph like this, on semilog coordinates, is useful in distinguishing first-order (straight-line), higher orders (concave upward), and lower orders (concave downward). Further, it is apparent that in this case the usual scatter of data experienced in soil residue work would make it difficult, if not impossible, to distinguish between any of the four orders in question if the rate is followed for 1 half life at one concentration. To determine the effective rate law with sufficient precision to be useful in estimating the residue accumulation one should estimate residues over a sufficiently large change of concentration, whether this is accomplished by using a number of starting concentrations or a number of half lives. Though this may seem obvious, it has been overlooked.

The kinetics of the degradation reaction can make a significant difference, as is shown in Table III. The accumulated residue for each

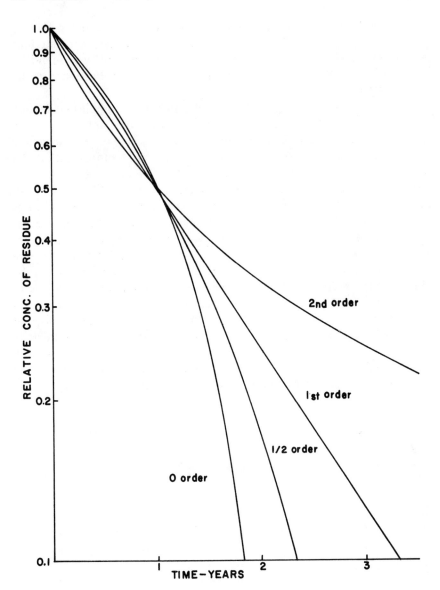

Figure 2.   Decay curves for different rate laws, half life of 1 year for unit concentration

of the four rate laws previously referred to was calculated on the basis of an annual addition rate of one concentration unit, and a pseudo half life of 1 year. It is apparent that the higher the order of the reaction, the lower the eventual accumulated residue. The mathematical integration for each order is straightforward, and a general formula for accumulated residue could probably be derived, but it is much simpler to solve numerically. The values for maximum residue for the four orders, for which the loss in 1 year was exactly one unit, was found by numerical approximation. In all instances, one unit was assumed to be the annual dose.

Degradation of pesticides in soil is frequently accomplished biologically, as indicated by inactivation by sterilizing the soil. Cases may therefore be found in which the kinetics are determined by enzymatic activity, and the classical case of this is Michaelis-Menton kinetics. An important feature of this type of kinetics is that the order of the reaction changes with concentration of the reactant, specifically, from first order at zero concentration toward zero order as the concentration increases without limit. The physical interpretation of this is that an enzyme catalyzes the reaction in question by forming a complex with the reactant, so that when the enzyme is completely complexed, the rate cannot increase further. A soil following these kinetics would not be able to decompose more than a certain maximum number of pounds of any given pesticide per acre, per year. It is not likely that many instances of uncomplicated Michaelis-Menton kinetics will be found, but it seems so probable that soils will have limited capacity to degrade some pesticides that I feel the possibility should be carefully examined.

Accordingly, Michaelis-Menton kinetics were examined in relation to the accumulation of pesticide. The pertinent mathematical expressions are shown below (1).

$$\frac{dc}{dt} = \frac{VmC}{Km+C}$$

$$\mathrm{Log}\,\frac{C}{C_o} + \frac{Vmt}{Km} - \frac{C_o-C}{Km} = 0$$

where

Vm = maximum rate of pesticide disappearance
C = concentration of reactant at time t
C_o = concentration of reactant at $t = 0$
Km = an equilibrium constant

The integrated expression is not easily solved for C; hence, unlike the case of first-order kinetics, no attempt is made to write a general expression for the accumulated residues. Instead, the equation was solved numerically for a range of values for the constants, Vm and Km, using the Newton-Raphson method for numerical approximation. This was programmed for a computer easily, although log table and slide rule or calculator will do the same job but in more time.

**Table III. Accumulation of Pesticide Residue in Soil for Annual
Addition Rate of One Concentration Unit and a
Loss of One Half in the First Year**

Kinetics of Decomposition	Relative Concentrations of Residues Accumulated after Indicated Number of Years Immediately Following Addition					
	0	1	2	3	4	∞
Zero order	1	1.5	2.00	2.50	3.00	∞
Half order	1	1.5	1.88	2.16	2.31	3.41
First order	1	1.5	1.75	1.88	1.94	2.00
Second order	1	1.5	1.60	1.62	1.62	1.62

The results of three of the runs for an annual addition rate of 1 unit
per year are shown in Figure 3. In these cases the limiting first-order
half life, which is approached as concentration approaches zero, was
fixed at 1 year, and the maximum rate was given different values. As
the maximum rate becomes more nearly equal to the annual addition
rate, the maximum value for accumulated residue will increase. This
is to be expected, for, since the maximum rate of decomposition is fixed,
the residue must increase without limit whenever the maximum decomposition rate falls below the annual rate of addition to the soil.

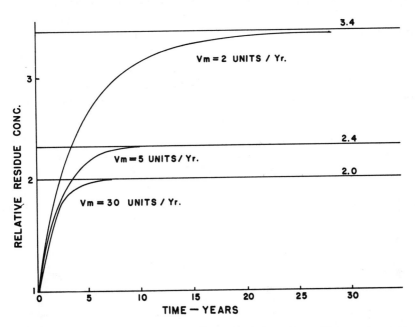

*Figure 3. Accumulated residue in soil. Calculated for Michaelis-Menton
kinetics limiting half life. 1 year, single annual addition of one concentration unit.*

In Table IV, equilibrium accumulated residues are presented for a larger range of constants and are compared with values obtained for comparable first-order kinetics. For these cases, the slow approach to limiting values can tax even the computer, and the values were therefore calculated by numerical approximation to that value of C for which the decrease in 1 year was just 1 concentration unit—i.e., the addition rate.

The obvious question at this point is, "Are there actual examples of Michaelis-Menton kinetics in soil?" Do some or all soils have a maximum rate beyond which they cannot degrade at least some pesticides? The answer to this would contribute to our understanding of the fate of pesticides in soil. In attempting to answer this question, it must be kept in mind that if the annual addition rate is much less than the maximum decomposition rate, the kinetics will approximate first-order. Table III shows that for the case of a maximum decomposition of 30 times the annual addition rate, Michaelis-Menton and first-order kinetics are not distinguishable in practice. Apparent and genuine first-order kinetics could be distinguished in two ways—raising the dosage and lowering the maximum decomposition rate. The former might be represented by laboratory experiments using massive dosages to demonstrate the principle. The latter may be found for customary dosages in the cases of soils which decompose a pesticide poorly. There does not appear to be any published work that establishes this point.

This has been a theoretical treatment from the standpoint of reaction kinetics only, and I would like to reiterate the point made earlier—that a rate law for disappearance arrived at empirically could be, and perhaps would be, better used than a purely theoretical function.

Table IV. Limiting Maximum Accumulated Residues in Soil as Calculated for Michaelis-Menton Kinetics and a Single Annual Addition of One Concentration Unit

Maximum Rate Decomposition, Vm, in Concentration, Units/Year	Ratio of Maximum Accumulated Residue in Soil, r, to Total Annual Dosage, C_0 Indicated First-order Half Lives		
	1 Month	1 Year	10 Years
2	1.0159	3.414	29.21
5	1.0013	2.348	18.47
30	1.0003	2.047	15.46
∞ [a]	1.0003	2.000	14.9

[a] Michaelis-Menton kinetics approach equivalence to first-order kinetics, as the maximum decomposition rate increases without limit. These values are calculated by first-order kinetics for the half lives indicated.

The complex nature of soil and soil processes means that many factors besides the type of reaction kinetics can affect the course of the disappearance of a pesticide. An example would be a case of a volatile pesticide for which a significant part of the loss was caused by vaporization from the soil. A complete mathematical analysis would take into account chemical degradation, vaporization, and diffusion. It would yield a mathematical relation different from and more complicated than one expressing the chemical kinetics alone. An example is simultaneous diffusion and degradation of soil fumigants as described by Hemwall (3, 4).

The best that we may be able to do, in complex cases, would be to determine the decay curve with care, obtain a function by curve-fitting techniques, and use this function to estimate accumulated residues. Care must be taken on at least three points: (1) that the data be precise enough to give an accurate function (errors would accumulate in calculating accumulated residue), (2) the decay curve be determined over so wide a range of concentration that no extrapolation is involved in calculating accumulated residue, and (3) a careful study be made of the contribution of various factors to the decay curve. It would make an important difference whether or not the disappearance is caused partly by volatility, changes in microbial population, sorption, leaching, side reactions, etc.

The studies of soil decomposition of pesticides which have been published are generally not suitable for the type of analysis described. There are various reasons for this, including those listed above. There is no evident reason why such analysis could not be used successfully if a study were designed specifically for that purpose.

Literature Cited

(1) Bull, H. B., "Physical Biochemistry," 2nd ed., Wiley, New York, 1951.
(2) Decker, G. C., Bruce, W. N., Bigger, J. H., *J. Econ. Entomol.* **58**, 266 (1965).
(3) Hemwall, J. B., *Soil Sci.* **88**, 184 (1959).
(4) *Ibid.*, **90**, 157 (1960).
(5) Lichtenstein, E. P., Schulz, K. R., *J. Agr. Food Chem.* **13**, 57 (1965).

RECEIVED October 25, 1965.

11

Distribution of Insecticides Sprayed by Airplane on an Irrigated Corn Plot

ERVIN HINDIN, DONALD S. MAY,[1] and GILBERT H. DUNSTAN

College of Engineering, Research Division, Washington State University, Pullman, Wash.

The distribution of insecticides applied once to an irrigated plot was investigated. Samples of crop, soil, air, water applied, irrigation runoff water, and water-borne settleable silt were collected prior to insecticide application and periodically thereafter for the remainder of the growing season. Insecticide residues in the extracts of the samples taken were determined. DDT and diazinon were applied during the first year; DDT and ethion were used during the second. Thirty-five percent of the DDT and diazinon was found at tassel height during 1963. In 1964, 22% of the DDT and ethion were found at this level. The relationship, plant to crop, varied throughout the growing season. Less than 0.01% of the insecticides applied was removed by the runoff water and water-borne silt.

The fate of insecticides once applied to cropland is not completely known. Available fragmentary evidence indicates that surface drainage from croplands treated with insecticides may contaminate the aquatic environment; however, relatively little is known about the transport of these insecticides through surface drainage. Nicholson (9) found toxaphene and the gamma isomer of BHC in a stream draining an insecticide-treated cotton area. In another study Nicholson *et al.* (10) evaluated the effect of parathion and other insecticides used in peach culture on the water quality of a pond adjacent to the orchard. Parathion was found in the pond water in concentrations of 0.02 μgram/liter, the pond bottom mud at 1.9 μgram/kg., and in the orchard soil at 1.7 μgram/kg.

[1] Present address: Water Pollution Control Administration, Department of the Interior, Corvallis, Ore.

The presence of parathion in the pond water and pond bottom muds was attributed to insecticide-laden soil washed in during a period of accelerated erosion. One-hundredth μgram per liter of parathion, 0.02 μgram per liter of DDD, and 0.01 μgram per liter of BHC were found in the pond water 4 months after the last application of insecticides. Dunstan, Proctor, and Hindin (2) reported the presence of DDT, aldrin, and the isopropyl ester of 2, 4-D in a number of irrigation return flow wasteways in the Columbia Basin Project of Eastern Washington.

Numerous reports indicate the distribution and persistence of chlorinated organic insecticides in soil. Ginsburg (3) found most of the accumulated DDT in the soil layer corresponding to cultivation or plow depth. Rodenheser (11) reported that in a study conducted in 1952, DDT and aldrin were initially in soil in concentrations of 38 and 140 mg. per kg., yet 6 years later 28 mg. per kg. of DDT and 95 mg. per kg. of aldrin were found in the same soil. Taschenberg, Mac, and Gambrell (14) found the accumulation of DDT in the soil resulting from three to four applications per year for 6 years to be approximately 9 p.p.m. and over a 12-year period to be approximately 13.5 p.p.m. About half of the DDT applied over the 6-year period and two thirds of that applied over the 12-year period were not recovered from the soil. DDE and DDT ratios were higher in the soils receiving applications over the 12-year period. Clore *et al.* (1) conducted a study in which five plots received applications of varying concentrations of DDT. An average of 70, 68, 47, 15, and 19% of the DDT present in the soil during the first year was present in the soil in the second, third, fourth, sixth, and ninth year, respectively. The more DDT applied initially, the greater the percentage remaining on the soil in subsequent years.

Lichtenstein and Schultz (7) found that the persistence of aldrin in soil depended largely on the presence of water in the soil. They concluded that once aldrin had been displaced by water from the soil particles, a major part of the insecticide was lost by volatilization. Unlike aldrin, DDT did not respond to displacement by water nor was it affected by enlargement of the surface onto which it had been deposited. Under field conditions, daily disking of a treated loam soil reduced 38% of the aldrin residue and 25% of the DDT residue after 3 months. In another study, Lichtenstein *et al.* (6) were able to recover aldrin and heptachlor residues ranging from 2.7 to 5.3% of the applied dosage 4 months after application to the soil surface. The persistence increased by a factor of 10 when the insecticides were mixed with the soil by rotatilling. One year after application 90% of the recovered insecticides was found in the upper 3 inches of the soil. Because two to three times more insecticide residues were recovered from crop-covered plots than from fallow ones, it was concluded that a dense cover crop increased the insecticide persistence by reducing volatilization at the soil-air interface.

From the literature cited it can be concluded that about 90% of the recoverable DDT residue will reside in the top 3 inches of the soil or at cultivation or plow depth. Certain persistent insecticides can be removed from the soil through volatilization. The extent of volatilization is determined in part by the vapor pressure of the insecticide, by displacement from the soil particle by other substances, by the presence and type of cover crop, and by the "turning over" of the soil. Insecticides from treated areas can enter the surface water sorbed onto eroded soil particles and/or desorbed from the soil by water.

Experimental Plan

A plot measuring 1 acre at the Othello Research Farm of the Irrigated Agricultural Research and Extension Center, 10 miles east of Othello, Wash., was assigned for use. To avoid boundary effects and to facilitate installation of equipment for flow measurements, a section measuring 0.46 acre was used for the study.

The Research Unit lies within the rain shadow of the Cascade Mountains of Washington. The average yearly rainfall of the area is 9.00 inches, only about 8% of which falls from mid-June to mid-September. During the same 3 months the rate of evaporation is three times as great as the average annual rainfall. Because of this and the low intensity of the rainfall, surface runoff occurs only from the shallow layer above the frost line.

The plot soil, of loessial origin, is a coarse silt loam belonging to the Shano series. The top soil, very fine and powdery, is high in inorganic nutrients and low in organic matter. The plot was irrigated down a 1.88% slope, having been cropped for only 3 years.

The entire plot was planted with Idahybrid-330 corn and cultivated and irrigated according to established agricultural practices. Cultivation was continued until the corn began to tassel. The crop was irrigated approximately every 10 days up to the time the corn began to mature. The irrigation water was Columbia River water conveyed to the station through the project's east low canal.

Sampling Sites

A careful examination of the topography of the plot determined the best site for the location of the return flow measuring equipment and aided in the selection of sampling sites. The plot assigned was 100 by approximately 435 feet. A square section of the plot (1225 sq. feet at the corner of the lowest elevation) was used for the installation of the return flow measuring equipment and construction of two bypass drainage ditches and one ditch draining the test area. To avoid boundary effects, a section of the plot measuring 50 x 400 feet was used.

Soil samples were taken at 50-foot intervals from rows 3, 7, 11, and 15. (The location of the sampling sites was recommended by T. S.

Russell, statistician for the Washington Agricultural Experiment Station.) In addition a series of seven samples (same intervals in the row) was taken from a row ¼ mile from the test plot, and constituted the control. The soil characteristics of the control were the same as those of the test area. The same variety of corn was planted in the control area as in the test area. As far as was known, the control area was free of insecticides. Sampling was duplicated within the test area by shifting the starting point from the 50-foot point to the 25-foot point and to rows 2, 6, 10, and 14. Samples from these sites were held in reserve if it became desirable to collect additional data.

To estimate the actual amounts reaching the plant and reaching the ground, a series of glass plates was installed, prior to spray application, at 11 locations selected at random within the test area. The plates were 1 sq. foot and installed on tripods at tassel height 8 feet above ground level. One aerial installation was placed in the control row to determine the extent of insecticide drift.

The apparatus used to sample the air for pesticides was placed in the center of the plot. The air intake was at tassel height.

Water meters were installed on the irrigated risers at the head of the plot to measure the water applied; each riser supplied water to two rows.

Equipment to measure, proportionally divert, and collect the surface runoff was installed at the end of the irrigation ditch-draining test plot. The measuring apparatus consisted of an up-channel and apron, Parshall flume, stilling well, and water level recorder. A flow-splitting device was attached to the downstream side of the flume. One third of the flow was diverted to a settling tank where it was sampled. A 3-hour retention time was allowed for the water-borne silt to settle. A proportional part of the settleable silt was collected for analysis.

To eliminate errors caused by insecticide spray falling into the collection ditch and onto the flow measuring and sampling equipment, sheets of plastic film were used to cover the installations during insecticide application.

Insecticide Application

Two insecticides—DDT and diazinon—were used in the 1963 studies, while DDT and ethion were used during the 1964 growing season. DDT in the form of an emulsifiable -2 EM DDT (Allied Chemical Co.), diazinon as emulsifiable 4E diazinon (Geigy Chemical Co.) and ethion as emulsifiable 4E ethion (Niagara Chemical Co.) were applied at the rate of 2, 1, and 1 pound of active insecticide per acre, respectively.

A Stearman 450 airplane, equipped with 32 spray nozzles and 46 plates having D-8s and D-10s orifices, was used to apply the insecticides. Two 45-foot swaths were made over the test area on each of 3 days during the 1963 study. During the 1964 season only one application consisting of two swaths was made. Applications were made at 7:00 p.m. on each day.

Collection and Analysis

Soil. The soil was sampled at the sites as described. Each sample consisted of a shallow block of soil taken by a specially designed scoop. The block had a surface area of 30 sq. inches, was 2 inches deep, and had a dried weight of approximately 1 kg. The block was placed in a paper bag and allowed to air-dry prior to insecticide extraction. Soil samples were taken prior to application, 1 day after the last application and 7 days after the last irrigation. The soil samples at a particular site were taken 3 inches from each other—e.g., at site 10, on July 29, 1963, a soil block was taken 100 feet from the head of the furrow; on August 8, 1963, the block was taken 100 feet 3 inches from the head of the furrow; and on September 5, 1963, the block was taken 99 feet 9 inches from the head of the furrow. Each block location was set off from the other by 4 inches.

The insecticides were extracted using a method developed by the Agricultural Division of the Shell Oil Co. (*13*).

EXTRACTION PROCEDURE. Approximately 1 kg. of the air-dried soil was blended with two 500-mg. portions of petroleum naphtha at 2500 r.p.m. for 30 minutes. The extracts were filtered through cheese cloth and then through No. 5 Whatman filter paper. The filtrate was sent through a column of anhydrous sodium sulfate to remove all traces of moisture. The filtrates were combined, and the solvent was removed by rotary vacuum evaporation carried out at 35°C. to a volume of approximately 4 ml. The concentration extract was transferred to a 10-ml. vial. Two 2.5-ml. portions of petroleum naphtha facilitated the transfer. The concentrate was evaporated to dryness using a stream of cool, dried air.

One-half-milliliter portions of petroleum naphtha were used to rinse down the walls of the vial. At time of analysis the residue was taken up in a measured amount (1 or 0.1 ml.) of petroleum naphtha.

In previous studies (*4*) it was found that 22.5% of either of the insecticides from Shano type soil is recovered using the above-mentioned extraction procedure. This value was rechecked periodically during the study and found to be consistent.

Water. The water used for irrigation was sampled at the diversion box while the section was being irrigated. During the 1963 study, the carbon adsorption method suggested by Middleton (*8*) was used to sample the water.

PROCEDURE. A measured amount of water, optimum quantity 5000 gallons (18,925 liters), was pumped through a column of Nuchar C-190, 30-mesh activated carbon 3 inches in diameter by 18 inches in height. The pumping rate used was 0.5 gallon per minute. After collection, the carbon was removed from the filter, air-dried, and placed in a modified Soxhlet extractor to remove the organic matter by benzene. Except for 250 ml., all solvent was removed by distillation. The remaining solvent was further reduced to approximately 4 ml. by rotary vacuum evaporation. The method of transfer and evaporation to dryness described for the soil extractants was used for the carbon extracts.

Rosen and Middleton (*12*) found that a 75% recovery of DDT can be anticipated using the above-mentioned adsorption and subsequent desorption procedures. Investigations carried out by Hindin (*4*) confirm the fact that 75% of DDT and 75% of diazinon can be recovered. The data for DDT in water are corrected for the 75% recovery. The irrigation return flow from the rills drained into a ditch; then was conveyed to the flow-measuring equipment. The flow after being measured was split proportionally. One third of the flow was diverted to a settling basin, where the settleable matter in the return flow was removed. The water in the settling basin was pumped through activated carbon and treated in the same manner as the irrigation water.

During the 1964 study a 18-liter composite sample of the irrigation water was taken. The insecticides were removed and concentrated using the extraction method of Teasly and Cox (*15*).

METHOD. One liter aliquots was extracted twice with 500 ml. of 1 to 1 ethyl ether–petroleum ether mixture. The combined extract was evaporated as described for the deadsorbant from the carbon adsorption method.

Settleable Water-Borne Silt. Wide-mouthed jars having an opening of known area were placed at the bottom of the settling basin to collect settleable silt. Three hours after the irrigation flow had ceased, the jars were removed, the excess water in the jars was decanted, and the settled silt was allowed to dry. The air-dried silt was weighed and treated in the same manner as a soil sample.

Spray Solution. Prior to each application of insecticides, 250 ml. of the spray solution were removed from the airplane's spray solution and analyzed directly by gas chromatography.

Aerial Plates. The insecticides adhering to the aerial and surface plates were removed by rinsing the plates with three 50-ml. portions of petroleum naphtha. The rinsings were collected and evaporated in the same manner as the filtered soil sample extracts.

Plants. To remove the insecticide residue on the plant, the plant sample was chopped, and the insecticide residue was extracted with 10% acetone in petroleum naphtha. The crop-solvent was placed in a 1-gallon press-top can with stainless steel baffles and rotated at 45 r.p.m. for 30 minutes. The solvent was decanted off, and the sample was extracted once again. The combined extracts were filtered through filter paper and evaporated in the same manner as the soil extract. Where lipid material was present, the corn extracts were re-extracted with acetonitrile.

Air Sampling. The apparatus used to sample insecticides in the air consisted of an insulated box housing two Smith-Greenburg impingers. A small battery operated the air pump and was used to draw a sample of air at the rate of 0.044 cu. meter per minute through *n*-decane contained in the impinger. The sampling period lasted 1 hour.

Analysis

Extracts from all samples were analyzed by gas chromatography as described by Hindin, May, and Dunstan (5). After the residue had been taken up in a measured volume (0.1 or 1.0 ml.) of petroleum naphtha, a 10-μliter aliquot was injected into a Beckman temperature programmer coupled with a Dohramann microcoulometric titration detector. The column-packing material used for the separation of the insecticides was 5% by weight of EPON 1001 on 60/80-mesh acid-washed, flux-calcined diatomite (Chromosorb P). This material was packed in aluminum tubing ¼ inch in o.d. by 3 feet.

To separate chlorinated organic compounds, a column temperature of 225°C. and a nitrogen carrier gas flow of 75 ml. per minute were used. The coulometer was operated at maximum sensitivity (512 ohms), at a damping position of 4 and a bias of 250. A silver–silver ion cell was used.

To separate sulfur-containing organophosphate insecticides, a column temperature of 180°C. and a nitrogen carrier gas flow of 39 ml. per minute were used. The coulometer was operated at maximum sensitivity (512 ohms) at a damping position of 4 and a bias of +100. An iodine–iodine ion cell was used.

Three standard solutions were prepared—one containing 1 mg. of DDT and 1 mg. of DDD per 10 ml. of solvent; the second containing 1 mg. of diazinon per 10 ml. of solvent; and the other containing 1 mg. of ethion per 10 ml. of solvent (benzene). The retention time (time required after injection of the sample for the component to reach its maximum peak height) was used as a qualitative measure to identify the component. Quantitative information was obtained from the direct relationship of the concentration of insecticide to the maximum peak height. Standards were analyzed periodically during the analysis of the residues.

Results

The test area was irrigated according to irrigation practices used in the Columbia Basin project area, where a 25 to 33% runoff flow from irrigated fields can be anticipated. Table I is a compilation of the results obtained from the flow measurements of the irrigation water applied and the runoff water.

Each irrigation lasted for 16 hours. The average percentage of runoff exceeded the maximum anticipated value in 1963 but was slightly less than the minimum value in 1964.

The quantity of water-borne silt removed by the irrigation water appears in Table II.

The concentrations of insecticide residues in the plants, soil, water, settleable silt, and air during the 1963 and 1964 investigations are shown in Tables III and IV, respectively.

Samples taken from the airplanes' spray tank prior to each application in 1963 revealed 0.26, 0.14, and 0.30 pound of DDT per gallon.

Table I. Flow Data

Date	Water Applied, Acre-Inches	Runoff Water, Acre-Inches	% of Flow Returned
7/29–30/63	3.93	1.6	40.9
8/8–9/63	5.43	2.21	40.7
8/17–18/63	4.35	1.84	43.5
8/28–29/63	5.24	2.04	38.9
Av., 1963	4.74	1.93	40.8
8/7–8/64	4.02	0.66	16.4
8/15–16/64	3.54	0.36	10.1
8/22–23/64	3.62	0.98	25.9
8/29–30	3.14	0.64	29.9
9/6–7/64	2.96	0.88	29.7
9/12–13/64	2.38	0.66	27.7
Av., 1964	3.28	0.75	23.3

Eight gallons of each spray solution were applied per application. The calculated amount of DDT sprayed was 5.6 pounds per acre over the test area. Because of analytical difficulties, the calculated amount of diazinon could not be determined. During the 1964 season, when one application of insecticide mixture was made, the spray solution was found to contain 0.25 pound of DDT and 0.125 pound of ethion per gallon. Eight gallons of the spray solution were applied: 2 pounds of DDT and 1 pound of ethion per acre.

The aerial plates at tassel height revealed that only 1.67 pounds of DDT and 0.98 pound of diazinon had reached that level. During the 1964 spray application, 0.44 pound of DDT and 0.49 pound of ethion were found at tassel height.

Based on the data obtained, the distribution of insecticides on the pound per acre basis can be determined (Tables V and VI).

Table II. Silt Data

Date	Silt Removed, Kg./Acre
8/8–9/63	18.8
8/17–18/63	6.7
8/28–29/63	4.7
8/7–8/64	12.3
8/15–16/64	22.2
8/22–23/64	15.1
8/29–30/64	8.7
9/6–7/64	5.4
9/12–13/64	3.3

Table III. Concentration of

Date	Insecticide	Plant	
		Test section, mg./plant [a]	Control, mg./plant [a]
7/29–30/63, 4 days prior to application	DDT Diazinon	< 0.01 [b] < 0.01 [b]	< 0.01 [b] < 0.01 [b]
8/8–9/63, 1 day after last application	DDT Diazinon	9.2 ± 3.1 0.07 ± 0.05	< 0.01 [b] < 0.01 [b]
8/17–18/63, 10 days after application	DDT Diazinon	....	....
8/28–29/63, 21 days after application	DDT Diazinon	....	....
9/5/63, 30 days after application	DDT Diazinon	4.8 ± 1.9 0.12	< 0.01 [b] < 0.01 [b]

[a] Averaged value, 30-sq. inch block.
[b] Less than sensitivity of detected method.

Conclusions

Not all of the insecticides applied could be detected at tassel height. Thirty percent of the DDT and 35% of the diazinon were found 8 feet

Table IV. Concentration of

Time	Insecticide	Plant	
		Test section, mg./plant [a]	Control, mg./plant [a]
7 days prior application	DDT Ethion	< 0.01 [b] < 0.01 [b]	< 0.01 [b] < 0.01 [b]
12 hr. after application	DDT Ethion	1.6 0.6	< 0.01 [b] < 0.01 [b]
7 days after application	DDT Ethion	1.0 0.2	< 0.01 [b] < 0.01 [b]
14 days after application	DDT Ethion	....	....
21 days after application	DDT Ethion	....	....
30 days after application	DDT Ethion	0.6 < 0.01 [b]	< 0.01 [b] < 0.01 [b]

[a] Averaged value 30-sq. inch block.

Insecticide Residue in Sample

Soil		Water		Settleable Silt
Test section, μg./block [a]	Control, μg./block [a]	Applied, mg./l.	Runoff Water, mg./l.	μg./kg.
< 1 [b]	< 1 [b]	< 0.10 [b]	< 0.16 [b]	....
< 1 [b]	< 1 [b]	< 0.10 [b]	< 0.16 [b]	....
54.6 ± 85.4	< 1 [b]	< 0.15 [b]	506.0	78
< 1 [b]	< 1 [b]	< 0.15 [b]	975.0	310
....	....	< 0.09 [b]	178.0	130
....	....	< 0.9 [b]	13.2	0.03
....	....	< 0.13	195.0	200.0
....	....	< 0.13	22.9	83.3
268.2 — 196.0	< 1 [b]	....	....	....
< 1 [b]	< 1 [b]	....	....	....

above ground level during application in 1963. During application of insecticides in 1964, 22% of the DDT and 49% of the ethion were found at this height. The inability to account for all the insecticides applied can be attributed to two factors: method of application and

Insecticide Residue in Samples

Soil		Settleable Silt	Air
Test section, μg./block [a]	Control, μg./block [a]	μg./kg. [a]	mg./cu. ft.
87.3	< 1 [b]	448.4	$< 1 \times 10^{-3}$ [b]
< 1 [b]	< 1 [b]	< 0.01 [b]	$< 1 \times 10^{-3}$ [b]
453.2	< 1 [b]	1598.0	0.3
49.1	< 1 [b]	408.0	0.09
....	....	660.8	0.05
....	....	25.0	0.01
....	....	677.2	2×10^{-3}
....	....	< 0.03 [b]	1×10^{-3}
....	....	469.6	$< 1 \times 10^{-3}$ [b]
....	....	< 0.01 [b]	$< 1 \times 10^{-3}$ [b]
458.6	< 1 [b]	468.0	$< 1 \times 10^{-3}$ [b]
< 1 [b]	< 1 [b]	< 0.01 [b]	$< 1 \times 10^{-3}$ [b]

[b] Less than sensitivity of detected method.

Table V. Distribution of

Date	Insecticide	Plant, Lb./Acre
4 days prior to application	DDT	$< 1 \times 10^{-3}$
	Diazinon	$< 1 \times 10^{-3}$
1 day after final application	DDT	0.46
	Diazinon	0.25
10 days after final application	DDT	. . . .
	Diazinon	. . . .
21 days after final application	DDT	0.23
	Diazinon	$< 1 \times 10^{-3}$

Table VI. Distribution of

Date	Insecticide	Plant, Lb./Acre
7 days prior to application	DDT	$< 1 \times 10^{-3}$
	Ethion	$< 1 \times 10^{-3}$
12 hr. after application	DDT	0.08
	Ethion	0.03
7 days after application	DDT	0.05
	Ethion	0.01
14 days after application	DDT	. . . .
	Ethion	. . . .
21 days after application	DDT	. . . .
	Ethion	. . . .
30 days after application	DDT	0.03
	Ethion	$< 1 \times 10^{-3}$

[a] Air samples taken over 1-hour sampling period.

method of collecting the insecticides. During application, insecticides are lost through drift, photo decomposition owing to exposure to sunlight, and errors in metering the volume of insecticide mixture applied. Loss caused by collection may result from scattering of the spray droplet into the air after striking the rigid glass surface. If upon impact the droplet is fragmented, vaporization may occur.

The soil, crop, and irrigation runoff water was found free of detectable amounts of DDT and diazinon prior to insecticide application in 1963. One day after application 40% of the DDT found at tassel height was found in the plant and soil. The amount found in the plant decreased as the season progressed. Plant tissue dilution of the insecti-

Data for 1963 Season

Soil, Lb./Acre	Irrigation Return Water, Lb./Acre	Settleable Silt, Lb./Acre
$< 2 \times 10^{-4}$	$< 3 \times 10^{-7}$	$< 1 \times 10^{-7}$
$< 2 \times 10^{-4}$	$< 3 \times 10^{-7}$	$< 1 \times 10^{-7}$
0.24	1.3×10^{-4}	3.2×10^{-6}
....	2.4×10^{-4}	12.9×10^{-6}
....	0.37×10^{-4}	1.9×10^{-6}
....	0.02×10^{-4}	4.8×10^{-6}
0.49	0.46×10^{-4}	2.2×10^{-6}
....	0.05×10^{-4}	0.9×10^{-6}

Data for 1964 Season

Soil, Lb./Acre	Settleable Silt, Lb./Acre	Air [a], Mg./Cu. Ft.
0.16	1.2×10^{-5}	$< 1 \times 10^{-3}$
$< 2 \times 10^{-4}$	$< 1 \times 10^{-7}$	$< 1 \times 10^{-3}$
0.83	77.0×10^{-5}	0.3
0.09	19.2×10^{-5}	0.09
....	1.2×10^{-5}	0.05
....	0.7×10^{-5}	0.01
....	1.3×10^{-5}	1×10^{-3}
....	$< 1 \times 10^{-7}$	1×10^{-3}
....	0.56×10^{-5}	$< 1 \times 10^{-3}$
....	$< 1 \times 10^{-7}$	$< 1 \times 10^{-3}$
0.84	0.34×10^{-5}	$< 1 \times 10^{-3}$
$< 2 \times 10^{-4}$	$< 1 \times 10^{-7}$	$< 1 \times 10^{-3}$

cides also contributes to the decline of residue level, on a plant basis, on a growing crop. This is confirmed by the results obtained during the 1964 study. Loss of the organic phosphate insecticides in the plant is thought to be caused primarily by hydrolysis. Loss of the chlorinated organic insecticide, DDT, can be attributed in part to plant falloff, anthers, dried leaves, and silk. An increase in the amount of plant debris in soil was observed as the season progressed. The transfer of DDT from the plant to the soil is shown in data obtained during the 1963 study and is less marked during the 1964 study.

Prior to application of insecticides in 1964, the plants were found free of detectable amounts of DDT or ethion. This shows that DDT has no systemic properties. Ethion was not present at this time in the soil, while DDT was present from the previous year's treatment. DDT was present in smaller amounts in the soil at the beginning of the 1964 sampling period than at the conclusion of the 1963 study. This difference is caused primarily by the cultivation of the soil.

The quantity of insecticides removed by irrigation runoff in 1963 in either the liquid portion and settleable silt for each irrigation or the total of three irrigations was minute compared with that found at tassel level or in the soil. Only 0.001% of the DDT found at tassel level was removed by all the irrigation runoff water. More DDT and diazinon were removed by the runoff water from the first irrigation after application than by subsequent irrigations. The runoff water in the first irrigation removed 60% of the total DDT. Each subsequent irrigation removed approximately 20% of this total. Virtually all the diazinon was found in the first irrigation after application. A near-constant quantity of DDT and/or diazinon was removed by the second and third irrigations after insecticide application. Twice as much diazinon as DDT was removed by the first irrigation, though supposedly twice as much DDT had been applied. The higher removal can be attributed to the relatively higher solubility of diazinon than DDT in water.

The quantity of insecticides sorbed on the settleable silt followed the same general pattern as that removed in the runoff water. Virtually all diazinon and 58% of the DDT sorbed on the settleable silt were removed during the first irrigation.

DDT was found in the settleable silt prior to insecticide application in 1964, due to its presence in the soil. The concentration of DDT in the settleable silt in 1964 was greater than that found during the 1963 study; the amount being carried by the irrigation water decreased with each successive irrigation after the last cultivation. The decrease in the amount of settleable silt in the runoff water of successive irrigations can be attributed in part to the removal of the loosely packed soil by the excess water and by the compaction of the soil particles by the downward movement of the water.

DDT and ethion were not found in detectable amounts in air prior to application but were present in detectable quantities as long as 2 weeks after application.

It was recognized at the outset of this investigation that the information from an insecticide distribution study is greatly influenced by such factors as climatic conditions, types of crop, soil, insecticides applied, method of application, size of plot, and collection and analytical procedures. The projection of the data obtained in a distribution study where the above-mentioned factors differ widely must be avoided.

Acknowledgment

The authors acknowledge the assistance given by C. D. Moodie and E. C. Klostermeyer in planning the study and reviewing the manuscript. Others contributing to the research program are R. A. McDonald, P. J. Bennett, F. Zitterkopf, and the personnel at the Columbia Basin Research Unit.

Literature Cited

(1) Clore, W. J., Westlake, W. E., Walker, K. C., Boswell, V. R., Washington State University, Washington State Agriculture Bull. **627** (1961).
(2) Dunstan, G. H., Proctor, D. E., Hindin, E., Proceedings of Pacific Northwest Industrial Waste Conference, 1963.
(3) Ginsburg, J. M., *J. Agr. Food Chem.* **3**, 322 (1955).
(4) Hindin, E., Division of Industrial Research, Washington State University, Research Rept. **63/12—155**.
(5) Hindin, E., May, D. S., Dunstan, G. H., "Residue Reviews," Vol. 7, p. 130, Springer-Verlag, New York, 1964.
(6) Lichtenstein, E. P., Mueller, C. H., Myrdal, G. R., Schultz, K. R., J. *Econ. Entomol.* **55**, 215 (1962).
(7) Lichtenstein, E. P., Schultz, K. R., *Ibid.,* **54**, 517 (1961).
(8) Middleton, F. M., Rosen, A. A., *Public Health Repts.* **71**, 112 (1956).
(9) Nicholson, H. P., *Proceedings of Tenth Pacific Northwest Research Symposium*, U. S. Department of Health, Education, and Welfare, 1961.
(10) Nicholson, H. P., Webb, H. J., Lauer, G. I., O'Brien, R. E., Grzenda, A. R., Shanklin, D. W., *Trans. Am. Fish. Soc.* **91**, 213 (1962).
(11) Rodenheser, H. A., *Agron. J.* **52**, 712 (1960).
(12) Rosen, A. A., Middleton, F. M., *Anal. Chem.* **31**, 1729 (1959).
(13) Shell Chemical Co., Agricultural Chemical Division, "Manual of Methods for the Determination of Pesticide Chemical Residues in Agricultural Products, Animal Products, and Soil," 1961.
(14) Taschenberg, E. G., Mac, G. L., Gambrell, F. L., *J. Agr. Food Chem.* **9**, 207 (1960).
(15) Teasly, J. I., Cox, S. W., *J. Am. Water Works Assoc.* **55**, 1093 (1963).

RECEIVED October 18, 1965. Study supported by Grants WP00215 and WP-00676, U. S. Public Health Service.

12

Insecticide Residues in Waterways from Agricultural Use

B. I. SPARR and W. G. APPLEBY

Shell Chemical Co., Agricultural Chemicals Division, New York, N. Y.

D. M. DeVRIES

Shell Chemical Co., Product Development Center, Agricultural Chemicals Division, Princeton, N. J.

J. V. OSMUN

Department of Entomology, Purdue University, Lafayette, Ind.

J. M. McBRIDE

Shell Chemical Co., Little Rock, Ark.

G. L. FOSTER

Shell Chemical Co., San Francisco, Calif.

Tests were conducted to determine the concentrations of insecticides found in waterways, fish, and mud from a cotton field treated three times with endrin at 0.3 lb./acre, corn fields (soil) treated with 5 lb. aldrin/acre/year, and rice paddies (seed) treated at a rate equivalent to 4 oz. aldrin/ acre. Endrin in the soil did not exceed 0.04 p.p.m., even after subsequent sprayings. Runoff water from the cotton field showed only low concentrations of endrin and only 50 p.p.t. after the last spraying. Traces of endrin were found in fish but none in mud. Similarly, aldrin and dieldrin residues were also low. Residues in water from corn fields or waterways draining rice fields did not exceed a few p.p.t. Residues in fish taken from waterways draining rice fields rarely exceeded 10 p.p.b. aldrin plus dieldrin.

The development of the gas-liquid chromatographic (GLC) method for analyzing chlorinated hydrocarbon insecticides has permitted an intensified effort to determine residues of these insecticides in our waterways. In earlier work, using the carbon-chloroform extract (CCE) and the less sensitive infrared spectrophotometric method to examine about 50 samples taken in 1957 from the National Water Quality Network stations, Middleton and Lichtenberg (6) reported one sample with aldrin and several with DDT. Other insecticidal compounds, which were thought to be present, could not be detected. In 1962, water samples from 101 sampling stations were analyzed by Breidenbach and Lichtenberg (1). They found dieldrin in only six monthly samples from one location and DDT in only 12 locations but no other chlorinated hydrocarbons. They used carbon-chloroform extracts, measured by GLC with flame ionization detection, and obtained confirmation by infrared spectrophotometry. On September 24, 1964 Weaver and colleagues (12) obtained and analyzed grab samples from 96 locations on 12 major river basins. The samples were solvent-extracted, the extracts subjected to thin layer chromatography (TLC), and sections of the developed silica gel chromatographs were removed and extracted for GLC analysis with microcoulometric detection. They reported finite but minute residues of dieldrin, endrin, DDT, and DDE in all the river basins sampled. Heptachlor and aldrin were less prevalent. TDE was reported at only one station. Weaver *et al.* attributed the absence of heptachlor epoxide and BHC to the poorer sensitivity for these compounds. Toxaphene, which was expected in certain samples, could not be analyzed by this procedure.

The aforementioned work represents a part of the continuing USPHS (U.S. Public Health Service) program to survey U.S. surface waters, and as such it is not concerned with the question of how these compounds enter the water. However, other teams of workers have conducted studies to determine the contribution of various agricultural applications of pesticides to water contamination. One of the most comprehensive studies has been conducted by the USPHS Southeast Water Laboratory in Athens, Ga. which has been studying most of the more widely used pesticides in some typical applications. Of the chlorinated cyclodiene insecticides, this group of workers have given the most attention to endrin and its use in sugar cane production. This work was reported in a 1963 Progress Report from that laboratory (11) and by Lauer (5). Of 109 water samples, endrin was found in 34, in p.p.t. concentrations. The highest concentrations were found in a water body practically impounded by cane fields while the concentrations reported for samples from bayous flowing away from the cane fields contained residues barely within the limits of detection. Dugan and co-workers (2) reported water, soil, and mud residues in a New York watershed where apples are the main agricultural product. Of 15 pesticides used in apple production, they only examined residues for the chlorinated hydrocarbons and dinitrobenzene derivatives. They found p,p'-DDT, dieldrin, γ-BHC, and aldrin in some of the water samples. The concentrations varied considerably (from nil to a few p.p.b) over short distances along a stream. Also the absence of any geographical distribution pattern with respect to pesticide concentration suggested that the concentration in soil or water was primarily a function of local application. At any given site the concentration in the contiguous soil was greater than in the mud which, in turn, was greater than in the water. They also obtained data indicating that these compounds reach the water bound to the silt and concluded that any factor producing an increase in total suspended solids would also increase the pesticide content of the water. While they learned that endrin was used in the watershed and obtained a few soil and mud samples containing endrin, they found no endrin in any water sample.

Hindin and co-workers (4) reported on a survey of the Columbia Basin river, ground, and irrigation water for chlorinated hydrocarbon insecticides and certain 2,4-D esters. Some of their samples contained aldrin and endrin in p.p.t. concentrations and less, but no dieldrin.

Except for the endrin-sugar work there has been little reported work relating the contribution of farm use of aldrin or endrin to water contamination. This report deals with studies undertaken in 1964 and 1965 to determine whether the treatment of soil under corn, which is an important use, contributes significantly to water contamination. It also contains the results of tests conducted in 1964 to determine whether aldrin, as a rice-seed treatment, contributes to waterway contamination. A few preliminary results reported by Sparr and Mitchell (10) indicated that the contribution was negligible. The results of a 1964 study to determine whether the foliar application of endrin to cotton leads to significant waterway contamination are also reported.

Experimental

Sampling. A rather wide variety of sampling techniques was used. In general, they were selected for ease of adaptation to the local situation. The water sampling equipment was as follows:

(1) From bridges—a weighted pail tied to a rope.

(2) From boats—a Golden Thief hand vacuum pump which can lift from depths of 25 feet (W&W Mfg. Co., Chicago, Ill.).

(3) From ditches—direct immersion of the glass gallon sample jug, making 3–9 separate immersions per sampling.

(4) From standing water (rice paddies)—a glass tumbler-representative sampling.

(5) From runoff water—a metal pail.

All water samples were placed and kept in chemically clean, 1-gallon glass bottles, closed with a screw cap with aluminum foil insert.

The fish were taken by hook and line, poisoned, or netted. They were wrapped in aluminum foil, quick-frozen, and shipped to the laboratory packed in dry ice. Mud was taken usually down to a depth of 3 inches by scoop or wide-mouth container. Soil and rice field mud samples were taken with a ¾-inch i.d. soil corer down to a 3-inch level. Fields were crossed diagonally, and subsamples were taken at regular intervals. The samples were packed in wide-mouth, screw-cap jars with aluminum foil inserts.

Extraction. At the laboratory, water samples were usually allowed to stand, and the supernatant liquid was decanted and extracted. With some samples the decantate was filtered through 1-micron porosity glass filter paper. The filtrate and the material on the filter paper were analyzed separately, but because of the limitations of table space, we have shown in these cases only the sum of the two analyses, which corresponds to the "decanted" values. We used a "progressive extraction" procedure to remove the insecticide from water. Here, about 4000 ml. of water were divided into 6–8 portions, and each portion was extracted in a separatory funnel with the same 100 ml. of hexane. This procedure was repeated twice more with fresh solvent, and the extracts were then combined.

Soils and muds were slurried with water and extracted with a hexane/2-propanol mixture. Fish were chopped and extracted in a Waring blendor with a hexane/2-propanol mixture.

Cleanup of soil and fish extracts was carried out on 5:1 Florisil/Celite columns, and the eluate was concentrated or diluted to appropriate volumes.

Analysis. Analyses of the eluates were conducted by the GLC electron capture technique. The cleanup and detection procedures used were those developed and routinely used at our residue laboratories (8). The sensitivities for water analysis ran 1–5 p.p.t. for aldrin, heptachlor, and γ-BHC. For endrin and heptachlor epoxide they were 4–10 p.p.t. For dieldrin we obtained sensitivities ranging from 10–20 p.p.t. For DDT and its congeners, they were 7–75 p.p.t. For mud, soil, and fish, our limits of detection were about 1/1000 as much and were in the p.p.b. range.

Results

Aldrin from Rice. An important off-take for aldrin is in the treatment of rice seed to protect the seedling against grape colaspis larvae and rice water weevils. The seed is usually sprayed with sufficient volume of an aldrin-hydrocarbon solution to give 2–4 oz. of aldrin per bushel of seed. The seed is either flown onto flooded fields or drilled into dry fields and then flooded. The planting rate, which determines the amount of aldrin applied per acre, will vary with the variety and local cultural practices. The fields are drained and reflooded a few times before harvest, the frequency depending upon the amount of rainfall and degree of pest infestation. This particular use of aldrin was selected because: (1) it involved adding aldrin and dieldrin—its principal metabolite—directly to standing water which is admitted to a waterway, and (2) it allowed an unusual opportunity to relate quantitatively any water contamination to the amount of insecticide used.

A 0.4-acre test plot belonging to the USDA Rice Experiment Station near Stuttgart, Ark. was used. This and neighboring plots had been treated with an aerial application of aldrin at a dosage of 2 lb./acre in early May. The station and field are located in Arkansas County, which in 1964 had 76,500 of the state's 439,000-acre rice allotment. A hardpan exists 6–8 inches below the soil surface, which prevents water seepage and restricts deep root development. Vegold seed, a late rice variety, treated with 2 oz. of aldrin per bushel, was flown on at a planting rate of 2 bu./acre in late June 1964. This is equivalent to an aldrin application of 4 oz./acre. Essentially all the rice in the area had been planted in May, with some planting in April. About 70% of the seed used had been treated with aldrin. Samples of water and mud were taken from the irrigation ditch supplying the test paddy, the paddy itself, and a ditch draining the paddy. A large ditch, draining 200 acres of rice fields, was similarly sampled. The geographical relationship of the test plot to the Little LaGrue Bayou into which it and the surrounding fields drain is shown in Figure 1. The Little LaGrue serves also as a source of water for the irrigation of the test plot and many of the neighboring fields. The Little LaGrue was sampled near Almyra. Nearly 100% of the drainage into the bayou at this point is from rice fields. Also shown are sampling points on the White River and their relationship to the rice-growing area. The sampling point at Jack's Bay represents the confluence of the LaGrue Bayou and the White River. The acreage of rice within this watershed is estimated at 168,000. About 70% of this acreage was planted with aldrin-treated rice seed. The typical seed treatment rate in this area was 2 oz./bu., and its typical seed planting rate was 3 bu./acre. Therefore, the typical aldrin application rate was 6 oz./acre.

The analyses of the water samples taken from the experimental plot and the immediate environs are shown in Table I.

Water enters the paddy via a ditch from a reservoir filled by the Little LaGrue Bayou. At the time of filling, the paddy contained about 0.06 p.p.b. dieldrin. Since our test plot was sown with a late variety of rice, this bayou had received one or more drainings from the surrounding fields. About a month later the concentration of dieldrin in the irrigation water was reduced by about 40%.

The paddy was originally filled to a 6-inch height and, while in the flood stage, kept at this level by admitting more water to compensate for evaporation losses, which were substantial (75–90% over the season).

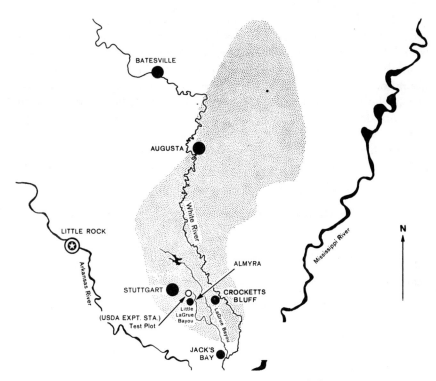

Figure 1.   Sampling points in White River watershed draining rice growing area. This area includes an estimated 168,000 acres of rice planted with an average of 3 bu. of seed per acre, equivalent to 6 oz. aldrin per acre.

Table I. Analysis of Water from Paddy Planted with Aldrin-Treated Rice

	Insecticide Concentration in Water, p.p.b.		
	Aldrin	*Dieldrin*	*Total*
Before seeding			
input H₂O from ditch	< 0.001	0.06	0.06
standing H₂O in paddy	0.02	0.02	0.04
2 Days after seeding	1.1	0.5	1.6
Theoretically possible conc.	. . . .	. . .	140.0
First drainage, 3rd week after seeding	0.4	0.9	1.3
After 2nd flooding			
Fourth week after seeding			
input H₂O from ditch	0.004	0.03	0.034
standing H₂O in paddy	0.007	0.31	0.32
Second drainage, 7th week after seeding	0.008	0.16	0.17
Ninth week after seeding	0.005	0.13	0.14
Third and last drainage,			
14th week after seeding	0.005	0.06	0.07

The highest dieldrin concentration—0.160 p.p.b.—in the paddy water occurred after seeding. At the time of the first drainage the water contained 130 p.p.t. aldrin plus dieldrin. If all the applied insecticide were in solution, the concentration should have been 140 p.p.b., which is near saturation for dieldrin. With each successive drainage, the concentration in the water decreased as expected, so that at the last drainage the concentration was essentially equal to the concentration of original input water.

As shown in Table II, the insecticide concentration in the top 3 inches of mud was substantially the same throughout the experiment— i.e., 0.07 ± 0.03 p.p.m.

Table II. Analysis of Mud from Paddy Planted with Aldrin-Treated Rice

	Insecticide Concentration in Mud, p.p.m.		
	Aldrin	*Dieldrin*	*Total*
Before seeding	< 0.01	0.05	0.05
2 Days after seeding	< 0.01	0.06	0.06
First drainage, 3rd week after seeding	< 0.01	0.04	0.04
After 2nd flooding, 4th week after seeding	0.02	0.08	0.10
Third and last drainage	0.03	0.03	0.06

Since, at the time of each drainage, the paddy contained 0.5 ft. of water, it is possible to calculate how much insecticide is in the water during each drainage. Table III gives the results of the calculations. During a rice-growing season, slightly under 1 gram per acre will enter a waterway. This amounts to under 1% of the applied insecticide. The remainder is assumed to be lost by some of the physicochemical and biodegradation routes mentioned by Mitchell (7).

We have attempted to show what happens to water, mud, and fish residues as we (1) proceed into the rice field drainage ditch and thence into Little LaGrue Bayou (which drains into LaGrue Bayou and thence

Table III. Estimated Quantities of Insecticide Admitted to Waterways from Aldrin Treatment of Rice Seed

	Grams/Acre
Insecticide added to paddy	113
Insecticide drained out	
1st drainage	0.8
2nd drainage	0.1
3rd drainage	0.04
Total	0.94

Table IV. Water, Mud, Fish Residues in Drainage Ditch and Little LaGrue

Location	Aldrin and Dieldrin Concentrations	
	July	Harvest
Water		
Drainage ditch	0.027 p.p.b.	
Little LaGrue	0.044 p.p.b.	0.018 p.p.b.
Mud		
Drainage ditch	< 0.01–0.02 p.p.m.	
Little LaGrue	< 0.01–0.02 p.p.m.	< 0.01 p.p.m.
Catfish		
Little LaGrue	0.07 p.p.m.	0.01 p.p.m.

the White River), and (2) proceed down the White River from Batesville, above the rice drainage area, through Augusta and Crockett's Bluff, within the area, to Jack's Bay, below the rice area but receiving the drainage of the whole area.

As Table IV shows, the drainage ditch and Little LaGrue Bayou show insignificant concentrations in the p.p.t. range of aldrin and dieldrin in the water, with indications that the very low level in mid-season declines to below the analytical sensitivity by harvest time. As shown in Table V, this was also observed along the White River, where mid-

Table V. Water, Mud, and Fish Residues in White River

Aldrin and Dieldrin Concentrations

Location	In water, p.p.b.	
	July	Harvest
Batesville	0.009	0.008
Augusta	0.023	~ 0.008
Crockett's Bluff	0.021	0.008
Jack's Bay	0.007	~ 0.006
	In mud, p.p.m.	
Batesville	< 0.01–0.02	< 0.01
Augusta	< 0.01–0.02	< 0.01
Crockett's Bluff	< 0.01–0.02	< 0.01
Jack's Bay	< 0.01–0.02	< 0.01
	In fish flesh, p.p.m.	
Batesville	0.04 (2 catfish)	< 0.01 (4 catfish)
Augusta	0.09 (4 buffalo)	< 0.01 (3 buffalo)
Crockett's Bluff	0.02 (3 catfish)	0.05 (10 whole carp)
Jack's Bay	0.21 (2 catfish)	0.04 (4 catfish)
	0.01 (2 buffalo)	

season residues in the rice growing area were very near the limit of sensitivity of the method. Harvest water residues were nil (i.e., <0.01 to 0.02 p.p.b.). At no time were aldrin or dieldrin residues found in the mud at the sensitivity of the method (0.01–0.02 p.p.m.). Thus, these data show that water and mud residues of aldrin and dieldrin in this heavily cultivated rice area, where 70% of the seeded acreage receives aldrin, are really negligible.

Residues in the meat of fish taken along the White River were all negligibly low from the standpoint of acceptable food residues, as indicated by aldrin and dieldrin tolerances in effect at the time. The residue in the two catfish taken at Jack's Bay, which were 0.21 p.p.m. aldrin plus dieldrin, are unexplained at present. The values represent one sample since the fish were combined for analysis. These data suggest that a trend toward lower residues from mid-season to harvest may exist. However, a more comprehensive, season-long study of fish residues in this area would be required to prove this.

We attempted to relate water flow rates on the White River at DeValls Bluff, which lies nearly midway between Augusta and Crockett's Bluff. The flow rates were measured by the U.S. Geological Survey and furnished by Sniegocki (9). However, the concentrations were so low and the variances in flow rate at the sampling times so minor that no relationship could be established.

Endrin from Cotton. The major off-take for endrin is for use on cotton, which it protects from bollworms, cabbage loopers, and numerous other pests. It is applied alone or in combination with other insecticides at a dosage of 0.2–0.5 lb./acre. Most application is by air.

A 5-acre field, belonging to the Arkansas Southeastern Branch Experiment Station at Kelso, Ark., was chosen as the experimental site. The relationship of the site to its environs is shown in Figure 2. Irrigation water was introduced from a head ditch on the north side of the plot and flowed through the ¼-mile furrows to a drainage ditch, which was sampled as it left the field. The ditch ran ⅝ mile until the water was held for reuse by a check dam. It was estimated that the water was diluted 20–fold at the dam site. The dam held the drainage of 800 acres of cultivated land.

We started our tests in late July when the cotton was slightly less than hip high and gave an average ground cover of 80%. The cotton was sprayed with an aqueous emulsion at a dosage of 0.4 lb. of endrin per acre. In all, three applications were made, the first with a ground rig and the other two from a plane.

While irrigating, water samples were collected, before and after spraying, from the irrigation and drainage ditches in the field. Rain runoff samples were taken from the end of a furrow during a rainstorm.

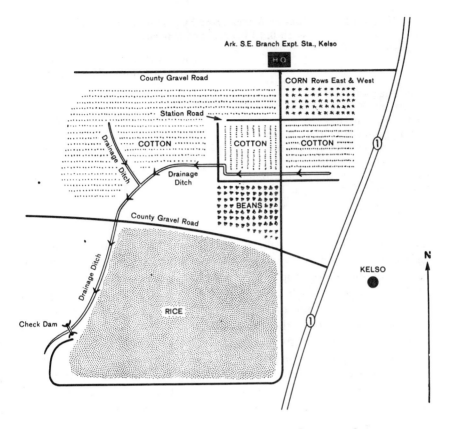

Figure 2.   Drainage from endrin-treated cotton plot

Soil samples from the cotton field were taken at various intervals, as was mud beneath the water impounded by the check dam. Fish were also taken from the impoundment. The results of the water analysis of samples taken from the cotton field are given in Table VI. These data show that a slight amount of endrin can be washed from a cotton field by irrigation. The first pair of analyses shows about a 4.5-fold increase in endrin concentration as the water courses over the ¼-mile of furrows. The second pair of values shows no total increment. On filtering the samples through 1-micron porosity glass filter paper, we found that 5/6 of the endrin in the first sample was held on the paper whereas only 1/10 of the endrin was retained from the second sample. These findings indicate that more soil particles were dislodged during the first irrigation than during the second. A 1.15-inch rainfall, which occurred seven days after the first application, gave rise to the highest water concentration measured in these tests. About ⅓ of the endrin in this sample was re-

Table VI. Residues in Water from Spraying a Cotton Field with 0.4 Lb./Acre of Endrin

	No. of Sprays	Interval from Last Spray, days	Endrin Conc., p.p.b.
Input irrigation H_2O	1	1	0.08
Used irrigation H_2O, from furrows [a]	1	1	0.36
Input irrigation H_2O	2	3	0.12
Used irrigation H_2O, from furrows [a]	2	3	0.11
Used irrigation H_2O, from furrows [a]	3	40	0.05
Rain runoff, 1.15 inches	1	7	0.66
H_2O held by check dam ⅝ mile from plot	1	2	0.006
H_2O held by check dam ⅝ mile from plot	1	3	0.008

[a] ¼ mile long.

tained on the filter. We believe that this higher endrin concentration resulted from washing the endrin off the foliage, which must hold the majority of the endrin applied. This belief is based on the soil residue data in Table VII, which indicate that only 10% or less of the applied endrin penetrates or runs off the foliar canopy at the time of application. If all the endrin reached the ground, the concentration in the soil should have been about 0.4 p.p.m. endrin.

The soil analyses also show that there is no measurable endrin in the top 3 inches (at a sensitivity of 0.01 p.p.m.) from the previous seasons' treatments. Moreover, the three applications during the test period did not result in a build-up above that initially deposited.

Table VII. Residues in Mud and Fish from Spraying a Cotton Field with 0.4 Lb./Acre of Endrin

	No. of Sprays	Interval from Last Spray, Days	Endrin Conc., p.p.m.
Soil, prespraying	0	0	nil
Soil, preirrigation	1	1	0.04
Soil, 3 days after irrigation	1	2	0.03
Soil, after two runoffs	1	17	0.03
Soil, after second application	2	0	0.04
Soil, after harvest	3	38	0.02
Mud at check dam	1	2	nil
Mud at check dam	1	3	nil
Mud at check dam (post harvest)	3	38	nil
Fish in drainage ditch			
whole perch (5 fish)	1	1	0.02 [a]
bluegill meat (5 fish)	1	1	0.01 [a]

[a] Apparent endrin; minimal analytical peak may be caused by toxaphene used to kill fish.

The concentration of endrin in the water held by the check dam (0.008 p.p.b.) was significantly less than could be accounted for by the 20-fold dilution factor. The water from this location does not drain into any waterways. Therefore, we believe that the water at the check dam is representative of water which may enter streams from cotton fields contiguous to them.

No endrin was found in the mud at the check dam with an analytical sensitivity of 0.01 p.p.m. The fish which were taken by poisoning with toxaphene contained concentrations of apparent endrin barely within the sensitivity of the method. Toxaphene was a poor choice here because the GLC smear can interfere with the analytical peaks for endrin. Rotenone, which was normally used when time did not permit sport fishing, was ineffective at this site.

Aldrin from Corn. The most important use of aldrin is as a soil insecticide under corn. Here it is usually incorporated in the soil at application rates of 1–2 lb./acre to a depth of 3–4 inches. In muck soils the rate may be as high as 5 lb./acre. It is used to control the corn rootworm and wireworm complexes plus other soil insects.

An area in northwestern Indiana was selected to determine whether soil usage of aldrin leads to significant residues in water. Since other chlorinated hydrocarbons are now or were in use there, we also measured those that are readily analyzable.

Water and mud sampling was set up at three locations. One was a railroad trestle over the Kankakee River immediately west of U.S. Route 421. Here water samples were taken from the middle and the side of the river. Mud samples were collected near the edge. This point represents the drainage of about 800,000 acres of land, much of which is farm planted with vegetables and corn.

Nearby at North Judson we sampled a large ditch, draining cornfields which had been treated with aldrin over a period of years including the test years. We also sampled a smaller ditch which receives the tile drainage and runoff from 100 acres of corn protected with 5 lb. of aldrin per acre.

The first sampling was in late June 1964, about 1 month after corn planting. Sampling continued on a semimonthly basis until September, when it was discontinued until December. From late March 1965 through early June, sampling was resumed on a semimonthly basis to determine the effect of spring runoffs and the renewal of planting and treating activity on the insecticide levels at these locations.

The range of analyses of the water samples taken from the Kankakee River between June and December 1964 is given in Table VIII. While aldrin and dieldrin residues are presented as a sum, only two of the 22 samples contained a finite concentration of aldrin—2 p.p.t.—barely

Table VIII. Range of H₂O Residue Concentrations in Kankakee River from Farm Usage of Chlorinated Hydrocarbon Insecticides [a]

| | Number of Samples in Concentration Range June–December 1964 | |
Conc. Range, p.p.b.	Aldrin and Dieldrin	p,p'-DDT, o,p-DDT, DDE
< 0.025	7	0
> 0.025 < 0.05	7	0
> 0.05 < 0.1	2	3
> 0.1 < 0.2	3	3
> 0.2 < 0.3	2	3
> 0.3 < 0.6	1	4
	22	14 [b]

[a] Endrin sought, but interference prevented detection, if present, in most samples. Under 0.025 p.p.b. detected in two samples.
[b] One sample about 12 p.p.b.

within the sensitivity of the analysis. Thus, the water residues from aldrin soil treatment are essentially dieldrin. The contribution by direct dieldrin application in the watershed is unknown. Sixteen of 22 samples are under 100 p.p.t., which we consider the lowest concentration that can be expressed with some degree of certainty. The highest concentrations of dieldrin found were under 300 p.p.t. The preponderance of the DDT-related compounds was found as p,p'-DDE. The concentrations of heptachlor expoxide and γ-BHC or lindane were lower than the other chlorinated hydrocarbons sought and were under 25 p.p.t. Although quantitative comparisons at these low levels may be, at best, shaky, there were no significant differences in water samples from the middle or side of the river.

As shown in Table IX, the concentrations of aldrin plus dieldrin in the small ditch were considerably lower than those in the river during the same time period, the highest being under 20 p.p.t. Since this ditch drains cornfields exclusively, the presence of DDT led us to believe the ditch may have received drift from aerial applications, runoff from foliage applications, or accidental contamination. The heptachlor epoxide and γ-BHC residues, which are not shown, were practically nil, suggesting that none has been used on these 100 acres in the recent past. Although endrin was sought in most of these samples, interference, absence, or lack of sufficient sensitivity prevented its detection in all but three water samples. These were samples taken in December from the middle and side of the Kankakee and from the large ditch; they contained about 17, 12, and 44 p.p.t. endrin. The larger ditch (#2) had essentially the same residues as the small ditch, #1.

Of 17 mud samples analyzed from the three locations, only one, taken in December from the larger ditch, showed a measurable amount of insecticide. It contained 30–35 p.p.b. aldrin. Although the analysis was repeated and confirmed, the sample integrity was regarded as suspect because a second mud sample taken at the same time from the same place showed no detectable aldrin at a 10 p.p.b. sensitivity. The water above showed no aldrin at a 3 p.p.t. sensitivity.

Of 24 water samples from the three locations analyzed for the March to June period, only one gave a finite residue. The remaining were free of insecticide residues at the level of detection. A sample of water taken from the small ditch on May 21 showed 45 p.p.t. dieldrin. Twelve mud samples from the Kankakee were free of insecticide within the limits of detection. As a frame of reference, the limits are given in Table X.

Reports that chlorinated hydrocarbons exist in samples taken from remote, unfrequented places are frequently the subject of much publicity. Most of the time there is a logical explanation for the finding. To find a logical explanation for the absence of residues in the heart of a

Table IX. Residues in Ditches Receiving Tile Drainage and
Runoff from Corn Fields with Soil Treatment
of 5 Lb. Aldrin/Acre—Indiana, 1964

	Number of Samples in Concentration Range	
Conc. Range, p.p.b.	Aldrin and Dieldrin	p,p'-DDT, o,p-DDT, DDE
Ditch No. 1 [a]		
< 0.01	2	0
> 0.01 < 0.02	7	0
> 0.02 < 0.05	0	1
> 0.05 < 0.075	0	2
> 0.2 < 0.3	0	2
> 0.3 < 0.4	0	1
	9	6
Ditch No. 2 [b]		
< 0.01	2	0
> 0.01 < 0.02	0	0
> 0.02 < 0.05	11	1
> 0.05 < 0.075	0	1
> 0.075 < 0.1	0	1
> 0.1 < 0.2	0	4
	13	7

[a] Ditch No. 1 drains 100 acres of soil treated with 5 lb. aldrin/acre.
[b] Ditch No. 2 receives drainage from ditch No. 1 and other cornfields and empties into Kankakee River above sampling point.

**Table X. Minimal Detectable Concentration Kankakee Study,
March–June 1965**

Insecticide	H_2O, p.p.t.	Mud, p.p.b.
Aldrin	5	5
Dieldrin	20	10
DDE	15	6
DDT	50	30
Endrin	25	10

high insecticide consumption area is quite a challenge. We are quite confident in the analyses because we obtained good recoveries from samples fortified near the sensitivity for the compounds sought. Since the pesticide patterns have been essentially unchanged in this area between 1964 and 1965, we assumed that the runoff during the winter and spring of 1965 was sufficiently high to dilute the insecticide concentrations beyond detectability. To check this assumption, we compared the daily flow rate of the Kankakee, as determined by the Geological Survey (3), with the dieldrin concentration found on a given date (Table XI). There is some qualitative evidence that the explanation is valid. Dunns bridge, which is the location of the Geological Survey gage, is 3 miles west of our railroad trestle, and there are no important tributaries in between. Therefore, we assume that the flow rate at Dunns bridge is the same as at the trestle. The differences in flow rates can be seen more dramatically in Table XII. The flow rate from January through

Table XI. Dieldrin Concentration vs. Flow Rate, Kankakee River

Date	Average Daily Flow Rate [a], Cu.Ft./Sec.	Dieldrin Conc., p.p.b.	
		Side of River	Middle of River
6/26/64	820	0.012	0.013
7/10/64	1340	0.016	0.067
7/24/64	638	nil	nil
8/5/64	407	0.011	0.028
8/22/64	384	0.209	0.169
9/19/64	301	0.017	0.200
12/12/64	855	0.207	0.083
3/29/65	1510	< 0.020	< 0.020
4/9/65	2530	< 0.020	< 0.020
4/23/65	1960	< 0.020	< 0.020
5/7/65	2070	< 0.020	< 0.020
5/21/65	1040	< 0.020	< 0.020
6/4/65	824	< 0.020	< 0.020

[a] At Dunn's bridge, 3 miles west of sampling point.

Table XII. Kankakee River Flow Rate

| Month | Mean Monthly Flow Rate, Cu.Ft./Sec. | | |
	1963	1964	1965
January	—	550	1578
February	—	481	1931
March	—	840	2156
April	—	1218	2375
May	—	936	1488
June	—	660	720
July	—	780	610
August	—	371	—
September	—	360	—
October	350	415	—
November	422	399	—
December	447	780	—

June 1965 was significantly higher than during the previous year. The flow rate is a direct function of precipitation runoff.

Conclusions

Aldrin from Rice. The maximum amount of insecticide that can be emptied from a paddy planted with aldrin-treated rice is below 1 gram per acre. At the end of a growing season, the paddy water and the top 3 inches of soil are the same as before the planting with respect to insecticide residue. The concentration of the drainage entering a waterway rapidly diminishes to a few p.p.t. by dilution and by physicochemical and biodegradation factors.

Fish taken from streams and rivers receiving the drainage of aldrin-treated rice fields contain residues well below acceptable tolerances on agricultural food commodities.

Endrin from Cotton. While the application of endrin to cotton leads to runoff immediately to the field, dilution and degradation reduce the concentration to barely discernible levels (< 10 p.p.t.) within a short distance on a watercourse from the treated field. While a fraction of the endrin reaches the soil surface, the concentration does not accumulate by multiple sprays during the growing season. Endrin concentration in the mud of a watercourse receiving the runoff is low and was analytically nil in our tests. Fish taken in the same watercourse have barely detectable, if any, endrin.

Aldrin from Corn. The aldrin-dieldrin concentrations of ditches draining cornfields receiving up to 5 lb. of aldrin per acre as a soil treatment are low—i.e., in the few p.p.t. range—throughout the year. When found, their presence is at best qualitatively detected. The heptachlor, heptachlor epoxide, γ-BHC, or lindane concentrations of the water in these ditches are of a lower order of magnitude, but their use pattern has not been established yet. The concentration of DDT and related compounds in the ditch water may be somewhat higher.

The mud in the ditches or in the river into which they empty does not appear to be an important insecticide reservoir; however, refinements of the analytical method to yield greater sensitivity would be required before a definite conclusion could be drawn. In any case, the muds are not seriously contaminated.

When rainfall causes runoff into the cornfield drainage ditches, the runoff does not increase the insecticide concentration in the river water. Winter or spring runoffs do not appear to increase the insecticide concentration of the Kankakee River or drainage from cornfields.

Stepped-up farming activities—i.e., preparing the soil for planting, planting, and insecticide application—do not appear to increase the insecticide burden of the drainage ditches or the Kankakee River into which they flow.

In general, it appears that normal sowing of aldrin-treated rice seed, spraying of cotton fields with endrin, or incorporation of aldrin into the soil of cornfields do not lead to a high degree of contamination of watercourses receiving drainage from the land masses on which these activities take place.

Literature Cited

(1) Breidenbach, A. W., Lichtenberg, J. J., *Science* **141**, 899 (1963).
(2) Dugan, P. R., *et al.*, *Research Rept.* No. **10**, Pt. 1, Project No. GL-WP-3, Syracuse University Research Corp., (1963).
(3) Hale, M. D., U.S. Geological Survey, private communications, 1965.
(4) Hindin, E., May, D., Dunstan, G. H., *Residue Rev.* **7**, 130 (1964).
(5) Lauer, G. J., *Proc. Am. Soc. Sugar Cane Technologists* **11**, 46 (1964).
(6) Middleton, F. M., Lichtenberg, J. J., *Ind. Eng. Chem.* **52** (6), 99A (1960).
(7) Mitchell, L. E., ADVAN. CHEM. SER. **60**, 1 (1966).
(8) Shell Development Co., MMS-43/64, October 12, 1964.
(9) Sniegacki, R. T., U.S. Geological Survey, private communication, 1965.
(10) Sparr, B. I., Mitchell, L. E., "Abstracts of Papers," 148th Meeting, ACS, Sept. 1964, p. 29A.
(11) U.S. Public Health Service, *Pesticide Pollution Progr. Rept.*, March 1963.
(12) Weaver, L., Gunnerson, C. G., Breidenbach, A. W., Lichtenberg, J. J., *Public Health Repts. (U.S.)* **80** (6), 481 (1965).

RECEIVED January 20, 1966.

13

Widespread Translocation of Pesticides by Air Transport and Rain-out

JESSE M. COHEN and CECIL PINKERTON

Cincinnati Water Research Laboratory, Federal Water Pollution Control Administration, U. S. Department of Interior, Cincinnati, Ohio 45226

There is increasing evidence that pesticides have contaminated extensive areas of the world not directly treated with pesticides. In many instances, the translocation can be attributed to food or water as the transmission vehicle. Another medium of dispersal of pesticides is the atmosphere. Analyses of rainwater and dust have revealed the presence of chloro-organic substances in all samples examined. Identification of specific pesticides has demonstrated that at least some of the chloro-organic compounds are pesticidal in origin. An analysis of dust, whose distant origin was documented by meteorological evidence, proved that pesticide-laden dust can be transported over great distances via the atmosphere and can be deposited over land surfaces remote from the point of application.

E vidence of increasing environmental contamination by pesticides has generated concern that is no longer limited to the people in the immediate areas where the pesticides are applied. During the past two decades, a huge volume of synthetic pesticides has been dispersed both intentionally and inadvertently, and many of these compounds are now found far from the area where they were applied.

The rapidly accumulating literature on the subject indicates that pesticides have contaminated land and water throughout the world. Pesticides have been found in fish and animals in areas remote from their application.

World-Wide Distribution of Pesticides

West (12) has reviewed some of the evidences of the world-wide distribution of pesticides. Blubber from a gray whale washed up on the California shore, she reported, contained 0.2 p.p.m. of DDT, 0.5 p.p.m. of DDE, and 0.2 p.p.m. of lindane. Moreover, DDT has been found in the oil of fish caught off the coast of the Americas, Europe, and Asia in concentrations ranging from 1 to 300 p.p.m. Residues of DDT have been found in duck eggs on the Yukon River, in 75% of 2300 species of birds collected from 22 states and three provinces of Canada, and in 31 of 32 eagles examined.

Humans in remote areas have also been contaminated with insecticide residues. Durham and Armstrong (6) report that the body fat in native Alaskans who lived in isolated, primitive areas contained a mean concentration of 1.4 p.p.m. of DDT and 3.8 p.p.m. of DDE. Since no DDT or DDE was detected in any of the native foods analyzed, these residues were presumed to have resulted from the consumption of a limited number of imported food items and from the hospital diet that had been served to the subjects.

Pesticide residues in fish, birds, and humans in isolated areas of the world can, in some cases, be attributed to distribution through the food chain; however, it is apparent from recent evidence that dispersion by air transport must also be considered. Paul (8) reported that 71% of all specimens of waterfowl and their eggs collected from selected areas of the United States and Canada during 1961, 1962, and 1963 contained chlorinated hydrocarbon residues. Significantly, chlorinated hydrocarbons were found also in samples of aquatic vegetation and snails obtained from the Far North waterfowl nesting areas of Canada, 500 miles or more from any known pesticide-treated area.

Sladen et al. (9) reported finding DDT products, in the range of 13–152 in the tissues of penguins and a seal captured in the Antarctic. They speculated on several modes of transport of DDT to this remote part of the world. Transmission via the food chain and by animal migration was considered to be the principal mode of contamination. Transport by contaminated air and water were considered unlikely.

The literature contains ample evidence that the atmosphere may become contaminated locally as the direct result of pesticide application, especially by air-spraying operations. Such occurrences have been documented, for example, by West (12) and Kraybill (7). Tabor (10) has shown that the air over both rural and urban communities contains pesticides, which reflect their use in local agricultural applications and in communities conducting mosquito-control operations. In this study, airborne particulate matter was collected by standard high volume air samplers located one-half to one mile away from the area of actual pesticide application. Analysis of the glass fiber filter collectors by electron capture gas chromatography disclosed measurable amounts of DDT and chlordan in the agricultural communities and DDT and malathion in the urban communities. Concentration of DDT ranged from below detectable levels to 23 nanograms per cu. meter for the rural samples and from below detectable levels to as much as 8000 nanograms per cu. meter for the urban communities conducting pest-control programs. These values were considered minimum because only an unknown portion of the particulate matter and none of the pesticide in vapor form was captured in the sampling procedure he used. Yates and Akesson (*14*) have reported the drift of pesticides to areas more distant than the local areas of application. Symptoms resulting from the drift of 2,4-D have been noted on grapes 8–12 miles from the point of application, and drift of tracers used in air pollution studies have been authenticated as far as 22 miles from the source.

The first quantitative evidence of the dispersion of pesticides, other than from the direct consequence of air spraying, was reported by Cohen, Evans, and Pinkerton (*4*). An experimental agricultural plot at Coshocton, Ohio, was hand-sprayed with 4 pounds per acre of atrazine and 2 pounds per acre of Esteron 99 (a polypropylene glycol butyl ether ester of 2,4-D). Three weeks later, an analysis of rainwater by microcoulometric gas chromatography revealed the presence of chloro-organic compounds. This chromatogram was strikingly similar to those obtained on samples of the treated soil located more than a mile away. The presence of atrazine in the soil was confirmed by injecting samples into three chromatographic columns, and the 2,4-D was confirmed by means of hydrolysis and methylation pretreatment.

Total organic chlorine in the rainwater was 0.3 p.p.b., with atrazine and the 2,4-D ester amounting to about 0.1 p.p.b. each. Since the soil one mile away contained 6 p.p.m. of atrazine, it can be calculated that no more than 16–17 mg. of soil per liter of rainfall would be sufficient to yield the 0.1 p.p.b. of atrazine actually found in the rain, and 16 to 17 mg. of suspended solids in a rain sample is not unusual.

These data led to the hypothesis that pesticides could exist in the atmosphere, adsorbed on soil particles, as was likely in this case, and could be redeposited by a rainfall washout on land areas remote from the site of original deposition of the pesticides.

Rainfall Analysis

Since this original discovery of pesticides in rainfall, additional samples have been collected and analyzed by microcoulometric gas chromatography. These data have been reported in part by Weibel *et al.* (*11*) and are summarized in Table I. Of the 90 samples of rainwater analyzed, none was free of organic chlorine, which ranged from 0.02 to 1.18 p.p.b. It is not certain that all of the organic chlorine content can be ascribed to pesticides; many peaks on the chromatograms have remained unidentified. The pesticides listed in Table I, however, have been identified as present in certain samples in the concentration ranges given. In addition, chlordan, heptachlor epoxide, aldrin, dieldrin, and the isooctyl ester of 2,4,5-T have also been identified in rainwater samples.

Table I. Organic Chlorine and Pesticides Content of Rainwater [a]

Compound	Range	Ripley, Ohio	Coshocton, Ohio	Cincinnati, Ohio
			Concentration, p.p.b.	
Organic chlorine	Max.	0.69	0.32	1.18
	Min.	0.10	0.02	0.09
	Mean	0.30 (36)	0.20 (15)	0.21 (34)
DDT	Max.	0.29	0.12	1.30
	Min.	0.02	0.02	0.07
	Mean	0.15 (23)	0.07 (3)	0.34 (8)
DDE	Max.	0.05	—	0.02
	Min.	0.01	—	0.005
	Mean	0.03 (13)	0.005 (1)	0.02 (7)
BHC	Max.	0.07	—	0.07
	Min.	0.01	—	0.01
	Mean	0.05 (23)	0.006 (1)	0.02 (10)

[a] Numbers in parentheses refer to number of samples analyzed.

Recent evidence has shown that the reported concentrations of pesticides in rainfall are low, perhaps by as much as a factor of 2, because the method used to collect the rainfall samples results in incomplete recovery of the pesticide material from the sampling trays.

Additional support for the finding of chloro-organic substances in general, and pesticides in particular, in rainwater was provided by Wheatley and Hardman (*13*). Monthly samples of rainwater were collected in a glass container placed inside the body of a rain gage, and supplementary samples were collected in glass trays by placing the collectors after a rain had started. Samples were analyzed by hexane extraction and thin layer chromatography and completed by gas chromatography using an electron capture detector. They imply in their data that the chloro-organic compounds in the atmosphere and subsequently in the rainwater resulted from the volatilization of the pesticides from the upper surfaces of pesticide-treated soils.

Their data suggest, however, that pesticide-laden dust in the atmosphere also must have been precipitated to earth by sedimentation and by rainfall. The average concentration found in the rainwater samples collected by exposing a sample collector for 1 month during the period November 1964 to February 1965 was for γ-BHC 100, for dieldrin 20, and for p',p'-DDT 3 parts per 10^{12} parts of rainwater (parts per trillion), whereas the samples collected only during periods of rainfall in January and March of 1965 averaged 29, 9, and 3 parts per 10^{12} parts of rainwater, respectively.

They conclude that, "in view of the world-wide use of organo-chlorine insecticides and the extensive distribution of their residues in soil, together with the foregoing evidence, it is possible that they might now contaminate the atmosphere continuously." This conclusion is entirely consistent with their data and with the evidence of organo-chlorine compounds in the rainfall samples reported by Weibel (11) and Cohen (4). Similar results were obtained from rain samples collected in the metropolitan area of London by Abbott et al. (1). These authors were also able to demonstrate the presence of pesticides in the atmosphere (2).

Long-Distance Transportation of Dust

Although the data cited clearly demonstrate the presence of pesticides in detectable concentrations in rainfall, there was no conclusive evidence that these compounds had been transported over great distances. Proof that pesticides can be transported by air over long distances and then precipitated to earth by rainfall was obtained from a deposit of dust on the Cincinnati, Ohio, area on January 26, 1965. During the morning a gentle rain, amounting to 0.15 inch, freed the air of local dust and vapor. Toward noon a dense reddish cloud darkened the sky and obscured the sun. A trace of rain at 12:30 p.m. precipitated the dust, which blanketed all surfaces with a reddish deposit. Newspaper accounts indicated that the origin of the dust was the Southern High Plains area. These accounts described a mammoth dust storm, spawned on January 25 on the Southern High Plains, that had blotted out the sun 300 miles to the east in Dallas and filled a rain gage in Lubbock, Tex., with more than 3 inches of sand.

Detailed information on the origin and movement of the dust mass was obtained from the Meteorology Section of the Public Health Service Air Pollution Division. Figure 1 shows the source area of the dust and the movement of the dust mass. The lines on the map represent the leading edge of the dust-bearing air mass marked at 6-hour intervals. The heavily cross-hatched area represents an estimate of the source

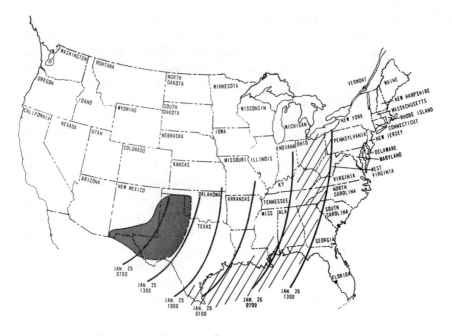

Figure 1.   Origin and movement of dust mass

of the dust. The northern and western limits are reasonably well known to about ± 30 miles; the eastern, and particularly the southeastern, limits are more uncertain, since there was no way of determining where the observed dust was being picked up from the ground or where it was being carried into the cloud by the winds. The cloud stretched out in a north-south direction and narrowed in an east-west direction, owing to the airflow pattern within the air mass. The lightly cross-hatched area represents the extent of the dust cloud at 1300 hours on January 26.

Collection of Sample

Because of the unusual amount of dust deposited and because the dust came from an area that has received heavy annual treatment with pesticides for many years, a large sample was collected for analysis at an installation that had previously been used to collect rainfall. Essentially, the collection surface is one fourth of a galvanized iron roof with the gutter arranged to discharge roof runoff into a collection tank. The collection area is 1090 square feet calculated from a horizontal projection. The day after the storm, the roof surface was flushed with 110 liters of Cincinnati tap water, and the dust slurry was collected in a stainless steel tank. The roof surface had been cleansed before the dust was deposited by the morning rain. The solids were recovered by filtration, air-dried, and weighed. The dust recovered amounted to 175 grams, which is equivalent to a dustfall of 4.8 tons per square mile. This value compares well with the 6 tons per square mile reported by the Air Pollution Control of Cincinnati.

Checks on Analysis

Before analysis of the dust was started, check analyses were made to determine the amounts of pesticides desorbed from the dust during the collection procedure and to insure against possible contamination by the wash water and solvents.

Analysis of the tap water used in the sample collection showed 0.08 p.p.b. of organic chlorine consisting principally of early eluting peaks; hence, the contribution of the contaminants in the water to the sample was insignificant. About 4% of the organic chlorine in the dust was found, however, to have been desorbed during processing. All solvents used in the analysis were entirely negative for organic chlorine compounds.

Preliminary Analysis

A preliminary analysis of a solvent-extract of the dust produced the chromatogram shown in Figure 2. The numerous, well-defined peaks and a content of 1.34 p.p.m. of organic chlorine indicated that a more intensive analysis of the dust was required.

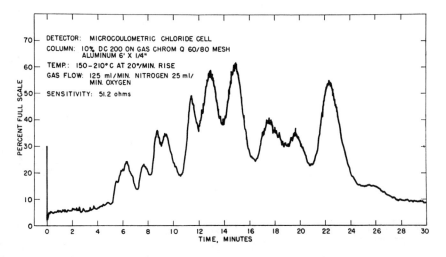

Figure 2.   Chromatogram of dust extract

For this analysis, and in all of the subsequent work, the gas chromatographic instrument assembly consisted of a Model 800 Perkin-Elmer, dual-column chromatograph equipped with temperature-programming facility. A Dohrman microcoulometric detector for both halide and sulfur ions was close-coupled to the chromatograph column exit. A variety of polar and nonpolar chromatographic columns were used. To obtain resolution of the complicated mixture of early and late eluting compounds, a temperature program of 150°–210°C. at 20° per minute rise was generally used in most of the work. Peak areas were quantitated with a mechanical Disc integrator.

Sample Extraction and Cleanup

Additional peaks and improved resolution of peaks were obtained after cleanup and column chromatography separations. The method of analysis is described by the flow diagram shown in Figure 3. An aliquot of the air-dried dust was slurried with water, adjusted to pH 3 with sulfuric acid, and then repeatedly extracted in a Waring blendor with a solvent mixture of hexane and diethyl ether, $1 + 1$ (v./v.). A portion of the extract was used for herbicide analysis in which methylation with diazomethane and gas chromatography were employed for the detection of the methyl ester of the chloro-alkyl phenoxy compounds.

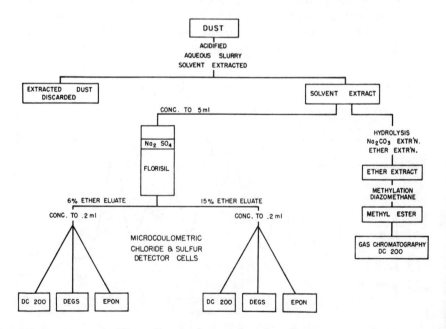

Figure 3.   Analysis of dust flow diagram

The remaining extract was filtered through a bed of sodium sulfate, concentrated to low volume in a Kuderna Danish evaporator, and then rinsed onto a column of activated Florisil. The Florisil column was eluted successively with 6 and 15% diethyl ether in hexane. Both eluates were concentrated to 0.2- to 0.3-ml. volumes to provide samples for identification by gas chromatography. The activity of the Florisil was checked by chromatographing a solution of hexane containing aldrin, heptachlor epoxide, dieldrin, endrin, and the *n*-butyl ester of 2,4-D. The column was judged acceptable when the first three compounds appeared in the 6% eluate and the last two in the 15% eluate.

Pesticide Identification

Identifying peaks in multicomponent mixtures is a difficult and time-consuming operation even under ideal conditions of concentration, sample size, and preknowledge of some of the components. None of these advantages existed with the dust sample; concentrations were known to be low, the sample size was limited absolutely, and the mixture could contain any of the 200 or so commercially important pesticides plus an unknown number of nonpesticide but halide-containing compounds.

Various procedures described by Crippen and Smith (5) are available for identifying components in a chromatogram. Because of the limitations mentioned above, the choice of method was restricted. Peak identifications for this sample relied on cleanup and preliminary separation by column adsorption chromatography with activated alumina and Florisil, use of the chlorine- and sulfur-specific microcoulometric detector, and parallel injections onto three or more columns containing liquid substrates varying widely in polarity.

The peaks on the chromatograms were identified on the basis of relative retention time (*vs.* aldrin) matches with reference compounds. The entire reference catalog of 115 pesticides was searched until the particular pesticide met the criteria of proper Florisil or alumina eluate and the relative retention times coincided on three columns.

Florisil 6% Eluate

The chromatograms obtained on the 6% Florisil eluate contained a series of distinguishable peaks on each of the three columns used. The relative retention times (*vs.* aldrin) of the sample and matching reference peaks are shown in Table II, along with the concentration of the identified components.

The relative retention times of an individual pesticide are, in most cases, sufficiently different on each of the three columns so that coinci-

Table II. Identification of Pesticides

Pesticide Identified	DC200 [a]		DEGS [b]		EPON [c]		Conc.[d], p.p.m.
	Ref.	Sample	Ref.	Sample	Ref.	Sample	
			6% Florisil Eluate				
Chlordan (tech.)	0.77	0.74	0.98	0.93	0.94	0.86	0.5
	0.88	0.92	1.07	1.12	1.10	1.06	—
	0.96	0.99	1.21	—	1.40	1.40	
	1.25	1.25	1.56	—			
Ronnel	0.92	0.92	—	—	—	—	0.2
Heptachlor epoxide	1.15	1.17	1.40	1.44	1.36	1.40	0.04
DDE	1.40	1.40	1.65	1.65	1.64	1.68	0.2
DDT (tech.)	1.42	1.40	1.70	1.65	1.92	2.00	0.6
	1.62	1.60	2.14	2.14	2.56	2.52	
	1.90	1.88	3.02	3.02			
			15% Florisil Eluate				
Dieldrin	1.45	1.50	1.80	1.88	1.96	1.87	0.003

[a] 5% DC200 silicone oil on 30/60 acid-washed Chromosorb P, 6 foot x ¼ inch aluminum.
[b] 10% Diethylene glycol succinate on 30/60 HMDS Chromosorb W, 6 foot x ¼ inch aluminum.
[c] 2.5% Epon 1001 on 30/60 Gas Chrom RZ, 4 foot x ¼ inch aluminum.
[d] Calculated on air-dried weight of dust.
Numbers shown are relative retention times *vs.* aldrin.

dence of sample peaks with reference peaks on three columns can be taken as proof of the presence of that component. The slight displacements shown in the relative retention time matches are well within the reproducibility of retention times by gas chromatography when temperature programming is being used.

In some instances, a single peak was used to identify two pesticides; however, the identification thus made can be justified, in every case, on the basis of the presence of additional peaks displayed by each compound. Ronnel was identified solely on the basis of a single match on the DC200 column. Additional evidence for this compound was obtained with the sulfur microcoulometer detector cell since the Ronnel molecule contains both chlorine and sulfur atoms. The identifications account for all peaks except one occurring at a relative retention time of 2.94 on the DC200 column.

Florisil 15% Eluate

Fewer peaks were obtained on the 15% Florisil eluate, and the total concentration of organic chlorine was low—0.05 p.p.m. compared with the 1.29 p.p.m. found in the 6% eluate. Of the six peaks that appeared on the chromatogram from the DC200 column, only dieldrin could be identified.

Herbicide Analysis

The original solvent extract of the soil was extracted with 3% aqueous sodium carbonate solution, which after acidification was serially extracted with diethyl ether. The ether extract was concentrated, treated with diazomethane to obtain the methyl ester derivative of the alkyl phenoxy compounds, and injected into the DC200 column. A single peak resulted from the injection, which matched the methyl ester of 2,4,5-T; reference relative retention time 0.76; sample peak 0.81; concentration 0.04 p.p.m.

Sulfur Cell Detector

Portions of the 6 and 15% Florisil eluate were injected into the DC200 and DEGS columns with the coulometer equipped with the sulfur-detecting cell. No peaks were obtained from the 15% eluate injection. Of the several peaks that appeared on the DC200 and DEGS columns from the 6% eluate injection, one was identified as Ronnel: DC200 reference 1.00, sample 1.00, DEGS, reference 1.00, sample 1.00, and concentration 0.2 p.p.m. Ronnel is chemically O,O-dimethyl O-(2,4,5-trichlorophenyl) phosphorothioate and thus should yield a peak with both the chloride and sulfur detectors. Identification was assured since a peak was found at the proper retention times with both detector cells; one column was used for the chloride, and two columns were used for the sulfur detector cells.

The total organic sulfur in the dust amounted to 0.5 p.p.m. The remaining peaks could not be identified, either because they represent thiophosphate compounds not in the reference catalog or because molecular changes had occurred in some compounds during residence on the ground and in the atmosphere. Moreover, organic sulfur compounds other than pesticides may be present in the sample and may have originated from the extensive oil and gas fields in the dust source area.

Alumina Column Chromatography

Another technique (3) was used to identify peaks. Essentially, the procedure consisted of column adsorption chromatography using activated alumina, fraction collection of successive portions of eluting solvent, and microcoulometric gas chromatography of each eluate fraction, again using three, and in some cases four, columns for retention time matches. Identification of peaks obtained with this technique rested on the knowledge of the elution fraction in which a pesticide should occur under the conditions of the column chromatography and on confirmation by retention times on three or four columns in the gas chromatograph. With the exception of 2,4,5-T, which was not determined, all of the pesticides previously identified by the Florisil–gas chromatography technique were completely confirmed by the alumina–gas chromatography method.

Pesticides Identified

Use of the techniques just described resulted in the identification and concentration values of the pesticides shown in Table III. The major pesticide components of the dust were DDT and chlordan, with DDE and Ronnel following closely. The remaining compounds, heptachlor epoxide, 2,4,5-T, and dieldrin, were present in relatively minor proportions. These seven pesticides accounted for a major portion of the organic chlorine content; however, certain peaks are still unidentified.

Table III. Pesticide Content of Dust

Pesticide	Concentration, p.p.m.[a]
DDT (tech.)	0.6
Chlordan (tech.)	0.5
DDE	0.2
Ronnel	0.2
Heptachlor epoxide	0.04
2,4,5-T	0.04
Dieldrin	0.003
Total organic chlorine	1.34
Total organic sulfur	0.5

[a] Based on air-dried weight of dust.

Arsenic concentrations of 26 p.p.m. were also found in the dust, but the evidence at hand does not indicate whether the arsenic was derived from natural sources in the soil or was contributed as residue from the use of arsenic compounds as cotton defoliant.

Conclusions

Pesticide residues in humans, animals, and fish in areas remote from pesticide application can, in many cases, be attributed to an intermediate such as the food chain. Thus, migratory fish and birds can easily accumulate pesticide residues from foods directly contaminated by pesticide application. In those instances where the food chain cannot serve as a reasonable explanation, then, clearly, the atmosphere, including dust and rainfall, offers an alternative solution to pesticides translocation.

Rainfall has been shown to contain organic chlorine in concentrations ranging from 0.02 to 1.18 p.p.b. (4, 10, 13). Identification of specific pesticides proves that at least some of the chloro-organic substances in rainfall are pesticidal in origin. Clearly, rainfall must be considered as one of the vehicles for dispersing pesticides in addition to food chain and water transmission; it also explains the appearance of pesticide residues in areas remote from pesticide usage.

By itself, the discovery of pesticides in rainfall, however, provides no evidence that the origin of the pesticides was local or distant. The analysis of dust, whose origin has been documented by meteorological evidence, does prove that pesticides can be transported over great distances via the atmosphere, that the pesticides can survive the photochemical processes of high altitude, and, finally, that these pesticides can be deposited over land surfaces remote from their application.

Although the dust storm cited was admittedly an uncommon occurrence, it was unusual only in its intensity. There is a constant rain of solids from the air—for example, the average monthly dustfall in Cincinnati, Ohio, is about 15 tons per square mile. Several samples of dustfall collected during the pesticide application season of June and July 1965 had an organic chlorine content of 7 to 83 p.p.m. Among numerous unidentified peaks, DDT was found in concentrations of 3–90 p.p.m. Hence, it is reasonably certain that soil is constantly being picked up by winds, transported at high altitudes over long distances, and deposited elsewhere either by simple sedimentation or by rain. While the data cited here would incriminate dust as the distributor of pesticides, it is entirely possible that they may also enter the atmosphere simply by volatilization. To date, however, no evidence is available to demonstrate this. Clearly, any appraisal of the contamination of the environment by pesticide residues must consider dustfall and rainfall as contributors.

Literature Cited

(1) Abbott, D. C., Harrison, R. B., Tatton, J. O. G., Thomson, J., *Nature* **208,** 1317 (1965).
(2) *Ibid.*, **211,** 259 (1956).
(3) Boyle, H. W., Burttschell, R. H., Rosen, A. A., ADVAN. CHEM. SER., **60,** 207 (1966).
(4) Cohen, J. M., Evans, F. L., III, Pinkerton, C., 37th Annual Conference of the Water Pollution Control Federation, Bal Harbour, Fla., Sept. 30, 1964.
(5) Crippen, R. C., Smith, C. E., *J. Gas Chromatog.* **3,** 37 (1965).
(6) Durham, W. F., Armstrong, J. F., *Science* **134,** 1880 (1961).
(7) Kraybill, H. F., Short Course on Occupational Health Aspects of Pesticides, University of Oklahoma, Nov. 20, 1963.
(8) Paul, R. M., *Am. J. Pub. Health* (Suppl.) **55,** No. 7 (July 1965).
(9) Sladen, W. J. L., Menzie, C. M., Reichel, W. L., *Nature* **210, 670,** (1966).
(10) Tabor, E. C., 58th Annual Meeting of the Air Pollution Control Association, Toronto, Canada, June 20-24, 1965.

(11) Weibel, S. R., Weidner, R. B., Christianson, A. G., Cohen, J. M., 85th Annual Conference of American Water Works Association, Portland, Ore., June 29, 1965.
(12) West, Irma, *Arch. Environ. Health* **9,** 626 (1964).
(13) Wheatley, G. A., Hardman, J. A., *Nature* **207,** 486 (1965).
(14) Yates, W. E., Akesson, N. B., Proceedings of 2nd Annual Conference on Use of Agricultural Chemicals, Davis, Calif., January 1963.·

RECEIVED January 24, 1966.

Potential Hazard in Using Dichlorvos Insecticide Resin

MITCHELL R. ZAVON and E. A. KINDEL, Jr.

The Kettering Laboratory, University of Cincinnati College of Medicine, Cincinnati, Ohio 45219

Dichlorvos, an organic phosphate insecticide, has been incorporated in a resin for continuous vaporization. The hazard in handling the resin strips and in home use of the resin strip vaporizer has been evaluated under simulated or actual use conditions. Use conditions included observations for as long as 6 months of persons using the vaporizers in their homes. Cholinesterase activity of the plasma and red blood cells of those exposed was determined serially. No significant degree of cholinesterase inhibition resulted either from handling the resin strips under the conditions of the experiment or from using them in the home over a 6-month period.

Dichlorvos (DDVP, dichlorovinyldimethyl phosphate) was first synthesized in the late 1940's, but active investigation of its insecticidal properties was not initiated until 1954. Investigations at that time revealed that low concentrations of the vapor of dichlorvos were toxic to adult mosquitoes and flies and that there appeared to be a relatively wide margin of safety between the insecticidal dose and the concentration required to affect man.

Research by personnel of the U.S. Public Health Service, particularly by George W. Pearce, resulted in the development of a solid formulation of 25% dichlorvos in montan wax, which when open to the air, released the vapor of dichlorvos continuously, in small quantities, over a prolonged period of time. This development led to a search for other, more stable formulations and eventually to the development of a formulation of 20% dichlorvos in a resin. This formulation, known as Vapona Resin Vaporizer, is referred to hereafter as the Vaporizer.

It is a strip of resin, 4½ by 10 inches, flexible, but tougher than leather, developed originally and primarily for use in controlling malaria by the World Health Organization. This particular formulation has gained wide acceptance in the United States for controlling flies and mosquitoes, and to a lesser extent, cockroaches in homes, offices, factories, barns, and other establishments.

The series of investigations described was initiated to evaluate the degree of hazard involved in handling and using this formulation of dichlorvos. The studies were designed to simulate as closely as possible the most severe conditions of actual use, while maintaining some degree of control of the subjects. Prior to these investigations, a thorough review of all relevant experiments involving animals and men had indicated the improbability of any significant effect from the procedures to be followed (*1–10, 12, 15*). A major concern throughout has been to make these experiments as meaningful as possible, without undue inconvenience to volunteer subjects.

Handling of Vapona Resin Vaporizers

To determine the effect on the skin and on the cholinesterase activity of the blood of persons engaged in handling the Vaporizers, 10 volunteers were selected for investigation: six men and four women. Before they handled the Vaporizer, blood was drawn by venipuncture from each subject, and the cholinesterase activity of the plasma and erythrocytes was determined. Two of the volunteers were used in a preliminary trial, one in handling the Vaporizer for 30 minutes, and the other by having the Vaporizer fixed to the volar aspect of the forearm for 30 minutes. Another sample of blood was drawn 24 hours after the experimental procedures (Table I).

Personal Data on Subjects

Subject	Sex	Age	Subject	Sex	Age
1	F	23	2	M	24
4	F	27	3	M	29
6	F	23	5	M	25
8	F	25	7	M	25
10	F	42	9	M	41
12	F	35	11	M	39
14	F	46	13	M	48
15	F	23	16	M	25
20	F	13	17	M	2
			18	M	14
			19	M	12
			21	M	52

Table I. Cholinesterase Activity [a] of Two Subjects in Preliminary Experiment

Cholinesterase Activity, ΔpH Units

Subject	Before Exposure		After Exposure	
	Plasma	Erythrocytes	Plasma	Erythrocytes
1	0.89	0.68	1.06	0.63
4	1.06	0.79	1.10	0.73

[a] Cholinesterase activity determined by Michel method (*11*).

The subjects were divided arbitrarily into two groups, A and B. Members of group A handled the Vaporizer for 30 minutes each day in the manner required for household or farm use. A portion of Vaporizer, 2½ by 5 inches, was affixed with adhesive tape in direct contact with the bare skin of the volar surface of the forearm of each member of group B, for 30 minutes of each of 5 successive days. Fresh Vaporizers were applied on the first and third of the 5 successive days. Cholinesterase activity was determined before the first period of contact and after the second and fifth (Tables I and II).

Table II. Cholinesterase Activity of Blood of Human Subjects During Experiment with Vapona Resin Vaporizers (*11*)

Cholinesterase Activity, ΔpH Units

Subject	Age	Sex	Pre-experimental		After 2nd period of contact		After 5th period of contact	
			Plasma	Erythrocytes	Plasma	Erythrocytes	Plasma	Erythrocytes
1	52	F	0.89	0.68	1.78	0.69	0.92	0.70
2	21	F	1.57	0.90	1.46	0.88	1.57	0.89
3	23	F	0.99	0.81	1.88	0.74	1.01	0.78
4	30	F	1.06	0.79	0.99	0.78	0.96	0.81
5	24	M	1.45	0.77	1.32	0.78	1.21	0.78
6	47	M	0.93	0.85	1.98	0.77	0.91	0.69
7	45	M	1.66	0.79	1.62	0.72	1.79	0.71
8	29	M	0.88	0.90	0.90	0.83	1.00	0.91
9	32	M	1.04	0.82	0.90	0.83	0.91	0.83
10	31	M	1.18	0.69	1.12	0.61	1.03	0.69

The brief periods of exposure and the close contact with the skin, whether of hands or forearm, made percutaneous absorption the most likely route of absorption. Inhalation, though possible, was certainly less significant, according to what is known of the rate of vaporization of the Vaporizer (*14*).

The results of this investigation indicate no detectable inhibition of the cholinesterase activity of either plasma or erythrocytes as a result of handling Vapona Resin Vaporizers under the conditions of this experiment or of maintaining Vaporizers in direct contact with the skin for 30 minutes per day on 5 successive days. The fluctuations in cholinesterase activity were well within the normal range of day-to-day variation. The second determination of the cholinesterase activity of the plasma of subject 6 was unusually high. No explanation can be offered for this unusually high value, except to note that the specimen was "very milky" (the probable result of lipemia) and that it was taken on the day following the death of the subject's mother.

It was concluded that Vapona Resin Vaporizers may be handled for at least 30 minutes per day without the necessity of wearing impermeable gloves.

Use of Vapona Resin Vaporizers in the Home

The use of Vapona Resin Vaporizers in the home poses the possibility of an adverse effect upon persons subjected day-in and day-out to the inhalation of the vapor of dichlorvos. In order to determine the extent of this hazard, the following investigation was undertaken.

Procedure. Initially, two families volunteered to have the Vaporizers installed in their homes in the recommended number of one per 1000 cubic feet of air. The members of the two families were observed regularly and tested for changes in the cholinesterase activity of their blood. They kept daily accounts of the amount of time spent in the house and maintained a continuous record of temperature and humidity. All were encouraged to report any hint of an adverse effect. These observations were made over the 6 months the Vaporizers were used in the homes. During the first 4 months of observation, new Vaporizers were installed monthly. Those installed at the beginning of the fourth month of observation remained, without change, during the fifth and sixth months of observation.

Just before and at intervals during the 6 months of the experimental regimen, blood was drawn from the subjects to determine cholinesterase activity. Table III presents the results over the entire period.

Subjects 1 and 2 live in an air-conditioned apartment of 5 rooms (5088 cubic feet), in which air-conditioning equipment operated intermittently during the period of observation. In effect, it is one big room since the doors to the two bedrooms are rarely closed and there are no doors between the living room, dining room, and kitchen. Five Vaporizers were installed in this area and changed at the frequency indicated above.

Table III. Cholinesterase Activity (ΔpH Units) in Blood of Persons in Homes in which Vapona Vaporizers Were Installed Over Period of Six Months [a]

Before Installing Vaporizers, 4/15/64

Subject	Erythrocytes	Plasma
1	0.74	0.76
2	0.62	0.83
3	0.68	0.96
4	0.57	0.79
Mean	0.65	0.83

After Installing Vaporizers

4/16/64		4/22/64		4/29/64		5/6/64	
Erythro-cytes	Plasma	Erythro-cytes	Plasma	Erythro-cytes	Plasma	Erythro-cytes	Plasma
0.83	0.74	0.65	0.92	0.75	0.85	0.62	0.68
0.78	0.71	0.61	0.81	0.84	0.70	0.59	0.75
0.78	1.06	—	—	0.65	0.87	0.61	0.91
0.66	0.79	—	—	0.66	0.82	0.53	0.78
Mean 0.76	0.83	0.63	0.87	0.73	0.81	0.56	0.78

5/13/64		5/27/64		6/10/64		6/24/64	
0.56	0.45	0.57	0.57	0.68	0.61	0.67	0.58
0.56	0.62	0.45	0.58	0.62	0.72	0.62	0.70
—	—	0.76	0.74	0.65	0.88	0.63	0.90
0.60	0.50	0.43	0.73	0.59	0.74	0.57	0.76
Mean 0.57	0.56	0.55	0.66	0.64	0.74	0.62	0.73

7/8/64		8/5/64		9/16/64		10/16/64	
0.63	0.55	0.42	0.68	0.65	0.79	0.60	0.79
0.60	0.70	0.43	0.73	0.54	0.82	0.55	0.71
0.60	0.98	—	—	0.65	1.01	0.53	1.16
0.50	0.74	0.43	1.05	0.47	0.73	0.43	0.89
Mean 0.58	0.74	0.43	0.82	0.58	0.84	0.53	0.89

[a] Fresh Vapona Vaporizers installed 4/16/64, 5/13/64, 6/16/64, 7/10/64.

Subjects 3 and 4 live in a detached, frame house which is not air-conditioned. The area lived in, approximately 8000 cubic feet, required eight Vaporizers. In this two-story house, Vaporizers were placed upstairs and downstairs.

Results. Samples were collected from the air of both residences on the morning of August 19, 1964, about one month following the latest replacement of new Vaporizers. All doors and windows were shut tightly at the time of sampling, and in each case the sample was collected in the middle of the living room, the largest room in each residence. Two Greenburg-Smith impingers, in series, containing together about 250 ml. of 0.13M phosphate buffer solution (pH 7.2), were used to collect each of the samples. One cubic foot of air per minute was drawn through the impingers by means of a Willson vacuum pump.

Subjects	Period of Sampling	Temp., °F.	Relative Humidity
1 and 2	9:40 to 10:20 A.M.	76	50
3 and 4	10:40 to 11:20 A.M.	70	59

Both samples of buffer solution were packed in dry ice, for transportation, and were received frozen and in good condition at the analytical laboratory. The results of the analyses are shown in Table IV.

Table IV. Concentration of Dichlorvos in Air of Homes in which Vapona Resin Vaporizers Were Installed

Source of Sample	Vol. of Sample, Cu. Ft.	Buffer Solution Volume, Ml.	Vapona Found [a], µg.	
			Per Cu. Ft. Air	Per Liter Air
Residence of subjects 1, 2	40	239	2.75	0.097
Residence of subjects 3, 4	40	240	2.45	0.087
Modesto Laboratory	—	1	—	

[a] Analyses performed by Agricultural Chemical Laboratory, Shell Development Corp., Modesto, Calif. (13).

The diaries indicated that subjects 1 and 2 spent considerably more time at home than subjects 3 and 4. The two couples lived in the same community and were subjected to the same ranges of temperature and humidity. During the period of these observations, there were wide variations in the out-of-doors temperature, which reached 100°F. on at least one occasion. Inside temperatures ranged between 60° and 82°F., with a tendency toward the higher end of the range in the non-air-conditioned dwelling during the summer months. The range of humidity was from 30 to 90%, with the air-conditioned dwelling having a lower humidity.

To extend the information concerning the use of Vaporizers to additional families under varying conditions of use, six additional volunteer families were enlisted, and the observations were initiated in September 1964 (Table V).

The procedure followed was similar to that previously described, except that the periods of exposure were shorter. Three pre-experimental

Table V. Cholinesterase Activity in Blood of Persons in Homes in which Vapona Vaporizers Were Installed Over Period of Two Months

Cholinesterase Activity before Installation of Vaporizers, ΔpH Units

Subject	9/16/64 Erythrocytes	Plasma	9/17/64 Erythrocytes	Plasma	9/18/64 Erythrocytes	Plasma
5	0.63	0.74	0.75	0.76	0.58	0.76
6	0.58	0.73	0.66	0.62	0.57	0.85
7			0.66	0.86	0.61	0.89
8	0.93	0.74	0.75	0.82	0.59	0.72
9	1.09	0.66	1.16	0.89	0.78	1.04
10	0.74		0.79	0.89	0.68	0.80
11	0.59	0.95	0.60·	0.68	0.67	0.89
12	0.70	0.92	0.85	0.95	0.60	0.92
13			0.58	0.79	0.60	0.82
14				0.89	0.64	0.98
15	0.57	0.66	0.65	0.52	0.69	0.58
16	0.56	1.04	0.81	0.91	0.79	
17					0.54	0.79
18					0.59	0.98
19			0.78	0.88		
20			0.95	0.91		
Mean	0.71	0.81	0.77	0.81	0.64	0.85

Cholinesterase Activity after Installation of Vaporizers, ΔpH Units

Subject	9/28/64 Erythrocytes	Plasma	10/9/64 Erythrocytes	Plasma	10/15/64 Erythrocytes	Plasma	10/23/64 Erythrocytes	Plasma	10/30/64 Erythrocytes	Plasma
5			0.57		0.59	0.61	0.73	0.73	0.64	0.57
6			0.61	0.52	0.54	0.43	0.69	0.53	0.58	0.50
7	0.64	0.76	0.74	0.68	0.70	0.75	0.61	0.76	0.59	0.66
8	0.45	0.45	0.61	0.53	0.67	0.45	0.82	0.48	0.83	0.38
9	0.73	0.54	0.85	0.35	0.85	0.46	1.04	0.58	1.05	0.36
10	0.69	0.59	0.58	0.64	0.59	0.63	0.70	0.71	0.72	0.60
11	0.40	0.78	0.64	0.75	0.59	0.76	0.78	0.83	0.61	0.82
12	0.56	0.78	0.61	0.65	0.59	0.78	0.96	0.75	0.73	0.74
13	0.52	0.65	0.63	0.60	0.56	0.65	0.57	0.74	0.58	0.74
14	0.52	0.11	0.65	0.55	0.62	0.58	0.78	0.78	0.70	0.80
15	0.58	0.65			0.51	0.53	0.62	0.64	0.61	0.56
16	0.46	1.08	0.67	0.95	0.67	0.85	0.77	0.89	0.74	0.69
17					0.58	0.66				
18					0.54	0.65				
19					0.55	0.80				
20					0.62	0.58				
Mean	0.56	0.64	0.65	0.62	0.61	0.64	0.76	0.70	0.70	0.62

determinations of the cholinesterase activity of the blood of the subjects were made. The temperature and humidity in two of the homes was recorded throughout the experiment and at two others during a portion of the time. The results of the cholinesterase determinations are recorded in Table V. The temperature and humidity were similar to those in the non-air-conditioned apartment noted above.

Discussion. Control of insects by the continuous vaporization of dichlorvos within enclosed spaces in which persons are housed intermittently or continuously constitutes a potential threat of the absorption of significant quantities of the material dispersed as vapor in the air. Despite extensive toxicological investigation of dichlorvos, which has included observations of human beings (4, 5, 6, 8, 12, 15), no work had been done to evaluate the hazard of Vapona Resin Vaporizers under actual conditions of use. The observations described in this report were designed to reveal the significance, if any, of such hazards.

Handling the Vaporizers does not appear to cause any significant decrease in cholinesterase activity among those doing the handling, nor is the cholinesterase activity affected by the prolonged contact of the Vaporizers with the skin of the forearm. In the ordinary day's work, the householder or the pest control operator would not be expected to handle the Vaporizer as much as 30 minutes each day even under the most unusual conditions. Under ordinary circumstances, the contact of the resin vaporizer with the skin would not persist for 30 minutes in any one day and would not be continued day after day.

The exposure to Vapona Resin Vaporizers in the general environment poses a somewhat different problem. Here, the potential hazard involves the combined effects of the absorption of the material through inhalation, through the skin, and from the alimentary tract (if swallowed). The observations made on two families over the period of 6 months, and of six other families over the period of 2 months, were designed to determine whether any adverse effect could be demonstrated.

Inhibition of the cholinesterase activity of the blood is the most sensitive means now available, with the possible exception of the inhibition of the esterase activity of the liver, for detecting the absorption of an organic phosphorus compound that is known to be capable of inducing this effect. The values indicative of cholinesterase activity are shown in Tables III and V. All subjects were exposed to the recommended dosage (one Vaporizer per 1000 cubic feet) except subjects 15 and 16, who were exposed to resin strips that contained no dichlorvos.

The data obtained were examined initially by plotting the cholinesterase activity of the erythrocytes and plasma against the day of exposure of each individual subject and summarizing the results obtained from each of the three test groups. These graphs revealed no consistent trend in any of the groups. The data were examined more closely for possible trends by fitting linear equations to each group. In all three cases, the slope of the best equation, determined by the method of least squares, was not significantly different from zero, indicating that the variations in the cholinesterase activity of the erythrocytes and plasma were not a function of the duration of the exposure of the subjects.

Dichlorvos is a known inhibitor of cholinesterase, and it is likely that under certain conditions of use, a significant degree of inhibition might occur. However, under the conditions of these experiments, no such effect appears to have occurred. The subjects indicated no adverse effects.

In addition to the human residents, two dogs and three cats were residents of the homes. None of the animals exhibited any difficulty during the period of exposure.

In these experiments the vaporizers were replaced at much shorter intervals than those normally recommended.

Conclusion

The handling and use of Vapona Resin Vaporizers, under the recommended conditions, are unlikely to result in adverse effects among persons so exposed.

Literature Cited

(1) Casida, J. E., McBride, L., Niedermeier, R. P., *J. Agr. Food Chem.* **10**, 370-7 (1962).
(2) Durham, W. F., Gaines, T. B., McCauley, R. H., Jr., Sedlak, V. A., Mattson, A. M., Hayes, W. J., Jr., *A.M.A. Arch. Ind. Health* **15**, 340-9 (1957).
(3) Durham, W. F., Hayes, W. J., Jr., Mattson, A. M., *Ibid.*, **20**, 202-10 (1959).
(4) Funckes, A. J., Miller, S., Hayes, W. J., Jr., *Bull. World Health Org.* **29**, 243-6 (1963).
(5) Gaines, T. B., *Toxicol. Appl. Pharmacol.* **2**, 88-99 (1960).
(6) Gratz, N. G., Bracha, P., Carmichael, A., *Bull. World Health Org.* **29**, 251-70 (1963).
(7) Hayes, W. J., Jr., *Ibid.*, **24**, 629-33 (1961).
(8) Hayes, W. J., Jr., "Clinical Handbook on Economic Poisons: Emergency Information for Treating Poisoning," U.S. Dept. Health, Education & Welfare, Public Health Service, 1963.
(9) Hodgson, E., Casida, J. E., *J. Agr. Food Chem.* **10**, 208-14 (1962).
(10) Kettering Laboratory, "The Immediate Toxicity of Various Formulations Containing Vapona Insecticide," Aug. 24, 1962.
(11) Michel, H. O., *J. Lab. Clin. Med.* **34**, 1564-8 (1949).
(12) Rasmussen, W. A., Jensen, J. A., Stein, W. J., Hayes, W. J., Jr., *Aerospace Med.* **34**, 593-600 (1963).

(13) Shell Chemical Co., "Method for the Determination of Vapona Insecticide in Crops and Animal Products. Enzyme Inhibition Spectrophotometric Method," **MMS-30/64** (July 1964).
(14) Shell Chemical Co., personal communication.
(15) Witter, R. F., *A.M.A. Arch. Ind. Health* **21**, 7-9 (1960).

RECEIVED November 1, 1965.

Determination of Organic Insecticides in Water by Electron Capture Gas Chromatography

WILLIAM L. LAMAR, DONALD F. GOERLITZ, and LeROY M. LAW

Water Resources Division, U.S. Geological Survey, Menlo Park, Calif. 94025

A convenient and extremely sensitive procedure for analyzing organic insecticides by electron capture gas chromatography is described. By this improved method these pesticides may be determined, in submicrogram amounts, on 1-liter samples of water. Recoveries are given for 13 common insecticides. Gas chromatographic columns which inhibit decomposition of the insecticides were prepared and applied. Interferences caused by sources of contamination in the laboratory are discussed, and corrective measures are prescribed.

The increasing development and use of insecticides and other pesticides constitute a growing hazard for contaminating our water supplies. To keep pace with the use (5, 6) of these toxicants, more information is needed on distribution, transport, exchange mechanism, degradation products, and metabolites of these substances. Thus, convenient and sensitive methods of analysis are essential to the success of research in this field. Furthermore, pesticide levels in water can be monitored more accurately by improved analytical techniques. Accurate and rapid procedures are especially needed when prompt information or action is necessary. Even when low concentrations of pesticides do not show immediate adverse effects, detrimental results may eventually occur, since it has been observed that a number of these toxicants are concentrated in a variety of aquatic plants and animals.

Identifying and measuring pesticides in water involve complex problems to which there have been many approaches (2, 3, 4, 7, 12, 13). No one method will be adequate because of the many different types of toxicants and the different conditions under which they are present in water. Further, water supplies may contain a wide variety of pesticides in low concentration. Selective and highly sensitive analytical methods are necessary to identify and measure these substances conveniently.

To avoid time-consuming and complicating factors which result from using large samples of water, the authors have given particular attention to the development of a highly sensitive procedure which can be performed with a convenient size sample. This report describes an electron capture gas chromatographic procedure for identifying and measuring organic insecticides which have high electron affinities, notably the chlorinated and phosphorothioate compounds.

Apparatus

Gas Chromatograph. Aerograph Hy-FI, Wilkens model 610-C equipped with electron capture detector, isothermal proportional controller, and differential flow controller.

Gas Chromatographic Oven. Aerograph Hy-FI, Wilkens model 550, equipped with electron capture detector, isothermal proportional controller, differential flow controller, and detector transfer switch. By using the detector transfer switch, this additional oven permits the use of two different columns without cooling which would otherwise be required to change columns.

Gas Chromatographic Columns. Two heat-resistant glass columns, A and B, ⅛ inch nominal o.d. (1.5 mm. i.d., 3 mm. o.d.) and 5 feet long, are used. Column A is packed with 60–70 mesh acid-washed Chromosorb G, coated by weight with 0.15% Carbowax 20M (a polyethylene glycol) and with 1.5% DC 200 (12,500 centistokes) silicone fluid; Column B is packed with 60–70 mesh acid-washed Chromosorb G, coated by weight with 0.10% Carbowax 20M and with 1.0% QF-1 fluorosilicone (also called FS 1265).

Recorder. Honeywell Brown Electronik, class 15, 1-mv. full scale response, 1-sec. pen speed.

Sand Bath. Tecam fluidized sand bath. A steam bath may be used in place of the sand bath.

Concentrating Apparatus. Kuderna-Danish concentrator, 250-ml. capacity.

Reagents

All reagents should be tested to ensure that they do not contain significant amounts of electron-capturing components.

Anhydrous Sodium Sulfate. Reagent grade, heated at 400°C. overnight and stored in a glass-stoppered bottle.

Hexane. The hexane should be checked by running it as a reagent blank. Most batches of reagent grade hexane can be purified by redistilling from a packed column after refluxing over bright sodium ribbon for 8 hours. Some batches of nanograde hexane (especially prepared for pesticide residue analysis) have been suitable without further purification, but other batches have contained high boiling impurities, requiring redistillation.

Distilled Water. The distilled water as commonly used in many laboratories can be a prime source of contamination of glassware and sample bottles. The section on Interferences discusses precautions to be observed in preparing organic-free distilled water.

Insecticide Standards. Analytical standards were obtained from City Chemical Corp., Panta Industries, Inc., and a number of pesticide manufacturers. The purity of the insecticides from the various sources was compared by infrared and gas chromatographic analysis. The concentration of the insecticide emulsions was determined by electron capture gas chromatography by using analytical standards.

Extraction

Water samples (900–950 ml.) are extracted with hexane in such a way that the water, or the water-sediment mixture, and the container itself are exposed to the solvent by the following technique.

Pour the water sample into a 1-liter separatory funnel. Add 25 ml. of hexane to the empty sample bottle and expose the sides of the container to the solvent. Then, pour the solvent into the separatory funnel, allowing the bottle to drain into the separatory funnel for several minutes. The hexane which remains on the sides of the sample bottle should be rinsed into the separatory funnel with small portions of the water sample. Shake the separatory funnel vigorously for 1 minute. Then allow the contents to separate for 10 minutes and collect the aqueous layer in the original sample bottle. If the hexane layer becomes emulsified, add distilled water in about 5-ml. increments and shake vigorously to break the emulsion. Pour the hexane layer from the top of the separatory funnel into a 125-ml. Erlenmeyer flask containing about 0.5 gram of anhydrous sodium sulfate.

Prepare a second and third extraction in the same manner, using 25 ml. of hexane each time, and each time add the extracts to the 125-ml. Erlenmeyer flask.

The combined extracts, contained over the sodium sulfate in the 125-ml. Erlenmeyer flask, are decanted quantitatively into a Kuderna-Danish concentrating apparatus. Remove most of the hexane by heating on a fluidized sand bath at 100°C. Since all the hexane is not evaporated, the temperature of the extract will not exceed the boiling point of hexane.

Transfer the remaining hexane extract quantitatively with a disposable pipet into a 5-ml. volumetric flask. Bring this solution to volume with hexane and then add about 50 mg. of anhydrous sodium sulfate. Mix the contents thoroughly and proceed with the gas chromatographic analysis.

Gas Chromatographic Analysis

A two-column electron capture gas chromatographic system, as described under Apparatus, is used for the analysis. Take 5.0-μliter aliquots of the concentrated extract and inject them into the gas chromatograph. The injections are made on two different types of specially prepared columns, designated as column A and column B (*see* section on Experimental Results).

The operating conditions for both columns are the same. The glass-lined injection ports are held at 210°–220°C., and the glass columns are maintained at 175°C. The nitrogen carrier gas, which is dried by a molecular sieve (Linde type 13X), is regulated at 30 ml. per minute by the differential flow controllers.

The insecticides are identified on the two different types of gas chromatographic columns by comparing the relative retention times of the recorded peaks of the samples with those of standards. If a closely eluting component interferes with the identification, a small amount of the suspected insecticide can be added to the sample which is injected into the column. This injection consists of a small measured amount of the insecticide standard drawn into a microliter syringe already charged with an aliquot of the sample extract.

Because the electron-capturing potential of each insecticide may be different, standardization curves must be prepared and maintained for quantitative analysis. The insecticides are measured quantitatively by comparing the area under the recorded peaks with those obtained from previously prepared standardization curves. Quantitative and qualitative insecticide standards are injected on the same day the samples are analyzed to provide corrections as necessary for the day-to-day fluctuations in operating conditions.

Retention times relative to aldrin are summarized in Table I. These results are given in the order of elution from the gas chromatographic columns A and B.

Interferences

In determining pesticides in water by electron capture gas chromatography, laboratory sources of contamination are a major problem. The principal sources of this contamination are described and illustrated in this section.

Organic substances will progressively adsorb on glassware. When this investigation was started, the glassware was rinsed with purified

Table I. Relative Retention Times of Insecticide Standards

Column A		Column B	
Insecticide	Retention Time Relative to Aldrin	Insecticide	Retention Time Relative to Aldrin
Lindane	0.57	Lindane	0.81
Heptachlor	0.81	Heptachlor	0.81
Aldrin	1.00	Aldrin	1.00
Methyl parathion	1.21	Heptachlor epoxide	2.07
Malathion	1.32	Malathion	3.21
Heptachlor epoxide	1.47	o,p'-DDT	3.27
Parathion	1.48	Dieldrin	3.32
Dieldrin	2.30	Methyl parathion	3.32
Endrin	2.56	Endrin	3.92
o,p'-DDT	3.36	Parathion	4.57
DDD (TDE)	3.70	DDD (TDE)	4.88
p,p'-DDT	4.75	p,p'-DDT	5.17
Methoxychlor	7.79	Methoxychlor	9.93

hexane, and the rinsings were checked by electron capture gas chromatography. We found that the glassware was contaminated with interfering compounds as illustrated by Figure 1. This contamination was largely caused by the distilled water used for rinsing. Although the distilled water was obtained from a high purity still, organic matter was derived from the valves, gaskets, connections, plastic piping, and storage tank and possibly also from the pump used to deliver water to the storage tank. The chromatogram in Figure 2 shows the interfering contaminants in the distilled water.

To avoid this problem, one can collect the distilled water directly from the condenser exit of the still. Depending on the quality of the feed water, it may be necessary to use a high purity still, with an organic remover cartridge (activated carbon) on the feed water. However, since some organic remover cartridges are made of plastic, this may be self-defeating. Organic-free distilled water also may be obtained by redistilling the water over alkaline permanganate in an all-glass system. Although water redistilled this way is satisfactory, a more convenient system for a distilled water supply was designed. The distilled water system now used is a gravity one that consists of a high purity still with an organic remover (activated carbon) on the feed water, a tin-silver lined storage tank with an ultraviolet lamp, and tin-lined piping, valves, and connections. Teflon tape was used to seal pipe joints in place of pipe "dope." An inorganic flux was utilized when any retinning of connections was necessary.

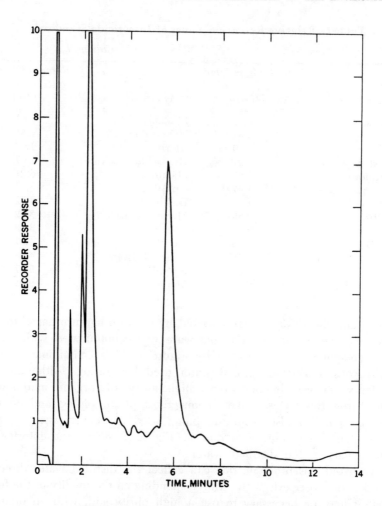

Figure 1.   Contamination from glassware

The purity of distilled water is usually specified on the basis of low electrical conductivity rather than organic contaminants. In distilled water systems, it is therefore common practice to use a variety of plastics or rubber materials, but from the previous experience it was apparent that these materials should be eliminated. When it is necessary to use similar material such as in gaskets, it has been found that Teflon, a fluorocarbon resin, is satisfactory.

The system described above provided a ready source of distilled water which eliminated interference problems as illustrated by Figure 3. This chromatogram represents the electron capture analysis of an extract obtained by extracting 2 liters of the improved distilled water with hexane.

Laboratory glassware and sample bottles should be checked for contamination before use. After conventional cleaning, heat treating the glassware at 300°C. overnight avoids interferences from this source. Volumetric glassware is cleaned with sodium dichromate in concentrated sulfuric acid. Rinsing the glassware with solvents may not remove all of the organic matter. For example, glassware was rinsed with hexane until the analysis of the rinsings indicated no contamination, but this hexane-rinsed glassware again contaminated hexane which remained in it overnight.

Another possible significant source of extraneous matter is the plastic screw caps used on sample bottles and reagent bottles. Even if the

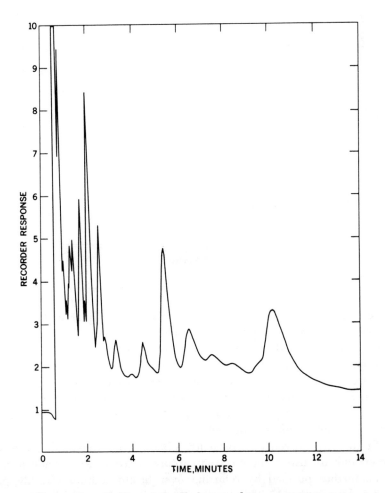

Figure 2.   Quality of distilled water before improvement

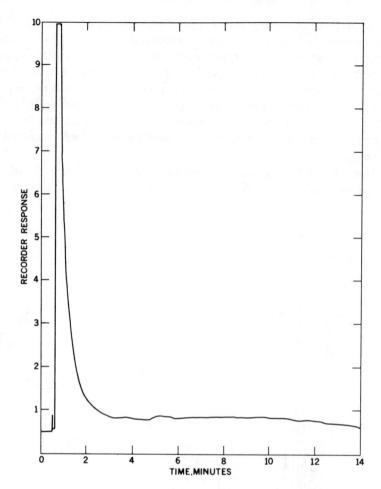

Figure 3.   Quality of distilled water after improvement

plastic cap itself does not cause contamination, the liner in the cap or the coating on the liner may do so. For example, the anhydrous sodium sulfate, which is used in drying the solvent extracts, was found to be contaminated. A chromatogram of these interfering substances is shown in Figure 4. In tracing the source, it was established that the screw-cap liner had contaminated the sodium sulfate. These impurities can be avoided by heat treating the sodium sulfate at 400°C. overnight and by storing it in an all-glass container.

Frequently, solvents as presently obtained on the market are not pure enough for use in the electron capture analysis. ACS-grade hexane can be further purified by refluxing over bright sodium (freshly prepared sodium ribbon). This treatment usually will purify hexane sufficiently to allow concentration of the extracts by a factor of about 20. Some batches of nanograde hexane, which is especially prepared for pesticide residue analysis, have been found suitable without further purification, whereas other batches have contained high boiling impurities, and redistillation from sodium was necessary.

High purity nitrogen gas is used for direct current electron capture detectors. This gas should be filtered and dry. An exhausted drier will allow passage of water and reduce the standing current.

Experimental Results

Column performance is the key to effective gas chromatographic analysis. The choice of column materials and the preparation of the col-

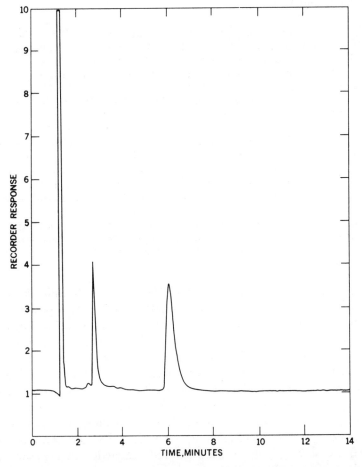

Figure 4.   Screw cap contamination of sodium sulfate

umns is particularly important. Some investigators (1, 9, 10) have observed that endrin decomposes on the gas chromatographic column, producing two or three peaks and reduced response. In a previous study (8) the authors had experienced difficulty in purchasing and in preparing columns that would not decompose some of the insecticides.

In our work, we observed that coating the column support with Carbowax 20M, prior to coating with the other liquid phase, increased response and appeared to inhibit decomposition of the pesticides. Apparently, this treatment blocks active sites on the column support. Endrin, which has a tendency to decompose on the analytical column, passed through the improved columns as a single peak. Others (10) have suggested conditioning the columns by massive injection of pesticides and waxy extracts from apples, but the following technique is more convenient and reliable.

The gas chromatographic columns are prepared by the frontal analysis technique (11). Each column is coated with Carbowax 20M first; then column A is coated with DC 200, and column B is coated with QF-1. This is done by pouring a measured volume of liquid phase, dissolved in a volatile solvent (anhydrous methanol for the Carbowax and ethyl acetate for the silicones), into a glass column (2 cm. diameter) that has a stopcock on the bottom and a glass joint on top. A weighed amount of Chromosorb G is poured into the column and allowed to settle. The liquid is drained and then blown from the column with nitrogen gas. The volume of liquid collected from the column is measured, and the amount of substrate on the support calculated. The column is back-flushed with nitrogen gas to take off the volatile solvent until the coated material is sufficiently dry to pour. Most of the remaining solvent is removed from the coated support in an evaporating dish under the gentle heat of an infrared lamp. Finally, any trace of volatile material is removed in a vacuum oven at 40°C. overnight. If greater accuracy is desired, the support can be weighed before and after coating with the liquid phases.

Appropriate addition of insecticides to water is difficult because many of these compounds are not very water soluble. In a previous study (8) the authors investigated two techniques of introducing organic insecticides into water—hexane solutions and emulsion suspensions. When the insecticides are added to the water from nonaqueous solvents, these substances do not immediately dissolve, and a nonuniform suspension usually results. By spiking with emulsified insecticides from aqueous suspension, a better exposure of these pesticides to the water or water-sediment mixture may be achieved. The emulsifiable concentrates of the insecticides must be thoroughly mixed with the water. This is accomplished by stirring with a glass-covered magnetic stirring bar at the time dilution or addition of the emulsion suspension is performed.

The emulsion technique was applied in the following manner: Microliter quantities of the emulsifiable concentrates of the insecticides were added to distilled water. Portions of each suspension were diluted, and the concentrations of the insecticides in the final suspension were determined by electron capture gas chromatography. Appropriate amounts of the diluted emulsion suspensions were then added to about 1-liter samples of distilled water to provide concentrations of these pesticides at levels of less than one part per billion.

Recovery tests were then performed on the prepared samples. The recovery of 13 common insecticides ranged from 86 to 121% as shown in Table II.

Table II. Recovery of Insecticides from Distilled Water After Addition as an Emulsion

Insecticide	Quantity Added, nanograms	Quantity Recovered, nanograms	Recovery, %
Aldrin	22	25	114
Chlordan	138	130	94
DDD (TDE)	97	117	121
DDT	514	549	107
Dieldrin	98	119	121
Endrin	106	96	91
Heptachlor	82	81	101
Heptachlor epoxide	63	61	97
Lindane	36	32	89
Malathion	785	862	110
Methoxychlor	360	435	121
Methyl parathion	126	140	111
Parathion	250	215	86

Recovery studies with unfiltered waters from streams are now in progress. In these tests, approximately 1-liter samples are used. Emulsifiable suspensions of the insecticide standards are added to one bottle of water, and another bottle of the same sample is used as a blank. Both bottles of the same sample are extracted and analyzed by the described procedure in the same way. The results obtained for the surface waters are comparable to those reported for spiked distilled water; however, this part of the investigation is being continued so that a variety of surface waters and conditions can be covered.

Discussion and Summary

The detectability (*1*) of hydrocarbon pesticides varies because of their differing chemical structure and physical properties. The practical minimum limits of analysis by this procedure are (a) 10 p.p.t. or less for aldrin, DDD, DDT, dieldrin, endrin, heptachlor, heptachlor epoxide, and lindane, (b) 50 p.p.t. for methyl parathion and parathion, (c) 100 p.p.t. for chlordan and malathion, and (d) 200 p.p.t. for methoxychlor. These values were derived from the gas chromatographic analysis of insecticides contained in 5.0-μliter aliquots of extracts that were concentrated to 5.00 ml. after recovery from 1-liter samples of water. When lower limits of measurement are desired, larger samples and/or greater concentration of the extract can be applied.

The samples are extracted with hexane in such a way that the water, or water-sediment mixture, and the container itself are exposed to the solvent. Improved analytical columns are used to analyze the extracts by electron capture gas chromatography. These columns are prepared by coating the support with Carbowax 20M, prior to coating with the selected liquid substrate. Using two different types of columns will substantially increase confidence in the results through the different partitioning action of two liquid substrates.

Recovery studies were performed on 13 common insecticides (chlorinated and phosphorothioate compounds). These pesticides were added as emulsifiable suspensions to distilled water and surface waters from streams. The results obtained so far for the surface waters are comparable to those reported in Table II.

Since the concentration of the insecticides in the spiking solution is determined by gas chromatography, a cumulative error can occur. At concentrations below one part per billion, the variations observed are not considered unreasonable. Considering the factors involved in monitoring waters for various pesticides, variations observed at these low concentrations can readily occur.

Hexane can be used to extract the insecticides efficiently from water. The efficiency of this extraction for insecticides sorbed on sediments in the water is under investigation.

At the high sensitivity of the electron capture detector, the laboratory is a prime source of contamination. All reagents and glassware should be checked for contamination. Heat treating the glassware to 300°C. overnight is a convenient way to avoid contamination from this source.

Literature Cited

(1) Bonelli, E. J., Hartmann, H., Dimick, K. P., *J. Agr. Food Chem.* **12**, 33 (1964).
(2) Breidenbach, A. W., Lichtenberg, J. J., Henke, C. F., Smith, D. J., Eichelberger, J. W., Jr., Stierli, H., *U.S. Public Health Serv. Publ.* **1241** (1964).
(3) Goodenkauf, A., Erdei, J., *J. Am. Water Works Assoc.* **56**, 600 (1964).
(4) Hindin, E., May, D. S., Dunstan, G. H., "Residue Reviews," Vol. 7, p. 130–156, Springer-Verlag: New York, Inc., 1964.

(5) Johnson, O., Krog, N., Poland, J. L., *Chem. Week* **92,** 117 (May 25, 1963).
(6) *Ibid.,* **92,** 55 (June 1, 1963).
(7) Kahn, L., Wayman, C. H., *Anal. Chem.* **36,** 1340 (1964).
(8) Lamar, W. L., Goerlitz, D. F., Law, L. M., *U.S. Geol. Survey Water-Supply Paper* **1817-B** (1965).
(9) Phillips, D. D., Pollard, G. E., Soloway, S. B., *J. Agr. Food Chem.* **10,** 217 (1962).
(10) Shuman, H., Collie, J. R., *J. Assoc. Offic. Agr. Chemists* **46,** 992 (1963).
(11) Smith, E. D., *Anal. Chem.* **32,** 1049 (1960).
(12) Teasley, J. I., Cox, W. S., *J. Am. Water Works Assoc.* **55,** 1093 (1963).
(13) Warnick, S. L., Gaufin, A. R., *J. Am. Water Works Assoc.* **57,** 1023 (1965).

RECEIVED November 15, 1965.

16

Determination of Silvex and
Its Low Volatile Esters in Water and Muds

JOHN D. POPE, Jr., WILLIAM S. COX, III, and ALFRED R. GRZENDA

U.S. Department of the Interior, Federal Water Pollution Control Administration, Southeast Water Laboratory, Athens, Ga.

Silvex acid and its propylene glycol butyl ether ester can be determined in soil and water by electron capture gas chromatography. Extraction of the water and soil, using organic solvents, is made by liquid-liquid and percolation, respectively. Recoveries from fortified water samples range from 65.3 to 94.0% of dosage levels of 1.0–1000.0 p.p.b. The recoveries from fortified soils range from 0 to 115.6% of dosage levels of 10–500 p.p.b. Silvex acid is esterified with 10% boron trifluoride in methanol before being chromatographed as the methyl ester.

Silvex [2-(2,4,5-trichlorophenoxy) propionic acid] is one of the phenoxy alkyl acid herbicides. Its salts and esters have been used in various formulations as selective herbicides for controlling and eradicating woody plants (2). Certain formulations have also been used to control several aquatic weeds (5). Although its disappearance in soils (1) and water (4) has been studied, little is known of its behavior in muds. This paper describes a method for extracting and determining the ester and acid forms of silvex in water and muds using gas chromatography.

The gas chromatographic determination of phenoxy acid herbicides was developed primarily by Yip (9), who found it the only satisfactory method for residues in plants. He found that several methods of preparing the methyl esters were satisfactory. For most of his work, he used diazomethane, which must be prepared in the laboratory. For convenience, we used methanolic boron trifluoride introduced by Metcalfe and Schmitz (7). The reagent is commercially available and may be stored indefinitely at room temperature. Since we wished to detect the propylene glycol butyl ether ester (PGBE ester) and the methyl ester near the part per billion (p.p.b.) level, we used an electron capture detection (6) system, whereas Yip used the microcoulometric detection system (3).

As part of a study of the persistence of silvex in water, the PGBE ester was applied as an emulsion. The ester is distributed as a 64.5% concentrate (42.8% acid equivalent). In this study, floating masses of alligatorweed (*Alternanthera philoxeroides* [Mart.]Griseb.) contained in 1500-gallon plastic swimming pools, were sprayed. To simulate natural conditions, the bottoms of the pools were covered with a 4 to 5-inch thick layer of soils, the tanks were filled with water, alligatorweed was added, and the system was allowed to equilibrate for 3 months prior to treatment. Three different soil types—Piedmont, Coastal Plains, and Florida muck—taken from their representative areas in the southeastern United States, were used as discrete bottom muds.

Samples of the water and bottom muds were taken after equilibration, and known amounts of the ester and the acid were added for the recovery experiments.

Experimental

Reagents. All organic solvents are redistilled, using all-glass distilling apparatus. The first 10% cut is discarded, and the next 80% is collected for use. The reagents used were acetone, benzene, chloroform, ethyl ether, hexane, petroleum ether (30°–60°C. b.p. range), boron trifluoride [(BF), 10% in methanol–Eastman No. 3706], Florisil (activated, 60–100 mesh-activated previously by manufacturer at 1200°F., stored in oven at 130°C. until ready for use).

Standard solutions used were:

Methyl ester prepared from silvex (99%+), the Dow Chemical Co., 1 microgram per ml. (μgram/ml.) in petroleum ether; protect from evaporation losses.

PGBE ester (Kuron), the Dow Chemical Co., 1 μgram acid equivalent/ml. Dissolve concentrate in petroleum ether and make up final solution in benzene.

Apparatus. Separatory funnels, with Teflon stopcocks—125-ml. and 4-liter capacities; Kuderna-Danish evaporators with Snyder three-ball columns; Immerex extractor, A. H. Thomas Cat. No. 1228-E; chromatographic tubes—25 mm. o.d. x 300 mm. glass tube with sintered glass in bottom and Teflon stopcock.

Gas chromatographic equipment was an electron capture gas-liquid chromatograph. Conditions should be as follows: Glass column, 6' x 4 mm. i.d., packed with 80/90 mesh Anachrom ABS coated with 10% DC 200 (12,500 cst); column temperature, 195°C.; injection temperature, 220°C.; carrier gas flow, 75 ml./min. of nitrogen; electron capture detector, radium source, concentric type. The complete system is adjusted so that 1 nanogram of lindane produces approximately 50% scale.

Procedure. MUD ANALYSES. *Sample Collection.* Using bottom sampler, take samples by scraping off top inch of mud along three radii, 120° apart, and composite to make at least a 1-quart sample after free water is decanted. Mark sampling points on outside of tank to prevent re-sampling of same radii.

Sample Preparation. Place sample in inert (glass or enamelled metal) pan or baking dish, and air-dry at ambient temperature. A fan may be used to hasten drying, but heat should not be applied. When sample just crumbles when touched, grind in mortar and pestle, quarter, and weigh for analysis.

Extraction and Isolation of Herbicide. (1) Place 100-gram portion of air-dried sample in basket of Immerex extractor. Add 250 ml. of acetone-hexane (1+9) to the metal container, and assemble extractor with basket in raised position. Using low heat setting on hot plate, extract the sample for 4 hours. Transfer extract to beaker, and evaporate just to dryness, using low heat and stream of dry air.

(2) Dissolve residue in beaker in 25 ml. ethyl ether-petroleum ether (1+1), transfer to small separatory funnel, and extract successively with three 25-ml. portions of 5% $NaHCO_3$ solution, shaking at least 1 minute each time. Combine the $NaHCO_3$ extract in a 250-ml. separatory funnel for step 3, and retain the ether extract for step 6.

(3) Extract the combined $NaHCO_3$ extract with 15 ml. $CHCl_3$ by shaking 2 minutes in small separatory funnel. Allow phases to separate, and discard the $CHCl_3$.

(4) Cautiously acidify with 5N HCl to approximately pH 3. Extract the aqueous layer with three 50-ml. portions of $CHCl_3$, combine the extracts, and discard the aqueous layer.

(5) Evaporate the $CHCl_3$ extracts to dryness on a steam bath with the aid of a stream of warm, dry air. Evaporate the final few milliliters with air only. Dissolve the residue in a few milliliters of ethyl ether. and transfer to a Kuderna-Danish evaporating tube. Evaporate the ethyl ether using gentle heat and air. Add 3 ml. BF_3 in methanol, assemble evaporator with Snyder column, and heat for 2 minutes on steam bath. Transfer the methanolic solution to a small separatory funnel using 20 ml. water followed by 30 ml. petroleum ether. Shake vigorously for 2 minutes, allow phases to separate, drain off, and discard aqueous layer. Retain petroleum ether extract for gas chromatographic analysis (protect from loss of solvent by evaporation). This solution contains the free acid as the methyl ester.

(6) Transfer the ether extract from step 2 to a small beaker, and evaporate just to dryness, using gentle heat and a stream of dry air. Dissolve the residue in a small amount of petroleum ether, and transfer to a chromatographic column containing 4 inches of Florisil, after settling, topped with about ½ inch of anhydrous Na_2SO_4, previously prewet with 35–40 ml. petroleum ether. Using 250 ml. each of mixed ethers (6+94 and 15+85), elute the column at approximately 5 ml. per minute. Discard the 6% eluate, and evaporate the 15% eluate just to dryness. Dissolve the residue in benzene for the determination of the PGBE ester by gas chromatography.

Determination. Using electron capture gas chromatography as the determinative step, inject 5 microliters (μliters) of each solution into the chromatograph. For high concentrations, further dilution will be necessary; conversely, low concentrations require larger aliquots. By comparison with standard solutions injected under the same operating conditions, determine the amount of silvex, using the peak height method for the methyl ester and the peak area method for the PGBE ester. Based on the aliquot used, calculate total amounts of esters in original sample and the residue levels of the free acid and the PGBE ester. The retention times of the silvex methyl ester and the PGBE ester are 0.47 and 2.33, respectively, as related to aldrin.

WATER ANALYSES. *Sample Collection.* Using Tygon tubing (6 mm. i.d.), siphon water into a 1-gallon (3.8-liter) glass jar, keeping the tubing at a depth of 5–7 inches and moving slowly around the circumference of the pool until the container is full. Extract sample immediately (*see* procedure below).

Extraction and Isolation of Herbicide. (1) Place a 2-liter sample into a 4-liter separatory funnel, and acidify to approximately pH 3 with 5 ml. hydrochloric acid (HCl).

(2) Using 100, 50, 50, and 50 ml. $CHCl_3$, extract the water successively, shaking vigorously for 2 minutes each time. After shaking, allow phases to separate, and drain off lower layer, including most of the emulsion. Combine the extracts, and remove the entrapped H_2O by passing through a 4- x 1-inch column of anhydrous sodium sulfate (Na_2SO_4). Wash column with 25 ml. fresh $CHCl_3$, and add to combined extract.

(3) Evaporate $CHCl_3$ on steam bath with stream of warm dry air to approximately 25 ml., transfer to a small separatory funnel, and extract successively with three 25-ml. portions of 5% sodium bicarbonate ($NaHCO_3$), retaining the $CHCl_3$ layer for step 6.

(4) Place the combined $NaHCO_3$ extracts in a 250-ml. separatory funnel, and cautiously acidify with $5N$ HCl to approximately pH 3. Extract the aqueous layer with three 50-ml. portions of $CHCl_3$, combine the extracts, and discard the aqueous layer.

(5) Prepare the methyl ester of silvex from the $CHCl_3$ extract as directed in step 5 of the procedure for mud samples.

(6) Evaporate the $CHCl_3$ layer (from step 3) just to dryness in a small beaker. Dilute to 5.00 ml. with benzene. This solution contains the PGBE ester. If the residue needs cleanup, proceed as directed in step 6 of the procedure for mud samples.

Determination. Using electron capture gas chromatography, determine the methyl ester of acid (step 5) and the PGBE ester of silvex (step 6) as outlined for mud analyses.

Discussion

The statistical significance of the recovery of silvex acid and PGBE ester from water was investigated (Table I). First, an analysis of variance was used for each formulation to estimate the variance owing to (1) differences in recoveries among triplicate analyses within dose levels (rows) and (2) differences in recoveries among dose levels (columns). The mean data were then subjected to additional analyses to estimate the variance owing to (1) differences in mean recoveries between formulations within dose levels (rows) and (2) differences in mean recoveries within formulations among dose levels (columns). The error mean square of each analysis of variance and the appropriate Q value were used to compute a difference among means (D) which would be significant at the 95% level (8). Thus, comparisons among mean recoveries within formulations among dose levels as well as comparisons between formulations can be made. For example, in Table I any difference among dose levels for the mean recovery of ester which exceeds ± 5.6 p.p.b. is statistically significant. Similarly, any difference between formulations which is greater than ± 13.9 p.p.b. is also statistically significant.

Table I. Recovery of Two Formulations of Silvex from Tap Water

Formulation	Percent Recovery				95% Significant Difference	
					Within Formulation	Between Formulations
	Dose Level, p.p.b.					
	1000	50	2.5	1.0		
Ester	94.0	86.8	84.9	77.0	± 5.6	± 13.9
Acid	94.0	94.7	68.0	65.3	± 20.1	

The replicate mean squares from the analyses of variance for acid and ester recovery were essentially the same (0.007 and 0.0015, respectively). In contrast, the mean squares for the dose levels were 0.022 for the ester and 0.116 for the acid. This indicates that the over-all precision of the method for both formulations is comparable regardless of differences in accuracy among dose levels. Thus, using 1-gallon samples and appropriate correction factors, data for the acid and ester are reliable for concentrations between 1 p.p.b. and 1 p.p.m.

The recovery of silvex acid and the PGBE ester from three soil types is shown in Table II. Residue recovery from Florida muck was substantially less than recovery from the Piedmont Plateau and Coastal Plain soils. However, differences within soil types are less apparent. The statistical significance of these data was investigated in the same manner as described for water samples. The D values are given in Table II.

There was no statistically significant difference between the mean recovery of silvex acid and ester from Coastal Plain soil. However, with one exception, such differences were statistically significant in the cases of Florida muck and Piedmont Plateau soil. The effect was most pronounced for the muck; for example, mean acid recovery was from 24–43% less than that noted for the ester.

Table II. Recovery of Two Formulations of Silvex from Three Soil Types

Formulation	Percent Recovery				95% Significant Difference	
	Dose Level, p.p.b.				Within Formulation	Between Formulations
	500	100	50	10		
			Piedmont Soil			
Ester	—	99.7	93.7	75.0	± 14.1	± 16.4
Acid	—	72.0	70.7	60.3	± 3.5	
			Coastal Plain Soil			
Ester	—	101.6	97.1	90.0	± 11.0	± 28.6
Acid	—	99.0	115.6	90.0	± 18.5	
			Florida Muck			
Ester	98.5	75.0	37.7	N.D.[a]	± 12.0	± 23.1
Acid	74.1	32.0	N.D.	N.D.[a]	± 27.5	

[a] N.D. = Not detected.

In Piedmont soil, mean recovery at 10 p.p.b. was significantly different from recoveries at 50 and 100 p.p.m. for both the acid and ester. However, even though recovery at 10 p.p.b. was lower, it was still adequate (60–70%) to retain reasonable sensitivity for residue analysis. With one exception, there were no statistically significant differences in mean residue recoveries among dose levels from Coastal soil. In Florida muck at a dose of 50 p.p.b., acid residue could not be detected, and only marginal recovery of ester (38%) was noted. Good recovery from muck was noted at 500 and 100 p.p.b. for ester and only at 500 p.p.b. for acid. Hence, the methods used would have serious limitations for a critical study of residue survival in mucky soils.

Thus far, only differences in accuracy have been discussed. The variance values owing to differences among triplicate analyses provide some precision. Among all formulations and concentrations, the mean squares obtained from the analyses of variance were 0.07, 0.13, 0.07, 0.53, and 1.48. The last two values are for ester and acid recovery from Florida muck, respectively. Therefore, residue recovery from muck, in addition to being the least accurate and sensitive, is also the least precise.

Conclusions

(1) The recovery of the PGBE ester of silvex from water was 85% or better for concentrations between 1 p.p.m. and 2.5 p.p.b.

(2) The recovery of free silvex acid from water was 95% or better for concentrations of 50 p.p.b. and 1 p.p.m. At 2.5 and 1 p.p.b. the recoveries were 65% or better.

(3) The precision of the method used for residue recovery from water was essentially the same regardless of concentration or formulation. Thus, in spite of differences in accuracy, the data can be corrected to give reliable estimates of residue levels between 0.001 and 1 p.p.m.

(4) The recovery of silvex acid from Piedmont Plateau soil and Florida muck was significantly less than ester recovery. The recovery of acid and ester from Coastal Plain soil was essentially the same.

(5) Many herbicides are adsorbed by colloidal particles. Since the amounts of mineral and organic colloids vary among soils, it is possible that this factor, as well as the pH of the spiked soils, played an important part in the recovery of the acid and PGBE ester.

(6) Future papers by others will deal with the characterization of the bottom muds, their effects on the disappearance of the herbicide, and changes in water quality parameters following treatment.

(7) The levels of accuracy, precision, and sensitivity noted for acid and ester recovery from Piedmont and Coastal soils are considered adequate to measure and detect silvex residues associated with the control of aquatic weeds. Similarly, the recovery of ester from Florida muck is judged to be acceptable down to 100 p.p.m. However, free acid recovery from muck is considered inadequate on all of these points.

Literature Cited

(1) Alexander, M., Aleem, M. I., *J. Agr. Food Chem.* **9**, 44 (1961).
(2) Crafts, A. S. Robbins, W. W., "Weed Control," 3d ed., McGraw-Hill Co., Inc., New York, 1962.
(3) Coulson, D. M., Cavanagh, L. A., Devries, J. E., Walther, B., *J. Agr. Food Chem.* **8**, 399 (1960).
(4) Goerlitz, D. F., Lamar, W. L., *U.S. Geol. Survey Open File Rept.* (1965).
(5) Hambric, R. N., *Proc. Ann. Meeting Southern Weed Conf., 18th,* Dallas, Tex. **18**, 458 (1965).
(6) Lovelock, J. E., Lipsky, S. R., *J. Am. Chem. Soc.* **82**, 431 (1960).
(7) Metcalfe, L. D., Schmitz, A. A., *Anal. Chem.* **33**, 363 (1961).
(8) Snedecor, G. W., "Statistical Methods Applied to Experiments in Agriculture and Biology," 5th ed., Iowa State College Press, Ames, Iowa, 1956.
(9) Yip, G., *J. Assoc. Offic. Agr. Chemists* **45**, 367 (1962).

RECEIVED February 7, 1966. Mention of products and manufacturers is for identification only and does not imply endorsement by the U.S. Department of the Interior.

Infrared Identification of Chlorinated Insecticides in Tissues of Poisoned Fish

H. W. BOYLE, R. H. BURTTSCHELL, and A. A. ROSEN

Cincinnati Water Research Laboratory, Federal Water Pollution Control Administration, Department of Health, Education, and Welfare, Cincinnati, Ohio

A method for identifying chlorinated insecticide residues in fish tissue is described. Whereas electron capture gas chromatography guides the isolation procedures and provides tentative identification and quantitative estimation, positive identification is made on the basis of the infrared spectrum of isolated insecticides. The procedure consists of hexane extraction of fish tissue, partition between hexane and acetonitrile, column adsorption and thin layer chromatography cleanup, and micro-infrared analysis in a potassium bromide disc. The practical limit of sensitivity needed to provide excellent infrared spectra of a number of the more common chlorinated insecticides is about 1 p.p.m. in the fish tissue; concentrations as low as 0.25 p.p.m. have given informative infrared spectra.

Unequivocal identification of pesticides that cause stream pollution and thereby affect aquatic organisms requires more evidence than can be provided by gas chromatography. Infrared spectrometry of these toxic substances recovered from the tissues of affected fish can supply firm proof of their identity (*1*). In using this technique, however, problems are introduced by the large proportions of interfering substances in typical samples. Infrared analysis, furthermore, is less sensitive than gas chromatography.

Infrared spectra of 1- to 3-μgram samples of pure chlorinated insecticides have been obtained by the micro-KBr disc method (*2, 8*). The minimum sample size is determined by traces of unremovable impurities. These impurities cause difficulties in analyzing pesticides in fatty biological materials, such as some foods (*3*). Published work on the analysis of pesticides in fish shows even greater difficulties. Eidelman (7) resorted to saponification and MgO-Celite cleanup to prepare a fish oil sample for pesticide residue analysis by gas chromatography, without eliminating all interferences. Other reported analyses of chlorinated insecticides in "normal" or poisoned fish (6, 12, 13, 15) did not include infrared identification.

The infrared identification method presented here is a selected combination of available methods for sample extraction, removal of interferences, separation and concentration of insecticides, and infrared spectrometry of micro samples. The method was developed using fish exposed in the laboratory to a variety of known pesticides; it was applied successfully to fish samples collected at the site of a large fish kill. The procedure consists of the following steps:

(1) Extracting frozen fish tissue in a Waring blendor.

(2) Partitioning the tissue extract between hexane and acetonitrile to separate the insecticides from the bulk of the oily extract.

(3) Column adsorption chromatography on activated alumina, which removes all but traces of oily matter and separates the insecticides into groups.

(4) Electron capture gas chromatography for tentative identification and quantitative analysis.

(5) Thin layer chromatography on alumina for separating mixtures of insecticides into their individual components and for a last stage of purification; also for confirmation of identification.

(6) Micro infrared spectrometry for final and definitive proof of identity.

The applicability of the procedure was demonstrated by the identification of 12 chlorinated insecticides isolated from fish tissue in quantities ranging from 10 to 40 μgrams.

Experimental

Reagents. Hexane: Burdick and Jackson Laboratories, b.p. 68°-69°C. (redistilled).

Acetonitrile: Matheson, Coleman & Bell, P-2726 (practical), b.p. 80°–82°C. (Redistill with 1 ml. 85% H_3PO_4 per gallon.)

Ethyl ether: anhydrous, reagent grade; Fisher E-138.

Alumina: Fisher A-540, 80 to 200-mesh, to which 1% water is added. The activity varies slightly from lot to lot. To obtain an activity corresponding to that of the alumina used in collecting the data in Table I, calibrate each lot with a known mixture of insecticides.

Acid alumina: Bio-Rad Acid alumina AG-4, 100 to 200-mesh.

Neutral alumina: Bio-Rad neutral alumina AG-7, 100 to 200-mesh.

Aluminum oxide G: According to Stahl, $CaSO_4$ binder, neutral; Brinkmann Instruments, Inc.

Table I. Order of Elution of Standard Insecticides from Alumina Adsorption Column [a]

Insecticide	Insecticides in 50-ml. Eluate Fractions, % of Total Recovered										Weight Insecticide Used, μgram	% Recovery, Av. of 3 Runs
	1	2	3	4	5	6	7	8	9	10		
DDE	95	5									10	94
Aldrin	93	7									10	97
Heptachlor	70	30									10	96
Chlordan (tech.)	30	30	40	Trace							20	99
Toxaphene	15	55	30	Trace							50	93
DDT	5	95									20	94
γ-Chlordan		2	80	18							10	99
DDD			60	40							10	93
Lindane			35	65							10	40
Endrin				45	55						10	95
Heptachlor Epoxide				35	50	15					10	95
Dieldrin						20	40	20	15	5	10	96
Methoxychlor						5	30	50	10	5	50	96
Lindane (Acid alumina)			25	60	15						10	100
Lindane (Neutral alumina)		3	75	20	2						10	91

[a] Eluting solvent—9:1 hexane/ethyl ether; elution rate—3.5 to 4.0 ml. per minute.

Potassium bromide: Powdered, infrared quality; Harshaw Chemical Co.

Apparatus. Infrared spectrophotometer: Perkin-Elmer model 421 recording spectrophotometer or equivalent, equipped with 6X beam condenser and holder for 1.5-mm. diameter KBr, discs.

Micro KBr Equipment: Perkin-Elmer KBr ultramicro-die, equipped with holder, pin, discs, funnel, and tamper for 1.5-mm pellets, and a press capable of exerting 500 pounds pressure.

Blender: Waring blendor, Model EP-1, explosion proof, with an Eberbach stainless steel, hermetic, 1-quart container.

Procedure. SAMPLE PREPARATION. The fish should be preserved by freezing as soon after collection as possible. It is a matter of convenience whether it is frozen whole or first processed into portions suitable for extraction. Only the muscle tissue and unseparated fat and viscera were used as samples in this investigation.

If the fish is not prepared for extraction at the time of collection, thaw it, and remove the head, skin, and fins. Remove the fat and viscera for separate handling. Cut off portions of the muscle tissue. Weigh out 20-gram samples of muscle and of fat-and-viscera for extraction. Refreeze these samples.

EXTRACTION. Cut the frozen sample of fish tissue quickly into small pieces (roughly 1-cm. cubes), and place with 175 ml. of hexane in the

Waring blendor. Homogenize for about 30 seconds. Remove the stainless steel container, and hold under a hot water tap for 1 minute; replace on the blendor, and homogenize for 2.5 minutes. Decant the supernatant liquid, and reblend the tissue with another 175-ml. portion of hexane for 3 minutes. Decant, combine the extracts, and filter through Whatman #1 paper into a 400-ml. beaker. If fine solids remain in the filtrate, filter again through Whatman #3 paper. Evaporate the extract to less than 50 ml. on a hot water bath under a gentle stream of filtered air; transfer to a 50-ml.-beaker, and evaporate to about 10 ml.

HEXANE-ACETONITRILE PARTITION. Transfer the extract to a 125-ml. separatory funnel, and bring to a 25-ml. volume with hexane. Extract with four 25-ml. portions of redistilled acetonitrile previously saturated with hexane. Combine the acetonitrile extracts, and evaporate just to dryness on a hot water bath under a gentle stream of filtered air. Take up the residue in 10 ml. hexane. Muscle tissue extracts are usually pure enough at this point for gas chromatography.

COLUMN ADSORPTION CHROMATOGRAPHY. In a 2-cm. diameter glass tube, prepare a 15-cm. column of 80 to 200-mesh adsorption alumina, and prewet it with 50 ml. of hexane. Adjust the elution rate to 3.5–4.0 ml. per minute. The adsorption alumina must be slightly deactivated, and each lot is calibrated by adding 1.0–1.5% water to give the activity required for the degree of separation of the insecticides listed in Table I.

Transfer the hexane extract to the column, washing it in with an additional 10 ml. of hexane. Take 10 50-ml. fractions while eluting with 9:1 (v/v) hexane/ethyl ether.

GAS CHROMATOGRAPHY. Electron capture gas chromatography guides the isolation procedures and provides quantitative estimation. Any system of instrument and column suitable for use with chlorinated insecticides is satisfactory for this purpose. The examples described here were carried out using a 3 ft. x ⅛ in. glass column containing 5% Dow 11 silicone grease on 60 to 80-mesh Chromosorb W.

Chromatograph 1 μliter of each 50-ml. fraction from the alumina column. Tentatively identify the insecticides by their retention times. Composite the fractions on the basis of the gas chromatographic results, and concentrate each composite to 5.0 or 10.0 ml. in graduated centrifuge tubes. Determine the insecticides in each composite by gas chromatography and by comparison with a reference standard giving the same peak heights as the sample.

THIN LAYER CHROMATOGRAPHY. Coat 8- x 8-inch glass plates with a 0.25-mm. layer of aluminum oxide G, and air-dry overnight. Activate in an oven at 155°C. for 2.5 hours, and store over Drierite until used.

Concentrate the composited pesticide fractions remaining after chromatography to 0.1–0.2 ml. in a hot water bath, with a gentle stream of filtered air. Spot the entire fractions on the plate along with appropriate reference standards, and develop the chromatogram with 1% ethyl ether in hexane. Additional developments with the same solvent system, following a brief air drying are necessary to separate some pairs of insecticides; two developments are necessary to separate dieldrin and methoxychlor.

Locate the insecticide spots by spraying lightly with 0.01% Rhodamine B in 95% ethanol. Insecticides are revealed as purple spots on a pink background. Remove each spot from the plate by vacuum, using a glass medicine dropper tube plugged with a small amount of glass wool. Elute the insecticides from the adsorbent in the tube with 5 ml. of 4:1 (v/v) hexane/ethyl ether into a 5-ml. centrifuge tube, and concentrate the eluate to approximately 0.1 ml.

INFRARED SPECTROPHOTOMETRY. A research grade infrared spectrophotometer equipped with a 6-power reflectance type beam condenser and a micro-die for 1.5 mm. KBr pellets was used.

Weigh out 7 mg. of infrared-quality powdered KBr into a 2-cm. micro-porcelain boat, and with a spatula lightly tamp into a small cake at one end. Add the concentrated eluate from the thin layer plate to the KBr in 2.0-μliter increments, allowing sufficient time (about 30 seconds) between additions for the solvent to evaporate. After all the sample has been evaporated onto the KBr, prepare the disc, and obtain the spectrum in the usual manner. It is advisable to record the spectra of a blank KBr pellet and a reference standard on the same paper for comparison.

Two precautions must be observed. First, the sample solution must not be added in larger increments or without allowing full time for evaporation of the preceding portion; otherwise sample will be leached from the KBr powder. Second, substantially all of the oily contaminant must be removed before the disc is pressed; otherwise the insecticide will be lost with the oil pressed out of the disc.

Discussion

Extraction. A modification of the Shell method for extracting animal products proved highly effective (13). The tissue should be cut quickly and extracted while still frozen to ensure good dispersion of the sample. The recovery of insecticide drops markedly when samples are allowed to thaw before the initial blending.

There is no absolute method for checking extraction efficiency, but the residual solids from a number of hexane extractions were re-extracted with acetone in a Soxhlet extractor to test the efficiency of the hexane extraction step. The acetone extract was carried separately through the purification steps. Recoveries by this method in the course of 18 trials ranged from zero to 10% of the total insecticide recovered.

Partition. Most of the noninsecticide impurity is removed in the hexane-acetonitrile partition step (9, 11). The effectiveness of this and the column chromatography step is shown in the following data recorded in the processing of a sample of fat and viscera from a large carp:

Fish tissue extracted	20.0 grams
Hexane extract	3.64
Extract after hexane-acetonitrile partition	0.129
Extract after column chromatography	Trace

If the analysis is to be used for samples of unusually high oil content (above 35%), corresponding modifications of partition cleanup or sample size may be required.

The bulk of the hexane extract is a clear, yellow oil that partitions into the hexane layer. The small amount of impurity which accompanies the pesticide into the acetonitrile layer is removed easily later by column adsorption chromatography. The acetonitrile is removed by evaporation on a hot water bath with a gentle stream of filtered air. In this way the extract may be evaporated just to dryness without loss, the small amount of oil remaining being sufficient to prevent losses by volatilization.

Extracts of muscle tissue are usually sufficiently pure for quantitative gas chromatography at this point, but fat-and-viscera samples require further cleanup. The small sample requirement of the electron capture detector permits a close check on the purification without a significant expenditure of sample. Gas chromatography provides tentative identification at this stage, even in impure samples, and guides the ensuing chromatographic cleanup steps.

Column Adsorption Chromatography. Almost all of the remaining interferences are eliminated by column adsorption chromatography. Alumina is more effective than silica gel or Florisil (4, 5).

In addition to eliminating interferences, the column also separates those insecticide pairs that are poorly resolved by gas chromatography— e.g., dieldrin and DDE. Figure 1 shows the improvement resulting from alumina column cleanup and separation on the gas chromatogram of the dieldrin fraction. The activity of alumina as purchased was found to vary slightly with age and lot; therefore, 1.0–1.5% water had to be

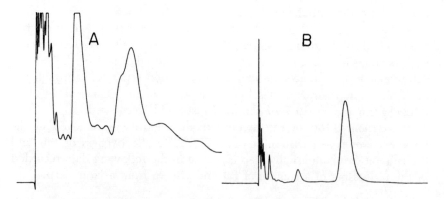

Figure 1.   Effect of alumina column cleanup in gas chromatography of dieldrin
A.   Muscle tissue of poisoned fish after acetonitrile cleanup
B.   Muscle tissue of poisoned fish after alumina column cleanup

added to attain the activity required to give the separations of the insecticides shown in Table I. The treated alumina was calibrated by using a standard mixture of aldrin, dieldrin, and endrin.

The most favorable elution rate is 3.5–4.0 ml. per minute for a 2- by 15-cm. column. Higher rates give poor separation, and lower rates do not improve the separation. Table I shows the observed order of elution of 13 insecticides in 50-ml. eluate fractions from the column.

Lindane is decomposed into two components with only 35–40% recovery of the unaltered compound when chromatographed on the usual basic alumina. If the preliminary gas chromatography following partition cleanup indicates significant concentrations of lindane, then acid alumina or neutral alumina (1.0–1.5% water added) is used. The recovery of lindane with these adsorbents is quantitative as measured by gas chromatography. The infrared spectrum, however, still shows slight decomposition in the form of minor shifts of a few bands. A single band at 775 cm.$^{-1}$ is changed to a double band at 765 cm.$^{-1}$ and 780 cm.$^{-1}$ while a narrow double band at 840 cm.$^{-1}$ and 845 cm.$^{-1}$ is changed to a single sharp band at 840 cm.$^{-1}$

Infrared spectra also show a minor alteration of aldrin on the basic alumina column as evidenced by a shift of the 720 cm.$^{-1}$ band to 710 cm.$^{-1}$ The same shift occurs when aldrin is chromatographed on acid or on neutral alumina. This band shift is more pronounced at lower concentrations, while at higher concentrations both the 720 cm.$^{-1}$ and the 710 cm.$^{-1}$ bands are observed.

The cleanup steps described failed to remove a trace of impurity that accompanied heptachlor, DDE, and aldrin in the alumina column chromatography. This impurity later appeared in infrared spectra obtained from small samples of these insecticides.

Thin Layer Chromatography. Thin layer chromatography has been used very successfully in separating the chlorinated insecticides (*10*); it also provides the final cleanup necessary before infrared identification. The R_f value may be determined as an independent confirmation of the gas chromatographic identification. The insecticide is extracted from the plate quantitatively and in a very pure condition suitable for infrared analysis. Some pairs that are not separated on the alumina column are separated in the thin layer chromatography step—e.g., dieldrin and methoxychlor. They elute together on the alumina column but can be separated on the thin layer plate with two solvent developments.

Aluminum oxide G was found to be superior to silica gel G or Florisil in separating power and convenience. Several solvents, consisting of hexane containing 0–4% ethyl ether, were tried. The combination with 1% ether was optimum. A spray solution of Rhodamine B in ethanol reveals the insecticides as purple spots on a pink background.

The dye remains on the alumina when the insecticides are eluted with hexane/ethyl ether after removal of the spot area from the plate by vacuum (*14*).

Recoveries are almost quantitative, except with toxaphene and chlordan, both of which streak on the thin layer plate and thus are not purified.

Infrared Spectrophotometry. The spectra of the chlorinated pesticides contain many sharp bands for easy identification once the compounds are separated from each other and the accompanying interferences. Column adsorption and thin layer chromatography furnish a sufficiently powerful means of cleanup to make infrared identification practical with fish extracts.

Micro equipment is required. With concentrations of only a few micrograms per gram in the fish tissues, it is seldom practicable to use samples containing more than 40–50 μgrams of a single pesticide. All the work reported here was carried out with a 1.5-mm. micro KBr pellet in a Perkin-Elmer model 421 infrared spectrophotometer, equipped with

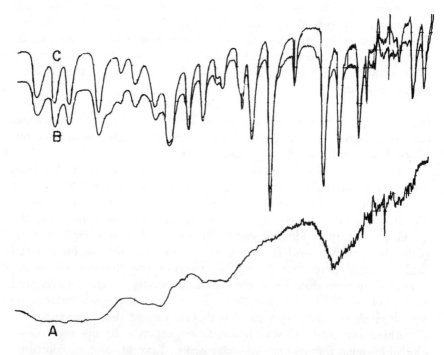

Figure 2.   Infrared spectra of endrin, showing efficiency of cleanup steps
A.   Muscle tissue of poisoned fish after acetonitrile cleanup
B.   Muscle tissue of poisoned fish after alumina column and thin layer cleanup
C.   Endrin standard

a 6x reflectance-type beam condenser. With this equipment, 20–30 μgrams of the pesticides tried gave excellent spectra. With 10μgrams, a usable spectrum was obtained, but smaller amounts showed only a few of the stronger bands because interferences owing to traces of impurities still present at this stage began to dominate the spectrum.

The efficiency of the cleanup steps for infrared identification is shown in Figure 2. The sample was a buffalo fish collected in a fish-kill in the lower Mississippi River; the muscle tissue contained 1.2 p.p.m. dieldrin and 4.2 p.p.m. endrin.

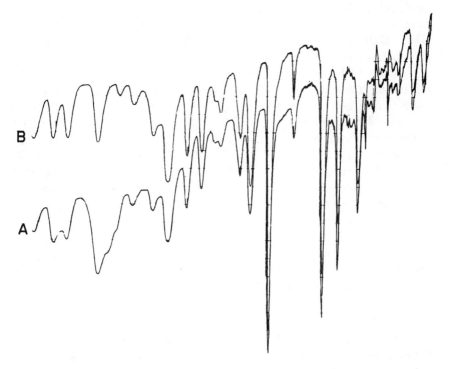

Figure 3. Infrared spectra of endrin, showing sensitivity of the procedure
A. 20 μgrams endrin from 80 grams muscle tissue of poisoned catfish, 0.25-p.p.m.
concentration
B. 20 μgrams endrin standard

The sensitivity of the procedure is demonstrated in Figure 3, which shows a clear infrared spectrum of endrin from the muscle tissue of a poisoned catfish. The tissue concentration was 0.25 p.p.m. To obtain sufficient endrin for the spectrum, two 20-gram samples and one 40-gram sample were combined in the thin layer chromatography cleanup step to give 20 μgrams of insecticide. The spectrum was recorded with 2x scale expansion.

Results

The infrared identification method was used for 19 fish samples containing 12 chlorinated insecticides, alone or in combination. Two samples were collected at the site of a large fish-kill; two others were controls from a reputedly uncontaminated source. A total of 14 samples consisted of fish exposed to insecticides in the water of an aquarium at a constant concentration (p.p.b. level) or dosed by oral ingestion once daily (p.p.m. level). Muscle tissue and viscera of the various fish samples were processed separately. The last sample was a can of California mackerel, packed in water and purchased at a local market (to serve as an example of marine fish). This sample contained both DDE and DDD; DDE was identified by infrared analysis in the small amount of oil separated in the container.

In the 14 laboratory-exposed fish, the insecticide concentrations in the muscle tissue ranged from 0.1 to 6.0 p.p.m. Concentrations in the viscera were generally higher, ranging from 0.1 to 8.8 p.p.m. In three exceptional fish, concentrations of 56.3, 93.8, and 273 p.p.m. were found in the viscera after oral ingestion of the insecticides. The most abundant insecticide was identified by infrared spectroscopy in the tissues of all fish samples, except the fish exposed to toxaphene and one control fish that showed no insecticide. DDT was identified in the second control sample. In five fish, more than one insecticide was identified by infrared.

Toxaphene was the only insecticide of the group studied whose spectrum was not sufficiently clear for identification; even 50 μgrams (2.5 p.p.m. concentration) was not adequate. All of the others gave spectra that were satisfactory in the 550 cm.$^{-1}$ to 1350 cm.$^{-1}$ range of interest. Examples of these results are shown in Table II.

Discussion

This method accomplishes the extraction, isolation, and infrared identification of a number of common chlorinated insecticides when present at concentrations of 1–2 p.p.m. or more in fish tissues. In the course of testing the method, certain related observations (noted in Table II) were provided by analyzing fish which were fed insecticides under laboratory conditions. Aldrin was converted largely to dieldrin in both muscle tissue and viscera of a fish exposed to aldrin for 22 days. However, where death occurred in 5 days after a massive dose, the conversion was very slight in the viscera. Heptachlor underwent a significant conversion to heptachlor epoxide, and DDT to DDE. There was also a selective concentration factor—e.g., technical heptachlor (containing γ-chlordan) showed a considerably higher ratio of γ-chlordan to heptachlor in the fish than in the crude insecticide. Likewise, DDD in

Table II. Results of Tests with Laboratory-Exposed Fish

Tissue	Amount, grams	Insecticide Fed	Insecticide Found	Conc., p.p.m.	Amount Insect., μgrams	Infrared Identification
Viscera	8.5	Methoxychlor	Methoxychlor	2.4	20	Positive
Viscera	7.5	Tech. DDD	Tech. DDD	7.1	53	Positive
Viscera	11.0	Aldrin	Aldrin	0.2	2	
		(22 days— alive)	Dieldrin	2.3	25	Positive
Viscera	7.8	Aldrin	Aldrin	267.0	2090	Positive (without TLC)
		(5 days— dead)	Dieldrin	5.6	45	Positive
Muscle	20	Tech. Hepta- chlor: 72% Hepta- chlor	Heptachlor	4.8	95	Positive
		20% γ-Chlor- dan	γ-Chlordan	3.5	70	Positive
		0% Hept. epoxide	Heptachlor epoxide	1.9	38	Positive
Viscera	12.5	Tech. DDT:	DDT	72.0	900	Positive
		98% DDT	DDD	20.8	260	Positive
		2% DDD 0% DDE	DDE	1.0	12	Doubtful
Muscle	20	Lindane	Lindane	2.5	50	Positive
Muscle	20	Toxaphene	Toxaphene	2.5	50	Negative

technical DDT was preferentially concentrated, especially in the viscera; the original DDT contained only 2% DDD, but 22% of the total insecticide in the viscera of DDT-exposed fish was DDD. An alternate explanation for the abundance of DDD is by dechlorination of DDT (16).

Acknowledgment

The authors are indebted to D. I. Mount, Fisheries Research Biologist, R. A. Taft Sanitary Engineering Center, who provided the laboratory-exposed fish used in this study.

Literature Cited

(1) Blinn, R. C., Gunther, F. A., "Residue Reviews," Vol. 2, p. 99, Academic Press, New York, 1963.
(2) Chen, J. T., *J. Assoc. Offic. Agr. Chemists* **48**, 380 (1965).
(3) Cook, J. W., Williams, S., *Anal. Chem.* **37**, 130 R (1965).
(4) Cueto, C., Jr., *J. Agr. Food Chem.* **8**, 273 (1960).
(5) de Faubert Maunder, M. J., Egan, H., Roburn, J., Hammond, E. W., Thomson, J., *Analyst* **89**, 168 (1964).

(6) De Vries, D. M., Francis, E. K., Porter, P. E., "Abstracts of Papers," 147th Meeting, ACS, April 1964, p. 8A.

(7) Eidelman, M., *J. Assoc. Offic. Agr. Chemists* **42**, 182 (1963).

(8) Giuffrida, L., *J. Assoc. Offic. Agr. Chemists* **48**, 354 (1965).

(9) Jones, L. R., Riddick, J. A., *Anal. Chem.* **24**, 569 (1952).

(10) Kovacs, M., Jr., *J. Assoc. Offic. Agr. Chemists* **46**, 884 (1963).

(11) Mills, P. A., *J. Assoc. Offic. Agr. Chemists* **42**, 734 (1959).

(12) Senate Subcommittee Hearing on Government Operations, Part 1, p. 194, May 23, 1963.

(13) Shell Chemical Co., "Manual of Methods for the Determination of Residues of Shell Pesticides," Anal. Method M M S 53/64.

(14) Smith, D., Eichelberger, J., *J. Water Pollution Control Federation* **37**, 77 (1965).

(15) U.S. Department of Health, Education, and Welfare, Public Health Service, "Report on Investigation of Fish Kills in Lower Mississippi River, Atchafalaya River and Gulf of Mexico," April 6, 1964.

(16) Klein, A. K., Lang, E. P., Datta, P. R., Watts, J. O., Chen, J. T., *J. Assoc. Offic. Agr. Chemists* **47**, 1129 (1964).

RECEIVED January 21, 1966. Mention of commercial products and manufacturers is for identification only and does not imply endorsement by the U.S. Public Health Service.

An Atmospheric Survey for Aerosol and Gaseous 2,4-D Compounds

W. L. BAMESBERGER and D. F. ADAMS

Air Pollution Research Section, College of Engineering Research Division, Washington State University, Pullman, Wash.

A differential sampling system collected 24-hour fractions of airborne aerosol and gaseous herbicides at two Washington field sites for approximately 100 days in 1964. The continuously sampled air impinged on an impaction disk rotating through a collection fluid to retain the droplets of impacted aerosols. Adhering solution was removed from the disk with a Teflon squeegee. The gaseous fraction was collected in a modified midget impinger containing a two-phase n-decane and 3.0% aqueous NaHCO$_3$ solution. The n-decane phases were analyzed directly for 2,4-D esters by electron capture chromatography. The aqueous phases were acidified, extracted, methylated, and the parent 2,4-D compounds were determined by electron capture chromatography as their methyl esters. The system is suitable for differential collection of all types of airborne agrichemicals.

Previous study and evaluation of atmospheric concentrations of 2,4-D esters indicated a need for knowledge of the specific form in which 2,4-D compounds exist in the air. The presence of low volatile, isooctyl 2,4-D in 1963 air samples provided circumstantial evidence of herbicides existing in aerosol form (1). The sampling method did not permit separation of herbicides present into aerosol and gaseous fractions. This study provides quantitative data on the amounts of aerosol and gaseous phenoxy herbicides present in the air. These data were obtained as part of a broad study of the application of phenoxy herbicides near sensitive crops.

The apparatus used to collect aerosol and gaseous fractions from the air during this study has been described in another report (2). The samples were analyzed by electron capture gas chromatography. Phenoxy acids and their salts and amines did not chromatograph under the conditions used and were therefore determined collectively as the methyl esters by a method of hydrolysis, extraction, and esterification similar to that used by Yip (6) for 2,4-D acid. Since this work was completed, a reviewer indicated that a method developed by Getzendaner (4) for determining dalapon residues is applicable to phenoxy acids and salts. Persons doing analytical work involving phenoxy compounds should consider this method.

Since air samples may contain many substances which give a response with the electron capture detector, samples whose first chromatograms indicated the presence of phenoxy herbicides were analyzed on a second column to reduce the possibility of incorrect identification owing to interfering substances. Criteria for determining whether a chromatograph peak represented only one substance were essentially the same as those outlined by Crippen and Smith (3).

Experimental

Gas Chromatograph. Two Wilkens Aerograph Hy-FI chromatographs equipped with electron capture detectors were used interchangeably with a Leeds and Northrup model H recorder. The recorder had a 0-1-mv. span and a ½″ per minute chart speed.

Samples were routinely analyzed on a 5′ x ⅛″ SS column packed with 5% SE-30 silicone gum on 60-80 mesh Chromosorb W. A second column 7′ x 3/16″ SS packed with 5% SE-30 silicone gum on 80-90 mesh Anakrom ABS, was used to verify the presence of isopropyl 2,4-D. Water-pumped nitrogen carrier gas was filtered through a 13X molecular sieve at a flow rate of 25 ml./min. The injection block temperature was 250°C., and column oven temperatures between 190° and 205°C. gave optimum peak separation for the columns used. The detector was removed and cleaned whenever the standing current dropped below 200 with a detector voltage of 60 volts.

Air Sampler. The air-sampling system described by Bamesberger and Adams (2), for the differential collection of aerosol and gaseous fractions of airborne herbicides, consists of a rotating disk impactor for collecting aerosol droplets down to approximately 3-micron diameter, followed by a midget impinger to collect the gaseous fraction (Figure 1). The impactor was specially designed and constructed of glass, Teflon, and stainless steel to prevent contamination of the collection fluid with substances that interfere with electron capture gas chromatography (Figure 2). Incoming air impinges on the impaction disk, which slowly rotates through a fluid well containing n-decane. The impacted droplets wash off into the collection fluid. The disk then passes through a Teflon squeegee to remove the adhering droplets, presenting a smooth surface containing a fluid film upon which the air stream impinges. The entire sampling train was refrigerated at 1°C. to minimize absorbent evaporation and sample loss.

Sampling Sites. Two samplers were operated at the same sites in Pullman and Kennewick, Wash., used in an earlier study (*1*).

Reagents. Contact with rubber or plastics will contaminate reagents. The *n*-decane should come in contact only with metal, Teflon, or glass. Reagents used were: *n*-decane, Humphrey Wilkinson, North Haven, Conn.; $NaHCO_3$, 3% aqueous solution; H_2SO_4, 10% aqueous AR grade; diethyl ether, anhydrous AR grade, Mallinckrodt Chemical Works, St. Louis, Mo.; diazomethane solution, prepared from "Diazald" (*N*-methyl-*N*-nitroso-*p*-toluenesulfonamide) as recommended by manufacturer, Aldrich Chemical Co., Inc., Milwaukee, Wis.

Preparation of Standards. Standards of isopropyl-, butyl-, isooctyl-, and 2-ethylhexyl 2,4-dichlorophenoxy acetate (2,4-D) and 2-ethylhexyl and isooctyl 2,4,5-trichlorophenoxy acetate (2,4,5-T) were prepared by serial dilution of the pure ester in *n*-decane to a final concentration of 1–2 nanograms per microliter.

Standards of the methyl esters of 2-methyl-4-chlorophenoxy acetic acid (MCP), 2,4-D acid, and 2,4,5-T acid were made by preparing dilute solutions of each of the acids in 3% $NaHCO_3$ and treating suitable aliquots with diazomethane as described in the analytical procedure steps 3–8 below. A final standard concentration of 0.5, 2.0, 30 nanograms per microliter for 2,4,5-T, 2,4-D and MCP, respectively, was suitable. Standards containing a 1:1 mixture of isopropyl and butyl 2,4-D and a 25:2:1 mixture of methyl MCP, methyl 2,4-D, and methyl 2,4,5-T were prepared to simplify sample analysis by standard addition.

Sensitivity. The sensitivity of the electron capture detector is related to the electron affinity and, therefore, the chlorine content of the compound. The limit of detection for the various herbicides is defined as the number of nanograms contained in the sample aliquot to provide a peak height twice that of the background noise level. Thus, the limit of detection for methyl MCP, containing one chlorine atom per molecule, is 1.5 nanograms; for methyl 2,4-D, containing two chlorine atoms per molecule, it is 0.2 nanogram; for methyl 2,4,5-T, containing three chlorine atoms per molecule, it is 0.04 nanogram.

The limit of detection for all esters of a given acid is generally the same; however, it should be noted that esters with longer retention times give broader peaks and, therefore, higher limits of detection. For example, the limit of detection for methyl-, isopropyl-, and butyl-2,4-D is 0.2 nanogram while the limit of detection for 2-ethylhexyl 2,4-D is 0.5 nanogram, and for isooctyl 2,4-D it is 1.0 nanogram.

The lowest concentration of herbicide detectable in the atmosphere depends on the sample volume and the collection time. For an absorption sample volume of 5.0 ml. *n*-decane and a collection time of 24 hours, the lowest detectable atmospheric concentration is 1.0 μgram/cu. meter for methyl MCP, 0.14 μgram/cu. meter for the 2,4-D esters, and 0.03 μgram/cu. meter for methyl 2,4,5-T.

Analytical Procedure. The collected sample should consist of approximately 5 ml. *n*-decane and 5 ml. 3% $NaHCO_3$ solution and is treated as follows.

(1) Remove the aqueous phase with a capillary pipet after storing the sample in a refrigerator for several hours.

Figure 1. The rotating disk impactor coupled with a modified midget impinger as a differential collection system

(2) Measure the volume of the decane phase, and analyze an aliquot (usually 5 μliters) for esters by gas chromatography.

(3) Acidify the aqueous phase to approximately pH 2 with 10% H_2SO_4.

(4) Extract the acidified aqueous phase with three 10-ml. aliquots of ether, and discard the aqueous phase.

(5) Evaporate the ether extraction in air or under a stream of N_2 until a volume of 1–2 ml. remains.

(6) Add diazomethane solution dropwise until the yellow color of diazomethane persists for 8–10 minutes.

(7) Evaporate the sample to dryness under a stream of N_2 or allow the sample to stand in the hood overnight to dry. Drying removes volatile contaminants; however, heating to dryness should be avoided to prevent loss of esters.

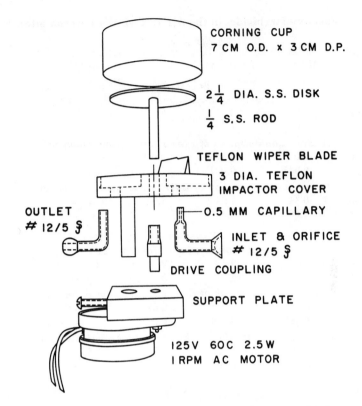

CORNING CUP
7 CM O.D. x 3 CM D.P.

$2\frac{1}{4}$ DIA. S.S. DISK

$\frac{1}{4}$ S.S. ROD

TEFLON WIPER BLADE

3 DIA. TEFLON
IMPACTOR COVER

OUTLET
#12/5 ƽ

0.5 MM CAPILLARY

INLET & ORIFICE
12/5 ƽ

DRIVE COUPLING

SUPPORT PLATE

125V 60C 2.5W
I RPM AC MOTOR

Figure 2.   The rotating disk impactor, disassembled

(8) Dissolve the sample in a suitable aliquot (2 or 5 ml.) of *n*-decane and analyze an aliquot (usually 5 μliters) on the gas chromatograph.

An aliquot of the suitable standard (1 or 2 μliters) is chromatographed with a second aliquot of the sample to provide positive identification of ester by peak reinforcement. This also provides a record of sample and sample plus standard peak heights. The standard peak height is obtained for calculations by subtraction.

Results and Discussion

Twenty-four hour air samples collected near Pullman and Kennewick Highlands, Wash., contained quantitatively detectable phenoxy herbicides on more than 75% of 113 days sampled between April 16 and August 6, 1964. The number of days each ester was detected, the average concentration of each ester during the total sampling period, and the maximum 24-hour concentration of each ester detected were calculated for the rotating disk impactor and midget impinger fractions of the daily samples collected at Pullman and Kennewick. These results are shown

Table I. Phenoxy Herbicides in the Air at Two Washington Sites, 1964

Collector	2,4-D Ester				2,4,5-T Ester
	Methyl	Isopropyl	Butyl	Isooctyl	Methyl
PULLMAN					
Number of Days Found (out of 99)					
Impactor	3	29	13	——	9
Impinger	5	1	——	——	——
Average Concentration of Ester Found, μgram/cu. meter					
Impactor	0.006	0.116	0.059	——	0.045
Impinger	0.031	0.007	——	——	——
Maximum Concentration of Ester Found, μgram/cu. meter					
Impactor	0.34	1.96	1.04	——	3.38
Impinger	1.00	0.69	——	——	——
KENNEWICK					
Number of Days Found (out of 102)					
Impactor	5	39	22	1	14
Impinger	4	15	5	——	7
Average Concentration of Ester Found, μgram/cu. meter					
Impactor	0.017	0.073	0.079	0.005	0.012
Impinger	0.055	0.078	0.028	——	0.013
Maximum Concentration of Ester Found, μgram/cu. meter					
Impactor	0.47	0.72	0.82	0.53	0.63
Impinger	5.12	1.30	1.27	——	0.78

in Table I. MCP, 2-ethylhexyl 2,4-D, 2-ethylhexyl 2,4,5-T, and isooctyl 2,4,5-T were not detected during the sampling period.

Data on the methyl esters include salts and amines which were converted to the methyl esters with diazomethane for analysis. It should be noted that methylation provides data on the sum of all salts and amines of each phenoxy acid present rather than data on specific formulations.

In a paper published after most of our analytical work was completed, Pursley and Schall (5) described a BCl_3-methanol reagent for transesterifying 2,4-D and 2,4,5-T esters. Preliminary investigations in our laboratory indicate that it may be superior to diazomethane as a methylating agent.

Figures 3 and 4 show the daily fluctuations in atmospheric concentrations of aerosols collected in the rotating disk impactor, gases collected in the midget impinger, and the daily temperature fluctuations. Isopropyl 2,4-D ester was detected most frequently at both sites. Most of the phenoxy herbicides collected at the Pullman site were collected in the RDI, which indicates that they were present primarily as larger aerosol droplets. Since the hotter, dryer climate at Kennewick encourages volatilization of weed sprays, it is not surprising that the midget impinger

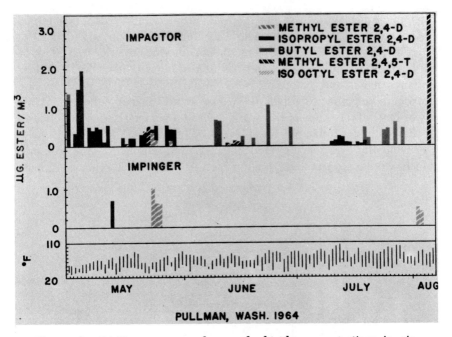

Figure 3.   24-Hour average phenoxy herbicide concentrations in air,
Pullman, Wash.

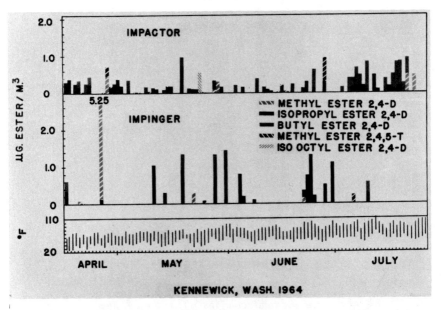

Figure 4.   24-Hour average phenoxy herbicide concentrations in air,
Kennewick, Wash.

fraction, representing smaller aerosol droplets and gases, contained phenoxy herbicides more frequently at Kennewick than at Pullman.

Since peaks not identifiable as phenoxy herbicides appeared in many of the samples, qualitative standards of systox, malathion, DDT, aldrin, lindane, BHC, and chlordan were chromatographed to establish approximate retention times for these insecticides in our columns. While it was beyond the scope of this work, quantitative detection of insecticides in these samples appeared feasible.

Difficulty was encountered in preparing chromatograph columns which would separate the phenoxy esters from each other and from

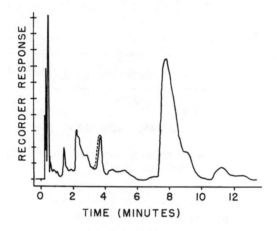

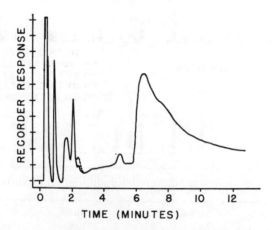

Figure 5. Chromatograms of a field sample on two different columns. The dotted lines show the change in curve on addition of a fixed aliquot of isopropyl 2,4-D ester standard.

interfering substances. Usable column packings were produced using a rotary evaporator. However, better results were obtained by gentle, manual stirring while evaporating over a steam bath. Chloroform was used as the solvent for SE-30 in preparing the column packings.

Some of the field samples contained a substance which was not separated from isopropyl 2,4-D ester on a 5′ x ⅛″ column containing 5% SE-30 on 60–80 mesh Chromosorb W. The presence of an interfering substance was indicated by peak broadening with little increase in peak height on adding isopropyl 2,4-D ester standard to the field sample. This is shown in the upper chromatogram in Figure 5. Efforts to separate the interfering substance from isopropyl 2,4-D on columns containing QF-1 and DC-200 separately and in combination on 80–90 mesh Anakrom ABS were unsuccessful. Separation adequate to determine isopropyl 2,4-D quantitatively was accomplished on a 7′ x 3/16″ column containing 5% SE-30 on 80–90 mesh Anakrom ABS as shown in the lower chromatogram in Figure 5.

Acknowledgment

This work was supported in part by the Hay and Grain Fund of the Washington State Department of Agriculture. The authors gratefully acknowledge the field work of Frank Lampson.

Literature Cited

(1) Adams, D. F., Jackson, C. M., Bamesberger, W. L., *Weeds* **12**, 280 (1964).
(2) Bamesberger, W. L., Adams, D. F., *J. Agr. Food Chem.* **13**, 552 (1965).
(3) Crippen, R. C., Smith, C. E., *J. Gas Chromatog.* **3**, 37 (1965).
(4) Getzendaner, M. E., *J. Assoc. Official Agr. Chemists* **46**, 269 (1963).
(5) Pursley, P. L., Schall, E. D., *J. Assoc. Official Agr. Chemists* **48**, 327 (1965).
(6) Yip, G., *J. Assoc. Official Agr. Chemists* **45**, 367 (1962).

RECEIVED September 27, 1965.

19

Fate and Persistence of Organic Pesticides in the Environment

C. H. VAN MIDDELEM

Pesticide Research Laboratory, Food Science Department, University of Florida, Gainesville, Fla.

The persistence and ultimate fate of pesticides in the food, soil, water, and air of man's environment is affected by such interrelated factors as volatility, solubility, ultraviolet irradiation, surface adsorption, systemic action, hydrolysis, chemical rearrangement, etc. The combined weathering action of rain, wind, temperature, and humidity exerts considerable influence on the exposed pesticide breakdown. However, the fate of pesticides in soils also depends on their chemical characteristics, soil type, moisture, microorganisms, cultural practices, etc. Pesticides usually find their way into surface and ground waters as a result of agricultural land drainage or industrial waste discharges. The persistence of a pesticide in ambient air is a function of the toxicant's properties, mode of application, and existing atmospheric conditions.

In varying degrees, pesticides may be contaminating and accumulating in man's food supplies as well as the soil, water, and air of his environment. During the past decade considerable information on the fate and persistence of pesticides has been investigated. By far the greatest emphasis in the past has been placed on man's food products, and consequently the majority of the available research has been concentrated on this aspect. Recently, however, increased emphasis has been placed on the fate and persistence of pesticides in soil, water, and air as well as the food products of the environment. This trend is encouraging since only by studying the total effects of the pesticide on our environment can we ultimately come to grips with all the possible adverse ramifications attributable to the use of pesticides. The presence of these toxicants in soil, water, and air does not constitute a possible immediate health hazard as in consumable foodstuffs; however, the long-range adverse potentialities are more subtle and perhaps ultimately more significant.

As pointed out by Westlake and San Antonio (46) such factors as temperature, light, humidity, air movement, volatility of the compounds, and microorganism activity are influencing the breakdown and mechanical dispersion of residues on plant surfaces and in soils. However, within plants and animals, probably the most important single factor in pesticide breakdown and transformation is through enzymatic action. As shown in Figure 1, when a pesticide is applied to plants, animals, soils, water or air, there are many factors that may effect chemical changes, and the rates of such alterations will depend on the nature of the compound and the particular environmental conditions to which

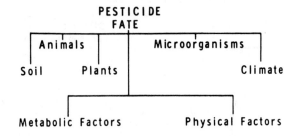

Figure 1. *Environmental factors affecting the fate of pesticides*

it is subjected. Various metabolic and physical factors will influence the fate or rate of degradation of the parent compound. The metabolic factors, as illustrated in Figure 2, affect the fate of the pesticides and involve either molecular alteration or migration phenomena. Molecular changes may be precipitated by chemical reactions such as oxidation,

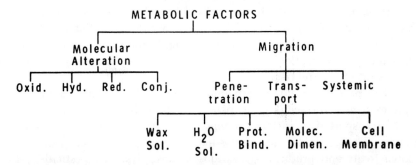

Figure 2. *Metabolic factors affecting the fate and persistence of pesticides*

hydrolysis, reduction, and conjugation. Migration in plants or animals may be considered to occur either through simple penetration or via a more involved systemic transport mechanism. Systemic transports are usually controlled by such factors as lipid solubility, cell membrane permeability, water solubility, protein binding, and the size and configuration of the toxicant molecule involved.

The physical factors (Figure 3) affecting the fate and persistence of pesticides in our environment are primarily climatic parameters such as sunlight, temperature, humidity, rain, wind, and the toxicant's vapor pressure (13, 42). Other important physical factors involve the plant's or animal's growth which will dilute and occasionally store pesticides in restricted sites, such as in oil or fat depots.

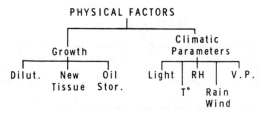

Figure 3. Physical factors affecting the fate and persistence of pesticides

As Figure 4 shows, pesticide persistence or disappearance relationships on and in crops will be affected by the type of toxicant involved, its dosage and formulation, as well as the number of applications. The crop's foliage development and growth characteristics and the type of insect to be controlled will be contributory factors in pesticide persistence. Of prime importance will be the local weather conditions to which the chemical will be subjected over a long period of time.

Pesticides and their metabolic products move through treated plants, soil, water, and air primarily by such interrelated weathering factors as rain, wind, and sunlight. An example of this interrelationship of climatic factors and the mode of pesticide movement transfer, transformation, volatilization, and eventual breakdown in our environment is illustrated by Figure 5.

The pesticide residues remaining in man's food and in animal feed may exist as a surface deposit, penetrate the cuticle to a limited extent, or be transported to various sections of the plant or animal by systemic action. The pesticide, once deposited, is usually metabolized or broken down to its end products by various means. Systemic pesticides often exhibit complex breakdown patterns which can differ somewhat, depending on whether a plant or mammalian metabolic mechanism is involved;

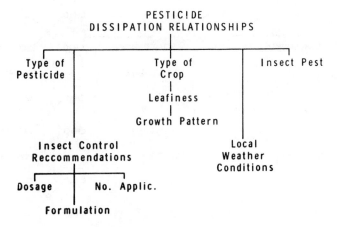

Figure 4. *Relationships affecting the disappearance of pesticides*

this is illustrated by the metabolism of dimethoate in Figure 6. Unlike many organophosphates, this pesticide readily passes into the aqueous tissues of plants, where it undergoes oxidation and hydrolysis. The selective toxicity of dimethoate may depend on the ability of the animal to attack the C-N bond more vigorously than the insect. As a result

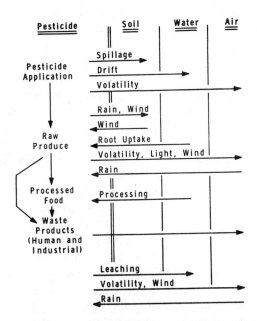

Figure 5. *Routes of pesticide loss in the environment*

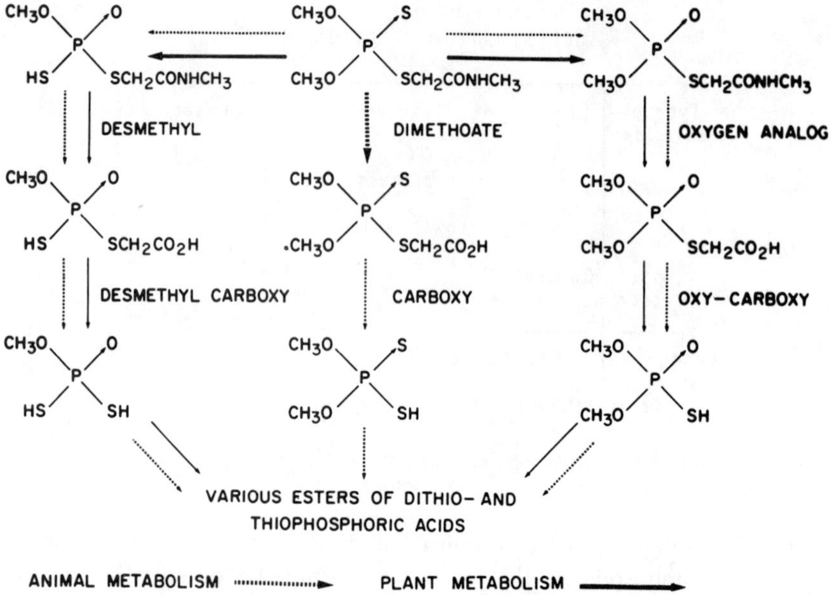

Figure 6. Dimethoate metabolism in plants and animals

of oxidation and hydrolysis, various metabolites are formed, of which the oxygenated analog is the most important from a purely toxicological viewpoint. Not only is this analog much more toxic to mammals, but it is also considerably more water soluble than the parent compound. It is believed that the oxygen analog is metabolized enzymatically within the plant and nonenzymatically on the plant surface. Dauterman et al. (10) reported that the important pathways for dimethoate in plant foliage are either to the oxygen carboxy and to a lesser extent to the desmethyl derivatives. In mammalian systems, however, these metabolites are relatively minor, with the primary product reported to be the carboxy derivative. Apparently the carboxy metabolite is not produced by applying dimethoate to plant leaves.

Phorate (O,O-diethyl S-ethylthiomethyl phosphorodithioate), although a systemic pesticide, is per se a relatively weak cholinesterase inhibitor. However, when the compound is chemically oxidized in nature, the final oxidized product (oxygen analog sulfone) is considerably more potent as a cholinesterase inhibitor. Fortunately, however, this oxidized metabolite is relatively unstable and does not seem to accumulate to any significant degree. Investigations have proved that oxidation attacks the coordinate sulfur and thioether linkages.

Although most of the present pesticides are not true systemics, some may undergo somewhat similar chemical transformations and degradation, resulting occasionally in metabolites as toxic or more so than the . parent compound.

An example of a few of these reactions that occur in our environment with several commonly used pesticides is illustrated in Figures 7–11. Fleck (15) has illustrated in Figure 7 that ultraviolet light catalyzes the decomposition of DDT. In the presence of air, one of the decomposition products is 4,4'-dichlorobenzophenone. However, when air is absent, 2,3-dichloro-1,1,4,4-tetrakis-(p-chlorophenyl)-2-butene is formed. This compound, through subsequent oxidation, may be converted into 4,4'-dichlorobenzophenone. In mammals 2,2-bis(p-chlorophenyl) acetic acid (DDA) has been identified and shown to be excreted in the feces and urine. The mechanism of formation of DDA is believed to be an initial dehydrochlorination to DDE, which is then hydrolyzed to DDA as shown in Figure 8. Mattson *et al.* (29) found both DDT and DDE in most samples of human fat, and Walker *et al.* (44) noted low levels of these same compounds in restaurant meals.

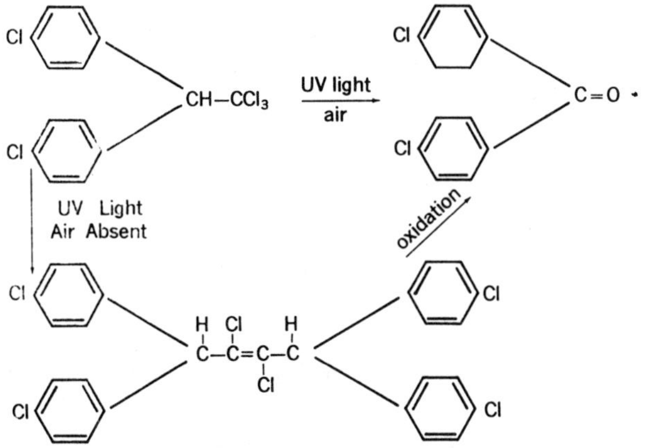

Figure 7.   Effect of ultraviolet light and air on DDT decomposition

The first of the organophosphorus insecticides to gain widespread use was parathion which is still an important commercial pesticide. This compound (Figure 9) is converted to the S-ethyl isomer by heating whereas paraoxon, a more toxic compound, is formed by enzymic action in plants. In animals, the additional products, p-nitrophenol and p-aminophenol, are also formed. At present, little information appears to be available regarding the decomposition products of parathion in soils.

Davidow and Radomski (11) found heptachlor epoxide as a metabolite of heptachlor in animals, as indicated in Figure 10. This report appears to be the first record of epoxidation of a foreign organic com-

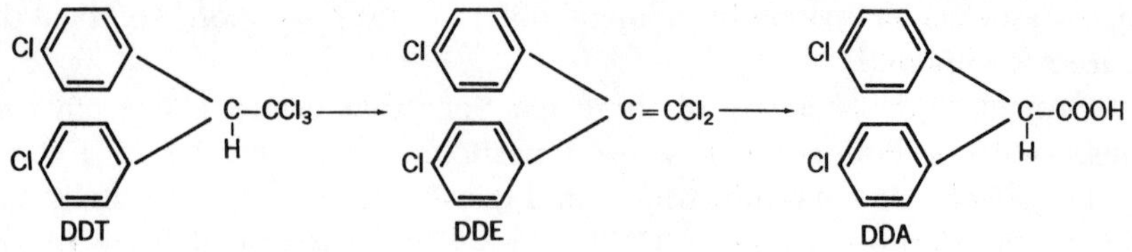

Figure 8.   Dehydrochlorination and hydrolysis of DDT to DDE and DDA in mammals

pound in an animal body. Ely *et al.* (*14*) detected heptachlor epoxide in the milk of cows fed technical heptachlor, and Gannon and Bigger (*16*) found the epoxide in soil treated with this insecticide. Bann *et al.* (*4*) reported the conversion of aldrin to dieldrin (Figure 11); this is another example of epoxidation in animals and verified the storage of dieldrin in fat. This conversion has been found to occur also in plants and in soils.

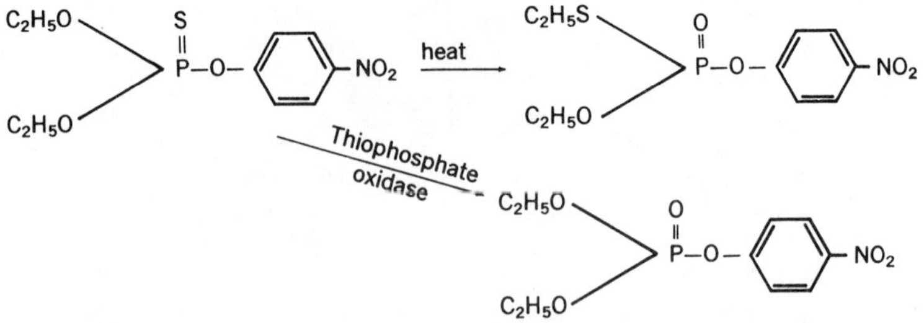

Figure 9.   Conversion of parathion to paraoxon by heat and enzymatic action

Space does not permit further discussion of the fate of various organic pesticides in man's environment. Some of the fate reactions involving the older pesticides have been extensively studied, but the picture is far from complete, even for such compounds as DDT and parathion. However, increasingly greater emphasis on more fundamental research is being made, particularly with the recently introduced pesticides, to determine all their possible metabolites under varying environmental conditions.

Food

It is well known that man's food may contain residues of various types of pesticides which may actually approach the legal tolerance limit or are significantly below it. However, as stated by Crosby (*9*), under practical conditions, a significant proportion of the pesticide applied directly to food crops is immediately lost to the environment such as to the air, soil, and inedible plant parts. Considerable research effort has been and continues to be underway to determine the breakdown of various classes of pesticides on various commodities and under different cultural and climatic conditions. Persistence of a pesticide might be considered as resistance to removal from a food product other than deliberate removal by man. Consequently, persistence is related to the length of time that a pesticide residue resists removal under conditions which may not be directly controlled by man. Persistence of a pesticide

Heptachlor   Heptachlor Epoxide

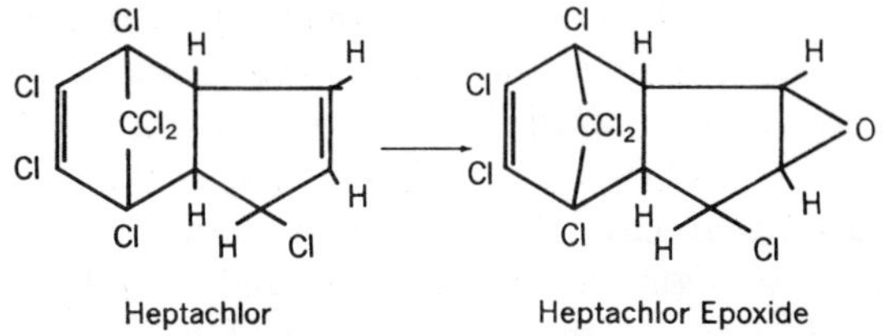

Figure 10.   Epoxidation of heptachlor in plants, soils, and animals

is associated with the host as well as with the chemical. As Cook states (8), one of the basic criteria for determining pesticide persistence is an adequate method of analysis which is designed for the proper residue and is sensitive enough to determine a significant level of residue. The method must also be judged by the general toxicity of the compound sought and proved to be applicable to the food product being analyzed. Adequate methodology is an important aspect of measuring persistence and one which has not always been properly considered.

Persistence is the net result of many interacting factors, but chemical properties of the pesticide can play a dominant role. Volatility, solubility, stability to ultraviolet irradiation, tendency to adsorb onto or dissolve into tissue surfaces, ease of hydrolysis, sensitivity to humidity, potentiality to polymerize with or without ultraviolet irradiation, possible isomerization or other molecular rearrangement are all important chemical properties which play a significant role in persistence. Weather conditions such as wind, rain, amount and intensity of light, air temperature, and humidity play important roles. Rainfall is usually con-

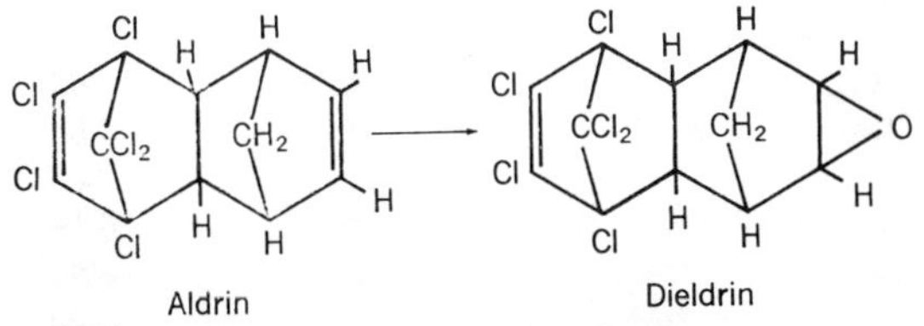

Aldrin   Dieldrin

Figure 11.   Epoxidation of aldrin in plants, soils, and animals

sidered the most severe of the weathering agents, and the amount of pesticide residue removed in this manner will depend largely on its chemical characteristics, the type of plant surface, the period of surface weathering, and the amount of toxicant originally deposited. High surface temperatures plus low humidity tend to reduce the effectiveness of pesticides more rapidly than low temperatures plus high humidity. High temperatures increase volatilization, resulting in greater pesticide loss. Under field conditions it is often difficult to separate the effect of temperature and sunlight on pesticide breakdown. The pesticide type and its particular formulation can be dominant factors in the overall sunlight effect on the disappearance rate of the toxicant.

Several years ago Van Middelem and Waites (42) studied the effect of various climatic factors on the breakdown of DDT residues on turnip and mustard greens. These workers attempted to study the separate effect of sunlight, wind, and rain, followed by varying combinations of two or more of these factors. In both experiments, as indi-

Table I. DDT on Turnip Greens
p.p.m.

Treatment No.	Weathering Factors	Interval Since Application			
		2 days	7 days	14 days	21 days
1	Sun	17.84	7.13	4.33	3.08
2	Sun + rain	14.40	5.14	3.16	2.48
3	Sun + wind	20.04	8.99	7.41	3.09
4	Rain	15.80	4.22	2.57	2.18
5	Rain + wind	15.15	6.74	3.17	1.98
6	Wind	19.40	10.33	6.18	3.65
7	Sun + wind + rain	10.40	4.38	3.05	1.61
Rainfall, inches			0.76	0.00	0.01
Sun, solar radiation			2773	1703	2701
Wind, miles			300	295	410

Table II. DDT on Mustard Greens
p.p.m.

Treatment No.	Weathering Factors	Interval Since Application		
		7 days	14 days	21 days
1	Sun	14.46	9.86	4.44
2	Sun + rain	14.17	9.37	3.16
3	Sun + wind	19.57	11.69	7.67
4	Rain	16.89	11.53	7.32
5	Rain + wind	11.71	9.83	6.34
6	Wind	17.66	17.06	7.43
7	Sun + wind + rain	14.76	8.14	2.69
Rainfall, inches		0.11	0.00	0.00
Sun, solar radiation		2704	1890	1367
Wind, miles		170	205	270

cated in Tables I and II, the combined effect of sun + wind + rain usually resulted in the greatest breakdown of the pesticide when sampled 1, 2, or 3 weeks after the DDT application. Table I illustrates the effect of 0.76 inch of natural rainfall on turnip greens 7 days after application. In the mustard green experiment (Table II) sunlight, as a single weathering factor, appeared to reduce the DDT residues more than wind or rain. Of course, it should be noted that there was only 0.11 inch of natural rainfall deposited on the mustard greens during the entire experiment. The interaction of sun + rain reduced the deposits more than the other combinations of sun + wind or rain + wind. It can readily be determined from experiments such as these that marked residue variations can occur in different parts of the country, owing primarily to unusual local climatic conditions during the growing season.

The characteristics of the plant on which the chemical is applied produce great differences in residue concentrations. The rate of growth, density of the foliage, shape of the plant, partial protection of edible portions from weathering by leaves, surface fuzz, the rate the plant produces a waxy surface, enzyme systems, rate of metabolism, etc., all may cause significant effects on chemical residues in or on growing plants. When animal products are considered, different but somewhat similar factors affect pesticide persistence and breakdown. For example, aldrin converts to dieldrin, heptachlor to its epoxide, thiophosphates to their sulfoxides and sulfones, both in animals and plants. However, the speed of these reactions and the disappearance rates of reaction products can and often do vary considerably, depending on the particular biological environment.

The penetrated or persistent residue remaining on a food or feed may be taken up by animals and eventually transferred to meat, eggs, and dairy products. However, when the plant product containing the pesticide residue will be eaten directly by man, the normal commercial processing procedures of trimming, washing, and cooking will further reduce the persistent residues that remained following weathering. In the field, during the harvesting operations, residues on certain crops are materially reduced by normal trimming and stripping operations. For example, the normal removal of the outer leaves of cabbage and the field-trimming of celery stalks usually will reduce the existing residues by several factors. Numerous studies have been conducted to determine the effect on pesticide residue removal of commercial washing operations. In a commercial packinghouse, water washing removed 40% of the initial residue remaining on celery cut two hours after an emulsifiable application. However, subsequent samples taken 2, 7, and 14 days following an application resulted in 25, 20, and 15% removal, respectively, of the original parathion deposited. Therefore, it was concluded that the longer parathion is allowed to "weather" on a crop such as celery, the more difficult it is to remove significant quantities of the remaining residue deposits by conventional water washings. This point is illustrated by Figure 12 showing parathion-treated celery which was subjected by Van Middelem and Wilson (43) to normal packinghouse water washing. It can be noted that as the samplings approached the

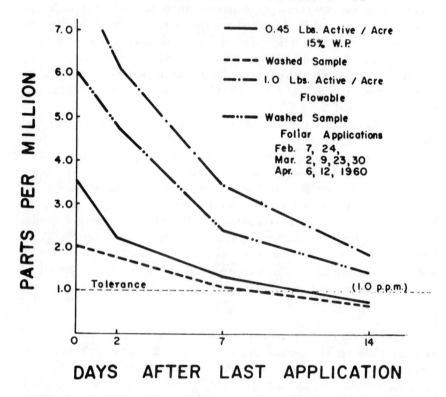

DAYS AFTER LAST APPLICATION

Figure 12. *Effect of washing on parathion residues remaining on commercial celery*

14-days-after-application period, less and less parathion deposits were removed by the washing operation. Table III summarizes a study by Thompson and Van Middelem (40), which compares the effect of packinghouse washing with and without surfactants on the removal of parathion residues from tomatoes, green beans, and mustard greens. Water washing alone was found to remove about 65% of the parathion residues on mustard greens sprayed 12 hours prior. Both detergents reduced the parathion residues significantly over water washing on all three vegetables. Table IV illustrates a similar study by these investigators involving toxaphene on four vegetables, indicating also that the detergents

Table III. Comparison of Washing with and without Surfactants on Removal of Parathion from Vegetables

Washing Treatment	Parathion, p.p.m.		
	Tomatoes	Green Beans	Mustard Greens
None	0.30	2.31	25.9
Water	0.25	1.47	8.9
0.1% Polyether Alcohol	0.25	1.13	4.4
1.0% Neutral Soap	0.27	1.12	3.4

removed considerably more toxaphene residues than the water wash alone. For example, the toxaphene residues on mustard greens which were harvested 12 hours after treatment, were reduced 57% by water washing alone and 90% following the detergent washings. The effect of commercial packinghouse washing on toxaphene residues on celery is noted by Van Middelem and Wilson (43) in Figure 13. Significant reductions in toxaphene residues caused by washing were noted, following two dosage levels applied to the celery in the field. Apparently the removal of DDT from mustard greens by water washing is more difficult. Somers and Mercer (38) report a study (Table V) which indicates that only 12.6% of the DDT residue was removed by water washing alone whereas 44.4% of the residue was removed by detergent washing followed by blanching.

Normal canning procedures involving blanching, pressure cooking, and freezing have been investigated to determine their effect on residue removal from fruits and vegetables. In one study, parathion residues were reduced from 30 to 100% by cooking whereas blanching and canning operations reduced parathion residues in certain vegetables by 40 to 95%. When Britten and Fairing (6) subjected three pesticides in pureed fruits and vegetables to thermal processing, pesticide losses ranged from 51–95% (Table VI). Two DDT isomers were subjected by Tressler (41) to 20 minutes of thermal processing in canned tomato juice, and

Table IV. Comparison of Washing with and without Surfactants on Removal of Toxaphene from Vegetables

Washing Treatment	Toxaphene, p.p.m.			
	Tomatoes	Green Beans	Celery	Mustard Greens
None	3.69	31.07	60.44	233.64
Water	3.31	24.91	25.81	100.02
0.1% Polyether Alcohol	3.19	13.18	76.99	23.09
1.0% Neutral Soap	3.27	12.25	16.42	20.77

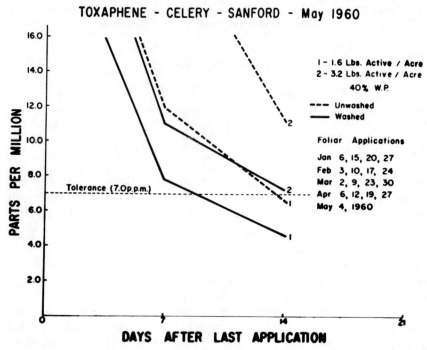

Figure 13. Effect of washing on toxaphene residues remaining on commercial celery, Sanford, Fla.

Table VII indicates that the recoveries were approximately 35%. It should be noted that many of these older residue data were obtained by analytical procedures which were not always specific for the molecule under consideration, and therefore small changes in molecular structure may have occurred during the processing procedures.

Soils

Soils are contaminated either through aerial spraying of crops or by applying pesticides directly. As Lichtenstein pointed out (23), the

Table V. Removal of Radioactive DDT from Spinach Using Varied Washing Conditions

Treatment	Residue Level, p.p.m.	Residue Removed (Percent)
No Wash	4.37	0.0
Cold Water Wash	3.82	12.6
Cold Water Wash and Blanch	3.31	24.2
Detergent Wash	2.75	37.0
Detergent Wash and Blanch	2.42	44.4

persistence of pesticides in soil depends on the physical properties and chemical reactivity of the toxicant, the soil type, moisture, temperature, microorganisms, cover crops, degree of cultivation, and mode and formulation of the pesticide.

Insecticides such as the chlorinated hydrocarbons are usually more persistent in soils than those of the organophosphorus or carbamate classes.

Large differences exist within each classification of pesticides whose half lives in soil range from a few days to several months or even years. One current problem with soil residues involves pesticides such as aldrin, dieldrin, or heptachlor that are applied to soils to control soil insects such as wireworms. There are recent reports of residues appearing in milk at very low levels, and it is suspected that the forage may be picking up minute pesticide residues from the soil and passing it on to the cow. Lichtenstein and Schulz (25) have recently reported residues of aldrin, dieldrin, heptachlor, and heptachlorepoxide on cucumbers and alfalfa that were grown on soils previously treated with aldrin and heptachlor. The fact that no aerial applications had been applied to these crops indicates that these pesticides were taken up by the cucumber and alfalfa plant to a very limited extent. It is well known that root crops such as potatoes, radishes, and carrots can absorb residues from the soil previously treated with these persistent pesticides.

Table VI. Effect of Thermal Processing on Pesticide Residues in Pureed Fruits and Vegetables

Pesticide	Average Pesticide Loss, %
Methoxychlor	95
DDD	51
Parathion	63.2

As an example of differences in soil residue persistence between the organophosphates and chlorinated hydrocarbon pesticides, parathion and malathion residues were present at the 0.1 p.p.m. level within 8 days of application whereas aldrin [according to Lichtenstein (23)] when applied at the same concentration, persisted 5 months longer as did aldrin and dieldrin at 40% of the applied dosage. Decker et al. (12) report that aldrin and dieldrin residues in soils never exceeded 13.2% of the total applied when tested one year after the last application. Other workers (24) have reported that on a loamy soil, under existing weather conditions, aldrin and dieldrin residues were present at a level of approximately 20% of the total applied insecticidal dosage over a 5-year period.

Table VII. Effect of Thermal Processing on Two DDT Isomers Added to Canned Tomato Juice

DDT Added, mg.		Heating at 212°F., min.	DDT Recovery,%	
o,p	p,p¹		o,p	p,p¹
0	0	0	0	0
0.70	0	0	104	0
0.70	0	20	37	0
0	0.70	0	0	97
0	0.70	20	0	31
0.37	0.70	0	113	90
0.30	0.70	20	63	31

Soils vary greatly in composition and reactivity. Many complex and dynamic processes occur continuously in most soils composed primarily of mineral and organic matter, water, and air. The soil atmosphere is composed of oxygen, carbon dioxide, nitrogen, and several minor gases whereas the mineral fraction varies in amounts of sand, silt, and clay and in types and amounts of clay minerals. Moreover, hydration and base saturation of the clay minerals also vary considerably. The organic matter and mineral colloids present in the soil contribute directly and indirectly to the extremely active nature of pesticide-soil systems. Since soil water contains many soluble compounds, it serves as an essential medium for many chemical and physical processes. The extreme complexity of these soil systems has been the primary reason that so few fundamental studies have been undertaken involving the ultimate fate of pesticides in soils.

Factors affecting the movement and persistence of pesticides in soils can involve leaching, fixation by soil colloids, chemical and microbial decomposition, adsorption, photodecomposition, etc.

Insecticides tend to persist longer in soils of high organic matter. In fact, in muck soils (50% or more organic matter), residues have been found bound to soil particles to such an extent that the same amount of toxicant is less effective in muck soil as compared with a sandy type. It has been noted that pesticides are absorbed into crops most readily from sandy soils and least from muck soils. Moisture enhances the release of volatile pesticides from soil particles and also influences the breakdown of other toxicants. Microbial attack has been found to oxidize aldrin to dieldrin, and parathion in the presence of yeast is reduced to the nontoxic aminoparathion in soil. As might be expected, increased soil temperatures can dramatically increase the rate of pesticide loss owing to volatilization and increased breakdown. Cover crops, such as alfalfa, can decrease pesticide volatility from soil whereas cultivation can accelerate the process. There are increasing reports of limited translocation of some chlorinated hydrocarbons from soils into edible parts of crops. Root crops such as potatoes, radishes, and carrots may absorb limited quantities of pesticide residues from the soil.

Herbicides present a special residue problem since many are applied directly to the soil as selective pre-emergence sprays and as nonselective soil sterilants. Sheets and Danielson (37) report that the factors affecting the movement and persistence of herbicides in soils include leaching, fixation by soil colloids, chemical and microbial decomposition, and volatilization. Persistence of several groups of herbicides in the soil is related to halogenation of the benzene ring, which has been demonstrated for certain chlorinated phenoxyacetic acids, carbamates, and phenylureas. Alexander and Aleem (3) indicated that the resistance of chlorinated phenoxyalkyl carboxylic acid herbicides or their derivatives to microbial degradation was governed by the position of the halogen rather than by the number of halogens on the ring and that the linkage and type of aliphatic side chain also influenced susceptibility to microbial breakdown. MacRae and Alexander (28) reported that the susceptibility of chlorobenzoates to microbial decomposition is related to the number of chlorine atoms on the aromatic ring. In the final analysis, according to Ward and Upchurch (45), complex structural relationships may mediate a herbicide's phytotoxic activity and can be presumed to involve a number of types of adsorptive sites. Such complex systems involving the herbicide, plant, and soil, can be understood only as the successive types of adsorptive sites involved in a given reaction are identified and the adsorptive mechanisms are clarified. The activity of most herbicides varies with soil composition since many are adsorbed by colloidal particles. Therefore, the variations in herbicidal activity can be attributed to differences in adsorptive capacity of the mineral and organic colloids in soils. The solubilities of pesticides in soils materially affect their degree of leaching. Minarik (32) points out that the various salts of 2,4-D are more soluble in water than the acid whereas salts of heavy metals, such as iron or copper, are less soluble than the acid. The adsorptive capacity of soils is influenced not only by the percentage of organic matter but by the amounts and types of clay minerals. The adsorption process is influenced by temperature and the nature of the solvent whereas the adsorptive characteristics of a pesticide are influenced by the pH of the solution. Therefore, since these factors influence adsorption, they must also materially affect the movement of herbicides in soils. Little is known about the direct effect of light on the breakdown of herbicides and other pesticides in soil. However, Hill *et al.* (21) postulate that in dry areas of the western United States some toxicants may be inactivated by ultraviolet irradiation.

Water

Apparently pesticides occur widely in surface water and to a lesser extent in ground water. Often pesticide levels of one part per billion or less originate from agricultural land drainage, industrial waste discharges, purposeful pesticide applications to water, and even by mere accidents. According to Nicholson and Thoman (35) the persistence of a pesticide will partially determine its impact (taste, odor, toxicity) upon a domestic water supply. This impact is related not only to the length of time required for a pesticide to become degraded or immobilized, but it also determines the length of time a water supply will be subjected to its presence from a renewable source, such as the surface of contaminated soil or an industry. Occasionally a pesticide will occur in water as a "slug" that rapidly moves downstream whereas at other times it may become chronic at low levels. Middleton and Lichtenberg (30) were the first to use chemical methods to determine pesticides in water, and they reported the presence of DDT in rivers and lakes by using infrared spectroscopy.

Thoman and Nicholson (39) reported that the following pesticides have been found in surface water in trace amounts: DDT, endrin, dieldrin, TDE, toxaphene, BHC, parathion, diazinon, 2,4-D, fenac, and 2,4,5-T. The U.S. Public Health Service (USPHS) has shown that agricultural usage of pesticides can result in widespread low level surface water contamination through land runoff. According to Nicholson et al. (33, 34), Grzenda et al. (18), and Lauer (22), this surface water contamination caused by land runoff seldom exceeds a concentration of 1 part per billion. Some pesticides, particularly the insecticides, are highly toxic to fishes and are readily detected in domestic water supplies when they are present in concentrations sufficient to kill fish. Pesticides, such as toxaphene and BHC, can impart undesirable taste and odor to water at levels of 5 and 20 p.p.b., respectively, according to Rosen and Middleton (36).

At present, there are generally two basic situations involving water supply contamination by pesticides: chronic contamination, which is usually at levels of less than 1 p.p.b., and short term and higher level contamination. The chronic contamination results from the more or less continuous bleed-off of pesticide residues from land and continuous or periodic discharges from industrial wastes. The second or high level contamination may involve accidents, massive runoff from land following heavy rains, or direct pesticide applications to water to control unwanted fish, insects, or aquatic plants.

Recently the USPHS reported a study by Grzenda and Nicholson (19) involving the distribution and magnitude of insecticide residues in a watershed and its adjacent cotton farms. In addition to water samples, residue results were obtained from the farm soils, stream sediments, and aquatic biota. The residues found were the highest in the farm soils and the lowest in the adjacent stream water. Toxaphene, DDT, and BHC residues were consistently found in farm soil and fish. DDT and DDE were the principal contaminants found in the stream mud and bottom fauna. Conversely, toxaphene and BHC were the primary residues noted in stream water. Bowman (5) concluded that the occurrence of DDT as only an occasional water pollutant is probably related to its exceptionally low solubility in water and its strong tendency to be sorbed by a variety of materials. The residues of toxaphene, DDT, and BHC in the streams were well below levels thought to be acutely toxic to fish according to Henderson *et al.* (20). Aquatic invertebrates are known to be less susceptible to toxaphene and DDT poisoning than are fish, but less is known about the toxicity of BHC to the invertebrates.

In the 1963 watershed study reported by Grzenda and Nicholson (19), the adjacent cotton field soils containing the following pesticide concentration ranges were reported in parts per million: toxaphene (0.16–1.60), DDT (0.02–0.53), and BHC (0.01–0.38). The untreated water from the adjoining streams during the spring and summer contained the following pesticide concentration ranges in parts per trillion: toxaphene (0–176), BHC (0–254), DDT (0–9), and DDE (0–4). Residues of DDT and DDE in mud collected from the basin ranged in parts per million as follows: DDT (0.006–4.62), and DDE (0.002–1.77). The bottom fauna in this basin contained the following ranges of pesticides in parts per billion: DDT (20–500), DDE (10–610), and toxaphene (0–1100). Fish collected from this basin contained the following residues in their edible portions and reported in parts per million: DDT (0.04–0.93), DDE (0.01–0.90), toxaphene (0.10–1.60), and BHC (0.01–0.04).

Air

Pesticides in the air are a man-made air pollution problem since they do not naturally occur in the atmosphere. The presence and persistence of pesticides in ambient air are functions of the chemical and physical nature of the toxicants, method of application, and atmospheric conditions. Air is constantly in a dynamic state, with both its physical and chemical characteristics constantly changing. While these toxicants clearly alter air quality by virtue of their presence, Middleton (31) has stated that the concentrations reported and the length of exposure are generally below those causing recognized adverse effects on the public health. Deleterious effects may be encountered as dosage is increased, and uptake by breathing, mouth admissions, and skin contact is prolonged.

The relationship of air concentrations and exposure time to the accumulation of the toxicant in tissues and organs and its effect on public health is much more difficult to assess.

The movement of air across the land mass and the area affected are largely determined by the direction and speed of the wind, topography, and the height of the containing inversion layer. As a result of agricultural applications, pesticides are present in the air mass for varying times and drift for varying distances. Studies on pesticide drift are currently underway in Arizona, California, Vermont, and other areas. Indirect evidence of the persistence of insecticides in air is found in the contamination of feed and foodstuffs and also surface residues. Akesson et al. (2) have reported on the drift of chlorinated hydrocarbon sprays applied by aircraft and on factors governing the amount of contamination to be expected on nearby forage crops. Their studies under windy, turbulent conditions show 1 pound of chlorinated pesticide resulted in residues of 8.0 p.p.m. in fields 100 feet distant. Levels of the same pesticide were detected at 0.01 p.p.m., 20,000 feet downwind under the same windy conditions. These workers have also demonstrated that the amount of drift residue is directly proportional to the amount of active chemical applied. For example, the drift from an application of ½ pound DDT per acre resulted in 0.01 p.p.m. at 3000 feet distance whereas a 1½ pound application deposited DDT residues of 0.04 p.p.m. at the same distance. Gerhardt and Witt (17) reported that DDT was detected at 0.1 p.p.m. 2600 feet downwind when 1 pound per acre was applied as a spray, and 1.4 p.p.m. DDT were detected at the same distance when the pesticide was applied as a dust. The reported presence of low levels of pesticides in fish and wildlife has been suggested as evidence of the persistence and distribution of pesticides in air.

It is well known that one of the most serious pesticide drift problems involves situations where chlorinated hydrocarbon pesticides are applied legally to fields or orchards adjacent to dairy cattle operations or to fields containing future dairy forage. MacCollom (26) advised Vermont orchardists to allow at least a 200-foot buffer zone for adjacent hayfields and to apply tedion dusts only when wind velocities were 3 m.p.h. or less.

Yoe (47) reports that sedimentation and impaction are usually the most important particle factors in drift hazard. Spray droplets, ranging from 10–50 microns in diameter, usually produce the greatest ground contamination several miles from the source of application, while droplets of 100 microns usually do not present a drift hazard unless winds are high. About 80% of the particles are deposited within short downwind distances when they are larger than 200 microns while droplets of less than 5 microns do not produce appreciable deposits and drift for many miles. Such small droplets, while not producing a deposit risk, probably constitute a serious respiratory hazard. A recent summary and critique of pesticide drift literature by Akesson and Yates (1) indicates the importance of particle size upon the drift potential of pesticides. These investigators reported that when a pesticide dust of 10 microns size was released about 10 feet above ground in a 3 m.p.h. wind, it drifted about 1 mile whereas those only 2 microns in diameter were carried 21 miles. Droplets of 50 microns in diameter drifted not more than 200 feet under the same conditions.

Certain phenoxy herbicides adversely affect sensitive crops (7) such as cotton, grapes, and tomatoes at distances of as much as 15 miles from the site of application. With this type of herbicide, not only are the physical state, particle size, and extent of the area treated important, but also the vapor phase of the toxicant. Highly volatile herbicides have been known to adversely affect sensitive crops some distance away for a duration of several weeks.

A recent pesticide drift study by MacCollom (27) has utilized air blast equipment using particle sizes from 20 to 200 microns in diameter. Using emulsifiable formulations or spray oils will increase droplet size, regardless of pressure or orifice size; thus, using wettable powders will tend to yield smaller droplet sizes. MacCollom reports that the most satisfactory results for controlling apple orchard insects and minimum drift appear to be with droplet sizes ranging from 40 to 100 microns in diameter. This author reports studies during the summer of 1965 with a speed sprayer using a fluorescent dye simultaneously with an aerial application of dust containing a different tracer. He was able to detect both the spray and dust tracer well over a mile from the target in concentrations which would have presented a hazard to dairy cattle if certain pesticides had been used.

In summary, an endeavor has been made to cover briefly the effect of several pesticides in our total environment, from the food we consume and the soil in which it is grown to the water we drink and fish in and even to the air we breathe. Of course, with a subject as broad as this, only a small fraction of the actual research conducted in this general area could be cited. Obviously, the fate and persistence of pesticides in our total environment are highly complex and worthy of our continued surveillance. However, we should always keep this problem of pesticide contamination of our environment in its proper perspective. Even though trace quantities of pesticide residues are found in our water, fish, milk, etc., and perhaps somewhat higher concentrations are found in some vegetables and fruit we may consume, there is no reason for unwarranted alarm. When pesticides are used properly, the concentration of residues reported are almost always far below levels judged hazardous to health by present medical standards. Indeed, we need to investigate and clarify all the ramifications of the fate and persistence of pesticides to be able to understand and predict their ultimate impact on our total environment. However, at the same time we must be rational and realize the benefits of these pesticides far outweigh their possible detriment to man.

Literature Cited

(1) Akesson, N. B., Yates, W. E., *Ann. Rev. Entomol.* **9**, 285 (1964).
(2) Akesson, N. B., Yates, W. E., Coutts, H. H., Burgoyne, W. E., *Agr. Avn.* **6**, 72 (1964).
(3) Alexander, M., Aleem, M. I. H., *J. Agr. Food Chem.* **9**, 44 (1961).
(4) Bann, J. M., DoCino, T. A., Earle, N. W., Sun, Yun-Pei, *J. Agr. Food Chem.* **4**, 937 (1956).
(5) Bowman, M. C., Acree, F., Corbett, M. K., *J. Agr. Food Chem.* **8**, 406 (1960).
(6) Brittin, W. A., Fairing, J. D., *J. Assoc. Offic. Agr. Chemists* **33**, 599 (1950).
(7) California State Dept. Agr. *33rd Ann. Rept. Bull.* **41**, 325 (1952).
(8) Cook, J. W., "Research in Pesticides," Part V, p. 205, Academic Press, New York and London (1965).
(9) Crosby, D. G., "Research in Pesticides," Part V, p. 213, Academic Press, New York and London (1965).
(10) Dauterman, W. C., Viado, G. B., Casida, J. E., O'Brien, R. D., *J. Agr. Food Chem.* **8**, 115 (1960).
(11) Davidow, B., Radomski, J. L., *J. Pharmacol.* **107**, 259 (1953).
(12) Decker, G. C., Bruce, W. N., Bigger, J. H., *J. Econ. Entomol.* **58**, 266 (1965).
(13) Ebeling, W., *Residue Rev.* **3**, 34 (1963).
(14) Ely, R. E., Moore, L. A., Hubanks, P. E., Carter, R. H., Poos, F. W., *J. Dairy Sci.* **38**, 669 (1955).
(15) Fleck, E. E., *J. Am. Chem. Soc.* **71**, 1034 (1949).
(16) Gannon, N., Bigger, J. H., *J. Econ. Entomol.* **51**, 1 (1958).
(17) Gerhardt, P. D., Witt, J. M., "Summary of Downwind Drift Limits, Comparison of Dust *vs.* Spray," Pesticide Residue Study, Univ. of Arizona, September 1963.
(18) Grzenda, A. R., Nicholson, H. P., Teasley, J. E., Patric, J. H., *J. Econ. Entomol.* **57**, 615 (1964).
(19) Grzenda, A. R., Nicholson, H. P., *Proc. 14th Southern Water Resources Pollution Control Conf., Chapel Hill, N. C.,* pp. 165–174, 1965.
(20) Henderson, C., Pickering, W. H., Tarzwell, C. M., *Trans Am. Fish Soc.* **88**, 23 (1959).
(21) Hill, G. D., McGahen, J. W., Baker, H. M., Finnerty, D. W., Bingeman, C. W., *Agron J.* **47**, 93 (1955).
(22) Lauer, G. J., Proc. *Conf. Amer. Sugar Cane Technol. Thibodaux, La.,* 1964.
(23) Lichtenstein, E. P., "Research in Pesticides," Part V, p. 199, Academic Press, New York and London (1965).
(24) Lichtenstein, E. P., Schulz, K. R., *J. Agr. Food Chem.* **13**, 57 (1965).
(25) Lichtenstein, E. P., Schulz, K. R., *J. Econ. Entomol.* **58**, 742 (1965).
(26) MacCollum, G. B., *J. Econ. Entomol.* **55**, 999 (1962).
(27) MacCollum, G. B., personal communication, August 1965.
(28) MacRae, I. C., Alexander, M., *J. Agr. Food Chem.* **13**, 72 (1965).

(29) Mattson, A. M., Spellane, J. T., Baker, C., Pearce, G. W., *Anal. Chem.* **25**, 1065 (1953).
(30) Middleton, F. M., Lichtenberg, J. J., *Ind. Eng. Chem.* **52**, 99 (1960).
(31) Middleton, J. T., "Research in Pesticides," Part V, p. 191, Academic Press, New York and London (1965).
(32) Minarik, C. E., *Proc. Northeast. Weed Control Conf.* (Suppl.) **5**, 29 (1951).
(33) Nicholson, H. P., Webb, H. J., Lauer, G. J., O'Brien, R. E., Grzenda, A. R., Shanklin, D. W., *Trans. Am. Fish Soc.* **91**, 213 (1962).
(34) Nicholson, H. P., Grzenda, A. R., Lauer, G. J., Cox, W. S., Teasley, J. I., *Limnol. Oceanog.* **9**, 310 (1964).
(35) Nicholson, H. P., Thoman, J. R., "Research in Pesticides," Part V, p. 181, Academic Press, New York and London (1965).
(36) Rosen, A. A., Middleton, F. M., *Anal. Chem.* **31**, 1729 (1959).
(37) Sheets, T. J., Danielson, L. L., *Symp. Nature Fate Chemicals Appl. Soils, Plants, Animals,* pp. 170–181, 1960.
(38) Somers, Ira I., "Abstracts of Papers," 145th Meeting, ACS, September 1963, p. 17A.
(39) Thoman, J. R., Nicholson, H. P., "Western Resource Papers. Water: Development Utilization Conservation," pp. 21–29, University of Colorado Press, 1963.
(40) Thompson, B. D., Van Middelem, C. H., *Proc. Am. Soc. Hort. Sci.* **65**, 357 (1955).
(41) Tressler, C. J., *J. Assoc. Offic. Agr. Chemists* **30**, 140 (1947).
(42) Van Middelem, C. H., Waites, R. E., unpublished data (1959).
(43) Van Middelem, C. H., Wilson, J. W., unpublished data (1960).
(44) Walker, K. C., Goette, Mary B., Batcheler, G. S., *J. Agr. Food Chem.* **2**, 1034 (1954).
(45) Ward, T. M., Upchurch, R. P., *J. Agr. Food Chem.* **13**, 334 (1965).
(46) Westlake, W. E., San Antonio, J. P., *Symp. Nature Fate Chemicals Appl. Soils, Plants, Animals,* p. 105–115, 1960.
(47) Yoe, D., *Rept., 1st Intern. Agr. Avn. Conf.,* p. 112–130, 1959.

RECEIVED October 13, 1965. Florida Agricultural Experiment Station Journal Series No. 2142.

20

Metabolism of Herbicides in Soils

PHILIP C. KEARNEY

Crops Research Division, U.S. Department of Agriculture, Beltsville, Md.

Soil microorganisms are responsible for the metabolic degradation of many organic pesticides. From products found in soils or in culture solutions of selected soil microorganisms, pathways of decomposition have been proposed for the phenylurea, phenylcarbamate, s-triazine, chlorinated aliphatic acid, and phenoxyalkanoic acid herbicides. Reactions associated with herbicide metabolism include N-dealkylation of the N,N-dimethyl-N'-phenylureas, ester or amide hydrolysis of the phenylcarbamates, side-chain degradation of the s-triazines, dehalogenation of the chlorinated aliphatic acids, and beta oxidation or ether cleavage of the phenoxyalkanoic acids. Enzymes responsible for the hydrolysis of the phenylcarbamates and dehalogenation of 2,2-dichloropropionic acid have been isolated and characterized.

The metabolic fate of organic pesticides in soils is currently of interest in relation to the over-all aspects of residues in our environment. Several processes in soils tend to dissipate herbicide residues—namely, volatilization, photodecomposition, leaching, adsorption, and microbial degradation. This paper concerns itself entirely with the microbiological aspects of decomposition. Specifically, it deals with recent biochemical studies on five major classes of herbicides: (1) the phenylureas, (2) the phenylcarbamates, (3) the s-triazines, (4) the chlorinated aliphatic acids, and (5) the phenoxyalkanoic acids. Primary emphasis is directed toward metabolic pathways elucidated in soils or in pure cultures of selected soil microorganisms. Where possible, specific details on the enzymes responsible for the initial decomposition reaction are discussed.

Phenylureas

The phenylurea herbicides have the same general structure as fenuron, shown in Figure 1. If a chlorine is substituted in the 4-position of the ring, the compound is called monuron. If chlorines are placed in the 3- and 4-positions of the ring, it is called diuron. Inspection of the N,N-dimethyl-N'-phenylureas might suggest that the classical urease type reaction would cleave this molecule directly to aniline, CO_2, and dimethylamine. Although urease is widely distributed in microorganisms, the enzyme shows an absolute specificity for urea. Sumner (39) examined many substrates, including the substituted ureas and related compounds, but reported no hydrolysis of these various substrates by urease.

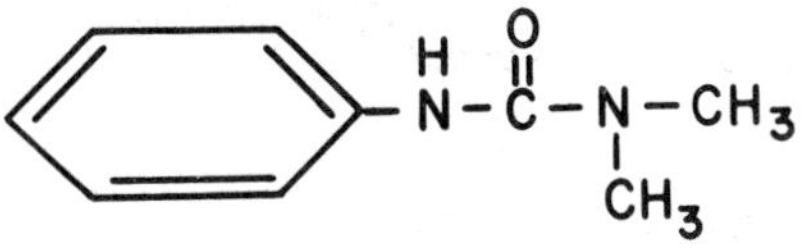

Figure 1. Chemical structure of 3-phenyl-1, 1-dimethylurea (fenuron) —a typical phenylurea herbicide

Recent reports from scientists working independently on phenylurea degradation in soils clearly show that dealkylation of the methyl groups probably precedes hydrolysis of the urea linkage. For example, Geissbuhler *et al.* (11) working with carbonyl labeled N'-(4-chlorophenoxy)phenyl-N,N-dimethylurea (chloroxuron) identified the monomethyl and completely demethylated urea in soil extraction studies. The metabolic pathway shown in Figure 2 was proposed. Demethylation of the herbicides monuron and diuron has also been reported recently. Decomposition of diuron proceeds by removal of first one and then the other methyl group, followed by hydrolysis of the urea to aniline (7). A similar process must be occurring with monuron since the monalkyl, urea, and aniline derivatives have been detected in soils (38).

Disappearance of the phenylurea herbicides from soils is caused partly by soil microbiological activity. Several bacteria (*Xanthomonas* sp., *Sarcina* sp., *Bacillus*, and two species of *Pseudomonas*) and fungi (species *Pencillium* and *Aspergillus*) have been reported to utilize monuron as a sole source of carbon in an agar medium (17). A bacterium of the *Pseudomonas* species isolated from a nonherbicide-treated Brookston soil was only capable of oxidizing monuron in the presence of exogenous growth factors (18). Metabolic products resulting from microbial decomposition of monuron by these soil microorganisms were not examined.

Although a cell-free system capable of degrading the phenylureas has not yet been reported, an enzyme system from rat liver microsomes has been isolated which requires reduced triphosphopyridine nucleotide

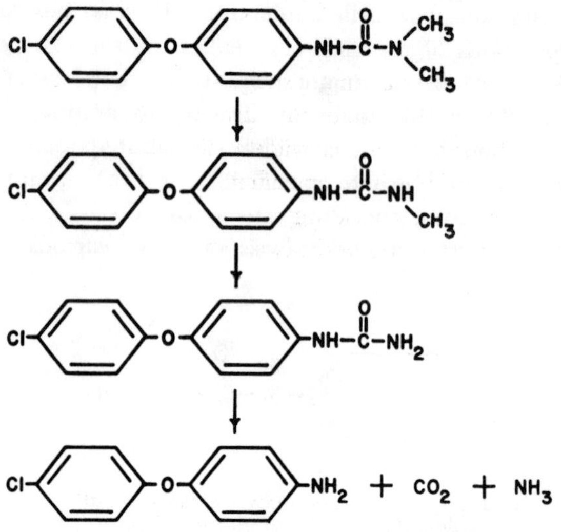

Figure 2. Proposed pathway for the degradation of carbonyl labeled N'(4-chlorophenoxy)phenyl-N,N-dimethylurea in soils [from Geissbuhler et al. (11)]

(TPNH) and oxygen to demethylate a number of closely related *N,N*-dimethylcarbamates (*21*). The same particulate system, however, exhibited a low order of activity on the urea herbicides: monuron, diuron, and fenuron. Apparently, substitution of a nitrogen atom for the oxygen atom of the ester linkage to form the corresponding urea substantially decreased the velocity of the reaction.

Continued study of the phenylurea herbicides in soils is needed. First of all, we must determine whether soil microorganisms are able to demethylate these phenylurea herbicides and secondly, whether enzymes may be present in plant roots which contribute to the phenylurea metabolites found in soils.

Phenylcarbamates

The phenylcarbamate herbicides are of the general structure shown in Figure 3. The particular compound shown is the isopropyl ester of 3-(chlorophenyl)carbamic acid (CIPC). Other herbicides in this class have various ring substituents and are esterified to different alcohols. At first glance the chemistry of the phenylureas and the phenylcarbamates would appear to be similar, but the phenylcarbamates are generally less persistent in soils. Previous studies with the phenylcarbamate herbicides in soils indicate a fairly rapid decomposition by soil microorganisms (*8, 10, 36*). Only recently, however, have the causative microorganisms been isolated and identified on two phenylcarbamates (*24*). Bacteria effective in degrading CIPC in soil perfusion columns were identified as *Pseudomonas striata*, a *Flavobacterium* sp., an *Agrobacterium* sp., and an *Achromobacter* sp. Microbes effective on 2-chloroethyl *N*-(3-chloro-phenyl)carbamate (CEPC) were an *Achromobacter* sp. and an *Arthro-bacter* sp. The herbicides served as sole carbon sources for the isolated bacteria.

Labeling experiments with isopropyl ^{14}C- and ring ^{14}C-CIPC revealed that both carbons gave rise to $^{14}CO_2$ when incubated in a soil perfusion column (*6*). A typical example of one type of microbiological breakdown observed in soils is shown in Figure 4. A lag period occurs and is followed by a rapid breakdown of labeled CIPC. Subsequent additions of CIPC to the adapted soils (open arrows) are rapidly metabolized. The bottom two curves represent $^{14}CO_2$ from carbonyl labeled banol (6-chloro-3,4-xylyl *N*-methylcarbamate) or the methylcarbamate insecticide. One of the banol samples is in sterile soil, the other in nonsterile soil. Apparently banol degradation in these soils is chemical and not microbiological. Adding banol to CIPC-adapted soils failed to alter the rate of banol decomposition. This observation does not preclude the possibility, however, that eventually soil microorganisms would be adapted to metabolize this methylcarbamate insecticide. Although certain chemical similarities exist between CIPC and banol, their mode of breakdown appears to be different in soils.

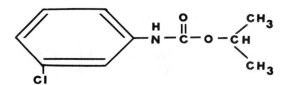

Figure 3.   Chemical structure of isopropyl N-3-chlorophenylcarbamate (CIPC)—a typical phenylcarbamate herbicide

One soil bacterium isolated from the soil perfusion columns and later identified as *P. striata* was capable of evolving $^{14}CO_2$ from the ring labeled portion of CIPC (*28*). The isopropyl moiety was lost as some volatile component that could not be recovered in the CO_2 traps. Products resulting from metabolism of carbon labeled CIPC have not yet been identified.

Enzymatic hydrolysis of CIPC by cell-free extracts of *P. striata* has been reported recently (*27, 29*). A 70-fold purified enzyme was obtained from the crude supernatant fluid of ruptured cells by a combination of

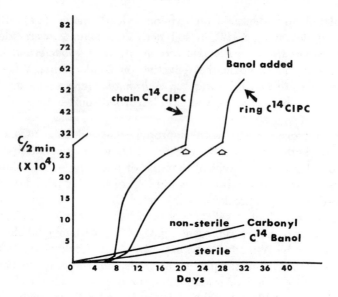

Figure 4.   CO₂ evolution from ring and chain labeled CIPC-¹⁴C and carbonyl labeled banol from soil perfusion columns

salt fractionation and chromatography on DEAE cellulose. The enzyme had a pH optimum near 8.5, was strongly inhibited by diisopropyl fluorophosphate, and apparently its activity was not enhanced by adding metal ions. The isolated enzyme catalyzes the hydrolysis of CIPC to 3-chloroaniline, CO_2, and isopropyl alcohol (Figure 5). It does not hydrolyze methylcarbamates. The mechanism of this reaction would appear to be, simply, hydrolysis of the ester linkage to yield isopropyl alcohol and 3-chlorophenylcarbamic acid. The latter compound is unstable and would

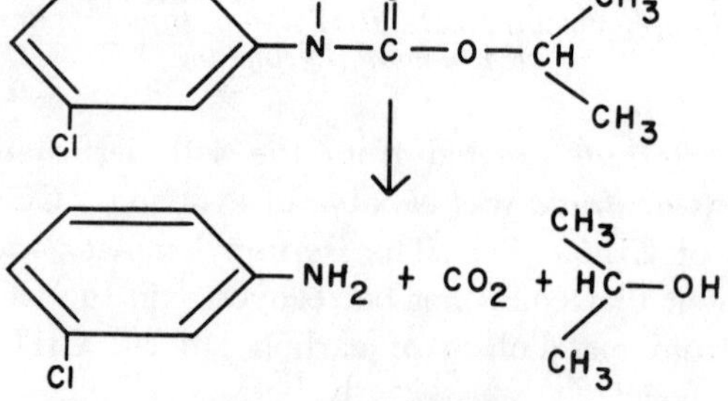

Figure 5.   Proposed mechanism of CIPC cleavage by an enzyme isolated from pseudomonas striata Chester

spontaneously give rise to aniline and CO_2. The partially purified enzyme from *P. striata* also hydrolyzes the amide bond in a number of closely related acylanilides. A similar reaction on CIPC would yield the identical products resulting from ester hydrolysis—namely, 3-chloroaniline and the isopropyl ester of carbonic acid. The latter compound would yield CO_2 and isopropyl alcohol.

Some interesting correlations between the rates of hydrolysis of different phenylcarbamates and their chemical properties have been elucidated (27). The electron density in the vicinity of the carbonyl carbon and the size of the alcohol moiety play an important role in governing the velocity of the reaction.

s-Triazines

Metabolism of the s-triazines in plants has been the subject of numerous investigations. Soil studies with the s-triazines have been confined largely to determining residue levels, with the *a priori* assumption that the pathway of metabolism in soils is similar to that in plants.

It is useful at this point to review briefly the current status of plant metabolism of simazine [2-chloro-4,6-bis(ethylamino)-s-triazine] and then consider this compound in soils. The conversion of simazine to hydroxysimazine [2-hydroxy-4,6-bis(ethylamino)-s-triazine] in corn apparently is catalyzed by a nonenzymatic reaction (4, 15, 37) (Figure 6).

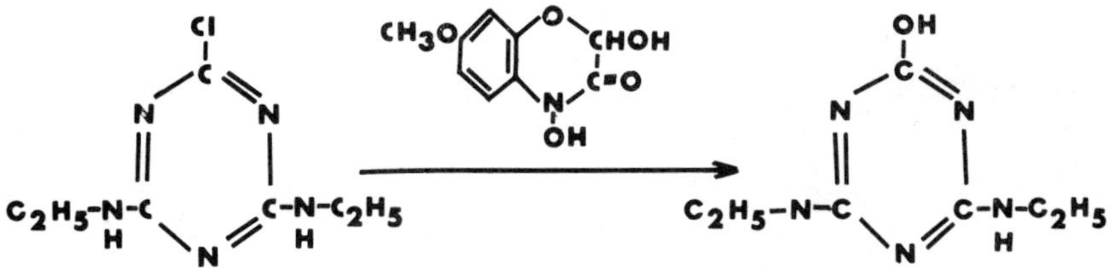

Figure 6. Proposed reaction for the conversion of simazine to hydroxysimazine as catalyzed by the cyclic hydroxamate in corn

A nonprotein, dialyzable, heat stable constituent was isolated from corn that could convert simazine to the innocuous hydroxysimazine (4). One plant constituent capable of carrying out the conversion has been identified as the cyclic hydroxamate (2,4-dihydro-3-keto-7-methoxy-1,4-benzoxazine) or its glycoside (15).

Hydroxysimazine has also recently been reported in four soils incubated 32 weeks with radioactive simazine (16). It is conceivable that a soil constituent with strong nucleophilic properties could also cause the conversion of simazine to hydroxysimazine.

There is evidence that a soil fungus, identified as *Fusarium roseum* is capable of degrading atrazine [2-chloro-4-ethylamino-6-isopropyla-mino-*s*-triazine] rapidly to its corresponding hydroxy analog (5).

Evidence for a different route of metabolism of simazine by soil fungi has recently appeared (23, 25) (Figure 7). A common soil fungus *Aspergillus fumigatus* Fres., liberated $^{14}CO_2$ only from chain labeled simazine and not from the ring labeled compound. A new metabolite was detected on paper chromatograms that possessed a different mobility from that of simazine or hydroxysimazine. Subsequent identification of the metabolite verified it as the 2-chloro-4-amino-6-ethylamino-*s*-triazine (26). Low concentrations of other ring labeled metabolites were also detected and indicated that dealkylation as well as deamination was occurring.

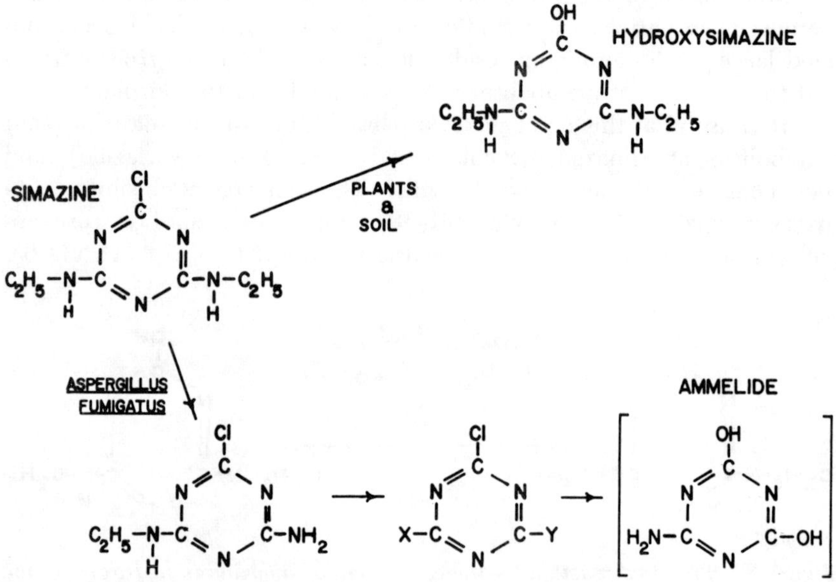

Figure 7. Proposed metabolic pathway for simazine decomposition in soils *[from Kearney et al. (26)]*

Evidence that dealkylation reactions associated with simazine degradation has been reported for other soil fungi. Results from $^{14}CO_2$ evolution studies indicated that side-chain degradation was occurring in culture solutions of four fungal species, *F. roseum*, *Geotrichum* sp., *Trichoderma* sp. and a *Pencillium* sp. (5). Whether or not side-chain degradation is unique to soil fungi is presently unknown.

Research on the metabolism of chloro-*s*-triazines is rapidly expanding, and significant gains are being made in several areas. However, much remains to be learned about the fate of these compounds in soils. Little is known, for example, about the metabolic fate of the 2-methoxy- and 2-methyl-mercapto-*s*-triazines in soils.

Chlorinated Aliphatic Acids

The two major herbicides that belong to the chlorinated aliphatic acids are dalapon (2,2-dichloropropionate) and TCA (trichloroacetate). General soil persistence studies indicate that dalapon is rapidly degraded while TCA is degraded more slowly. Abundant evidence exists that soil microorganisms can dehalogenate the two herbicides and use the carbon as a sole source of energy (*19, 20, 22*). At least seven species of soil bacteria, five species of fungi, and two species of actinomycetes have been shown to be effective in decomposing dalapon (*32*).

An adapted soil bacterium identified as an *Arthrobacter* sp. incorporated most of the labeled carbon from dalapon-2-^{14}C into various cellular components (amino acids, lipids, protein, and nucleic acids) while the carboxy carbon was accounted for mostly as $^{14}CO_2$ (*2*). Products identified on paper chromatograms were the amino acids alanine and glutamic acid (Figure 8). An enzyme preparation obtained from the supernatant fluid of broken cells of the same *Arthrobacter* sp. liberated Cl ion from dalapon to yield the organic acid pyruvate (*31*). The

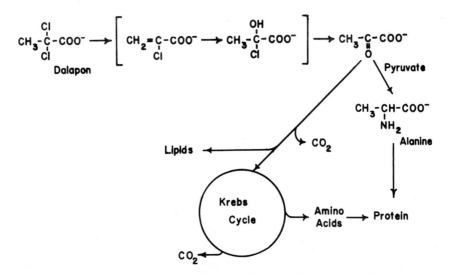

Figure 8.   Proposed pathway of dalapon degradation by Arthrobacter *sp. isolated from soil [from Kearney et al. (32)]*

partially purified enzyme showed no metal ion requirement, was not enhanced by reducing conditions, and was inactive on TCA and most β-chloro-substituted organic acids. It is difficult, however, to determine a requirement for reducing conditions since many of these reagents glutathione) have copious quantities of halide ion.

Some preliminary studies were conducted to determine whether one of two proposed reactions could account for the appearance of pyruvate from dalapon. The precursor of pyruvate in this system is probably the α-hydroxy-α-chloropropionate. This compound is unstable and will spontaneously give rise to pyruvic acid. The enzyme apparently forms α-chloro-α-hydroxypropionate from dalapon. One reaction system by which the enzyme could form α-chloro-α-hydroxypropionate from dalapon would involve a direct substitution reaction (Reaction 1). In this case there would be a direct nucleophilic attack at carbon-2, led by a hydroxyl group to form the desired product.

A second reaction would involve beta elimination—i.e., some basic group on the enzyme surface could abstract a proton from the beta carbon of dalapon to form α-chloroacrylate or the 1-chloropropene (Reaction 2).

Energetically, Reaction 2 would be far simpler for the enzyme to carry out. To study these two proposals, an experiment was set up in which the enzyme reaction was conducted in tritiated water (30). One could distinguish between the two reactions on the basis that Reaction 2 would incorporate tritium into the final product, pyruvate, during the addition reaction. In this case, Reaction 2 would yield tritiated pyruvate. When this experiment was conducted and the pyruvate was isolated from the tritiated water on a Dowex-1-Cl column, it was found that pyruvate was labeled with tritium. Unfortunately, however, when the boiled enzyme was incubated with pyruvate and tritium, the pyruvate was also tritiated. Apparently then at pH 8.5, pyruvate picked up tritium by enolization.

Since the specific activity of pyruvate from both boiled and nonboiled enzymes was identical, the appearance of an unsaturated intermediate can probably be ruled out.

Dehalogenation of TCA by soil microorganisms has been reported by several investigators (*12, 19, 20, 22*). Most of the isolated microorganisms grow feebly on TCA as a sole source of carbon. Gemmell and Jensen (*12*) reported that TCA and its theoretical dehalogenation product, oxalate, could serve as carbon sources for two species of *Arthrobacter*.

Metabolic studies with an unidentified soil microorganism incubated with TCA-1-^{14}C and TCA-2-^{14}C indicate rapid evolution of $^{14}CO_2$ from both forms of the labeled TCA (*33*). Coinciding with $^{14}CO_2$ evolution is the release of Cl$^-$ into the solution. Although growth is limited on TCA alone, radioactivity from TCA-1-^{14}C and TCA-2-^{14}C was incorporated into all cellular components—namely, transient intermediates, lipids, nucleic acid, and proteins. One of the early products detected in TCA metabolism was the amino acid, serine. Many scientists find it astounding that soil microorganisms are capable of metabolizing a compound as toxic as TCA. It must be remembered, however, that in this case we are dealing with the trichloroacetate not the acetic acid. Nevertheless, this represents a fascinating series of reactions in which a potentially toxic compound serves as an energy source for these soil bacteria.

Phenoxyalkanoic Acids

The metabolic fate of the phenoxyalkanoic acids has been widely studied, and the amount of written material concerning the fate of these compounds in soils is voluminous. Although any attempt to cover this material thoroughly is beyond the scope of this paper, some of the significant contributions to this area of knowledge will be discussed. At least 10 different organisms have been reported to decompose 2,4-D [2,4-dichlorophenoxyacetic acid] (*41*). The effect of specific structural characteristics of the phenoxyalkanoic acids on general soil persistence has been studied extensively (*1, 3*). Two pathways have been described for the metabolism of the 2,4-dichlorophenoxyalkanoic acids with aliphatic moieties containing more than two carbons by pure cultures of soil microorganisms. One mechanism involves beta oxidation of the alkanoic acid (*40*) while a second mechanism involves the initial hydrolysis of the ether linkage between the ring and the side chain (Figure 9).

Beta oxidation proceeds by the sequential removal of two carbon fragments from the functional end of the alkanoic acid. Recent evidence for the existence of an operative oxidative pathway in soils has been reported. The first intermediate of the beta oxidation pathway, 2-4-dichlorophenoxycrotonic acid, was detected in soils treated with 2,4-dichlorophenoxybutyric acid by gas chromatography (13). Previously, another intermediate in the beta oxidation process was identified as the beta-hydroxy-4-(4-chlorophenoxy)butyric acid in metabolic studies with *Nocardia opaca* (42). Further evidence for beta oxidation in soils was demonstrated with a natural soil population of microflora capable of metabolizing 2,4-dichlorophenoxyalkanoic acids, with alkanoic moieties ranging from butyric to undecanoic, to acids of shorter chain length (14). Phenoxyalkanoic acids with an even number of carbons in the side chain were oxidized to products containing an even number of carbons. Compounds with an odd number of carbons in the side chain were oxidized to the corresponding valerate, propionate, and phenol derivatives.

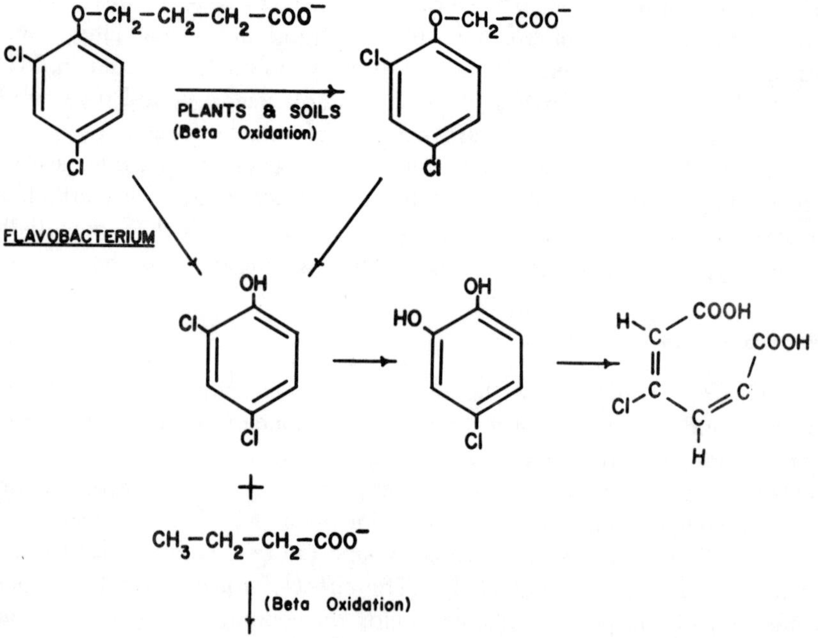

Figure 9. Two proposed pathways for 2,4-DB metabolism by soil microorganisms

Cleavage of the ether linkage of the 2,4-dichlorophenoxyalkanoic acids by a strain of *Flavobacterium* to yield the intact alkanoic acid and 2,4-dichlorophenol has also been observed (34, 35). The intact alkanoic acid is further metabolized by beta oxidation. The bacterium produced the free fatty acid corresponding to the aliphatic moieties of six omega-linked dichlorophenoxyalkanoic acids in the series from 3-(2,4-dichlorophenoxy)propionic acid to 8-(2,4-dichlorophenoxy)octanoic acid.

The fate of the ring structure in soils has also been studied. Detection of 2,4-dichlorophenol, 4-chlorocatechol, and chloromuconic acid (9) from either soil or pure culture studies suggests a sequence of reactions involving ring hydroxylation and cleavage and further metabolism of the open chain structure to CO_2.

Summary

The metabolism of the phenylureas, phenylcarbamates, s-triazines, chlorinated aliphatic acids, and the phenoxyalkanoic acids in soils has been considered from the standpoint of proposed pathways of degradation and isolated enzymes from soil microorganisms which catalyze the initial hydrolysis of these herbicides. Reactions associated with the degradation of these five classes of herbicides include dealkylation of N-alkylamines, ester or amide hydrolysis, dehalogenation, beta oxidation, and ether cleavage. Although significant gains are being made toward a better understanding of the metabolic fate of herbicides in soils, additional studies are needed on many of the new herbicides that are being used widely for weed control.

Of all the systems operating on the pesticides in our natural environment, the greatest potential for detoxification appears to exist in soils. From a biochemical standpoint the soil microbial population represents a complex system capable of producing unique enzymes to degrade a whole host of organic pesticides. It should be noted, however, that many pesticides stubbornly resist the attack of the soil microflora. The chemistry of the molecule that endows persistence to that compound must be elucidated. Additional information is needed on how processes such as adaption are involved in pesticide decomposition and what effect control systems have on pesticide degradation in soil microorganisms. Finally, detailed studies are needed at the enzyme level to determine what specific linkages are being hydrolyzed. Hopefully, such information should allow us in the future to synthesize pesticides that are capable of controlling pests but at the same time are somewhat more biodegradable than some existing pesticides.

Literature Cited

(1) Alexander, M., Aleim, M. I. H., *J. Agr. Food Chem.* **9,** 44 (1961).
(2) Beall, M. L., Kearney, P. C., Kaufman, D. D., *Weed Soc. Am. Abstr.* **5,** 12 (1964).
(3) Burger, K., MacRae, I. C., Alexander, M., *Soil Sci. Soc. Am. Proc.* **26,** 243 (1962).
(4) Castelfranco, P., Foy, C. L., Deutsch, Deborah B., *Weeds* **9,** 580 (1961).
(5) Couch, R. W., Gramlich, J. V., Davis, D. E., Funderburk, H. H., *Proc. Southern Weed Conf.* **18,** 623 (1965).

(6) Crops Protection Research Branch, Plant Industry Station, Beltsville, Md., unpublished data.
(7) Dalton, R. L., Evans, A. W., Rhodes, R. C. *Proc. Southern Weed Conf.* **18,** 72 (1965).
(8) DeRose, H. R., *Bot. Gaz.* **107,** 583 (1946).
(9) Fernley, H. N., Evans, W. C., *Biochem. J.* **73,** 22 (1959).
(10) Freed, V. H., *Weeds* **1,** 48 (1951).
(11) Geissbuhler, H., Haselback, C., Aebi, H., Ebner, L., *Weed Res.* **3,** 277 (1963).
(12) Gemmell, C. G., Jensen, H. L., *Arch. Mikrobiol.* **48,** 386 (1964).
(13) Gutenmann, W. H., Lisk, D. J., *J. Agr. Food Chem.* **12,** 322 (1964).
(14) Gutenmann, W. H., Loos, M. A., Alexander, M., Lisk, D. J., *Soil Sci. Soc. Am. Proc.* **28,** 205 (1964).
(15) Hamilton, R. H., Moreland, D. E., *Science* **135,** 373 (1962).
(16) Harris, C. I., *Weed Res.* **5,** 275 (1965).
(17) Hill, G. D., paper presented before the Weed Society of America, New York, 1956.
(18) Hill, G. D., McGahen, J. W., Baker, H. M., Finnerty, D. W., Bingeman, C. W., *Agron. J.* **47,** 93 (1955).
(19) Hirsch, P., Alexander, M., *Can. J. Microbiol.* **6,** 241 (1960).
(20) Hirsch, P., Stellmach-Helwig, R., *Zentr. Bakteriol. Parasitenk. Abt. II* **114,** 683 (1961).
(21) Hodgson, E., Casida, J. E., *Biochem. Pharmacol.* **8,** 179 (1961).
(22) Jensen, H. L., *Can. J. Microbiol.* **3,** 151 (1957); *Tidsskr. Planteavl.* **63,** 470 (1959); *Acta Agr. Scand.* **10,** 83 (1960); **13,** 404 (1963).
(23) Kaufman, D. D., Kearney, P. C., Sheets, T. J., *Science* **142,** 405 (1963).
(24) Kaufman, D. D., Kearney, P. C., *Appl. Microbiology* **13,** 443 (1965).
(25) Kaufman, D. D., Kearney, P. C., Sheets, T. J., *J. Agr. Food Chem.* **13,** 238 (1965).
(26) Kearney, P. C., Kaufman, D. D., Sheets, T. J., *J. Agr. Food Chem.* **13,** 369 (1965).
(27) Kearney, P. C., *J. Agr. Food Chem.* **13,** 561 (1965).
(28) Kearney, P. C., Kaufman, D. D., "Abstracts of Papers," 149th Meeting, ACS, April 1965, p. 18A.
(29) Kearney, P. C., Kaufman, D. D., *Science* **147,** 740 (1965).
(30) Kearney, P. C., Meloche, H. P., unpublished data.
(31) Kearney, P. C., Kaufman, D. D., Beall, M. L., *Biochem. Biophys. Res. Commun.* **14,** 29 (1964).
(32) Kearney, P. C., Harris, C. I., Kaufman, D. D., Sheets, T. J., *Advan. Pest Control Res.* **6,** 1 (1965).
(33) Kearney, P. C., Kaufman, D. D., "Abstracts of Papers," 150th Meeting ACS, September 1965, p. 16A.
(34) MacRae, I. C., Alexander, M., Rovira, A. D., *Intern. Cong. Microbiol.*, *8th, Abstr.*, **B16,** 4 (1962).
(35) MacRae, I. C., Alexander, M., *J. Bacteriol.* **88,** 1231 (1963).
(36) Newman, A. S., DeRose, H. R., DeRigo, H. T., *Soil Sci.* **60,** 393 (1948).
(37) Roth, W., Knusli, E., *Experientia* **17,** 312 (1961).
(38) Smith, J. W., Sheets, T. J., USDA, Plant Industry Station, Beltsville, Md., unpublished data.
(39) Sumner, J. B., Somers, G. F., "Chemistry and Methods of Enzymes," 3rd ed., Academic Press, Inc., New York, 1953.
(40) Taylor, H. F., Wain, R. L., *Proc. Roy. Soc.*, **268B,** 172 (1962).
(41) Thiegs, B. J., "Down to Earth," pp. 7–10, The Dow Chemical Company, Midland, Mich., 1962.
(42) Webley, D. M., Duff, R. B., Farmer, V. C., *Nature* **179,** 1130 (1957).

RECEIVED October 13, 1965.

21

Persistence of Pesticides in Orchards and Orchard Soils

L. C. TERRIERE, ULO KIIGEMAGI, R. W. ZWICK,[1] and
P. H. WESTIGARD[2]

Departments of Agricultural Chemistry and Entomology,
Oregon State University, Corvallis, Ore.

When soils from two Oregon orchards were examined for residues of halogenated insecticides, most of the residues found were DDT analogs and metabolites. Approximately 40% of the DDT applied to the orchards since 1946 is still present in the soil, most of it in the top 12 inches. Only traces of these pesticides are found at the 3-foot depth. Part per billion levels of the pesticides were present in water thought to emanate from one of the orchards. Waste land adjacent to the orchards has accumulated about 5 pounds of DDT per acre. Considering all avenues of loss except evaporation and degradation, approximately 50% of the DDT applied to the orchards has been accounted for.

Orchard crops are among those most heavily treated with pesticides and are therefore most likely to serve as points from which pesticides are disseminated into the surrounding environment. It is not uncommon for an orchard to be treated with several types of pesticides for a yearly total of 50 pounds per acre. In the 20 years since modern insecticides were introduced, therefore, as much as ½ ton of pesticides could have been applied to every acre of many commercially operated orchards.

There has been much interest in the fate of the persistent pesticides, especially DDT, in orchard soil. This subject has been reviewed by Ginsburg (4). Although most authors agree that the build-up of DDT in orchard soil is not linear with application, one recent publication (11) reports a continued accumulation of DDT in forest soils during the 3

---

[1] Present address: Mid-Columbia Branch Experiment Station, Hood River, Ore.
[2] Present address: Southern Oregon Branch Experiment Station, Medford, Ore.

years after treatment of the forest. Foster (2) concluded that DDT builds up in the soil at a rate almost equal to the rate of application. On the other hand, Lichtenstein (7), who studied 14 orchards with DDT treatment histories of 9 to 11 years, reported that the soil contained an average of 26.7% of that applied during the period.

All reports examined show that most of the DDT still present in the soil of orchards remains in the surface layer. New Jersey orchards (3) were found to contain up to 113 pounds per acre, most of it in the top 4 inches. In a study of 35 Indiana orchards (9) it was found that 70–90% of the pesticides still present was concentrated in the top 2 inches of the soil profile.

This report concerns a further examination of the orchard as a source by which the environment is contaminated with pesticides. The investigation extended to the sub-soil regions of the orchards, the ground water moving from the orchard, and the surface soil of the adjacent waste land areas. DDT was chosen for the study because of its stability and continuous use in orchards.

Experimental

Field Plots. An apple orchard in Hood River, Ore., in the northern part of the state, has been treated with DDT every year since 1946 for a total application of 388 pounds per acre. Until 1949 the sprays were applied with hand-controlled hydraulic equipment. Since 1949 air carrier sprayers have been used. The orchard is never cultivated, and the soil type is Wind River sandy loam. It is located on the edge of a low plateau about 300 feet above Hood river, a tributary of the Columbia river.

A pear orchard in Medford, in the southern part of the state, received DDT treatments each year between 1947 and 1959, for a total estimated dosage of 169 pounds per acre. Until 1953 applications were made with hand-controlled hydraulic systems, after which spraying was done with air carrier sprayers. The soil type is Meyer clay adobe, and the orchard is kept free of vegetation by cultivation.

Between 1947 and 1951, soils were collected from both orchards and analyzed for DDT, using total chlorine or labile chlorine methods. In late 1964 and early 1965 another series of analyses were made using methods capable of resolving the major isomers and metabolites of DDT.

Sampling Procedures. Five or six sub-samples were taken around the drip zone of the tree with a ¾-inch soil auger and composited. In the Hood River orchard the samples were taken at 0–6-, 7–12-, 13–24-, and 25–30-inch level. The samples from Medford were obtained at 0–6-, 7–12-, 13–24-, and 25–36-inch level. Analysis of samples collected radially from a tree trunk showed that the soil residue was highest at the drip zone or at about 9 feet from the trunk.

The Hood River water samples were collected from a small spring below the orchard. It was assumed to originate, at least in part, from drainage from the orchard. Because of the low water flow, a container was buried in the spring, allowed to fill with water, and the sample taken from that container.

Extraction of Soils. The soil samples were pulverized, thoroughly mixed, and their moisture contents were determined. They were extracted by shaking in a mechanical shaker for 1 hour with isopropyl alcohol, 1 ml. per gram, and redistilled hexane, 1 ml. per gram. The extract was recovered by decantation, washed free of alcohol, and dried with anhydrous sodium sulfate. This extract was used without cleanup for thin layer or gas chromatography. To check on the extraction procedure, some samples were re-extracted with isopropyl alcohol–hexane mixture or with acetone. These additional extracts did not contain significant amounts of the pesticides.

Extraction of Water. The water samples were extracted by shaking a 1200-ml. aliquot with three 480-ml. portions of redistilled hexane for 10 minutes. The combined hexane extracts were dried with anhydrous sodium sulfate and analyzed without cleanup.

Analysis by Gas Chromatography. All soil samples were analyzed by gas chromatography using a Dohrmann instrument equipped with a microcoulometric detector and an 18-inch, 5% Dow 11 column. This column did not separate the individual pesticides present, indicating only the total halide content of the sample (*10*). All results were calculated in terms of DDT and based on the dry weight of the sample.

A more complete resolution of the DDT-derived compounds in the soil extracts was achieved by electron capture gas chromatography. A mixed column of 5% QF-1 and 5% Dow 11 was used in a Wilkens gas chromatograph. This column satisfactorily separated the pesticides present except in a few cases when an unknown material appeared in the same regions as p,p-DDT. In these cases, a column composed of either SE 30 or 2% neopentyl glycol succinate on Chromasorb W resolved this mixture. The unknown amounted to about 3 p.p.m. calculated as p,p-DDT.

The reliability of the analytical method was confirmed by analyzing insecticide-fortified extracts of untreated soil. An average recovery of 85% was achieved with DDT. The gas chromatograph was standardized by injecting known amounts of pesticides before and after every two or three unknowns.

Analysis by TLC. Confirmation of the identity of the halogenated compounds in the soil samples was achieved by resolution of selected extracts on TLC plates, followed by gas chromatography of the separate compounds eluted from the plates. The thin layer chromatography system of Kovacs (*6*) was used, and the halogenated compounds were detected with the silver nitrate–2-phenoxyethanol reagent. Comparison with standards chromatographed on the same plates permitted an estimate of the pesticide concentrations.

Results and Discussion

The distribution of DDT in the top 3 feet of the soil profile of the two orchards is remarkably similar (Table I) in spite of the climatic, cultural, and soil differences between the two locations. When the soil

Table I. Comparison of DDT Distribution in Hood River and Medford Orchard Soils, 1965

Soil Level, inches	DDT Distribution [a]			
	Hood River		Medford	
	p.p.m.	percent [b]	p.p.m.	percent [b]
0– 6	59.8	88.3	38.0	86.8
7–12	3.9	5.3	3.3	8.7
13–24	1.5	4.7	0.5	2.9
25–30	1.1	1.7	—	—
25–36	—	—	0.3	1.6

[a] Calculated from MCGC short column analysis of 10 composite samples of Hood River soils and five composite samples of Medford soils. Samples collected from drip zone of five trees. Includes all DDT-derived compounds.
[b] Based on estimated distribution in pounds DDT per acre.

concentrations are recalculated on a pounds per acre basis, a maximum of 130 pounds per acre in 3 feet is estimated in the Hood River orchard and 73 pounds per acre in the Medford orchard. This amounts to approximately 33 and 42%, respectively, of the total weight of DDT applied during the 20-year period. These are probably maximum values because they are based on analyses of the most heavily contaminated regions of the orchard.

Tables II and III show that downward leaching of DDT and its analogs is very slow, with less than 3% of the total residue having penetrated below the 1-foot level. The amount of o,p-DDT, p,p-DDE, and p,p-TDE [1,1-dichloro-2,2-bis(parachlorophenyl)ethane] present is expressed as a ratio with p,p-DDT in order to relate the soil concentrations of these analogs with their concentrations in the technical DDT originally applied. The p,p-DDT to o,p-DDT ratios range from 7 to 14 at the various soil depths analyzed, while in technical DDT the ratio is about 3. This change in relative concentration suggests that the o,p-isomer is less persistent in soil. This result is contrary to that of Woodwell and Martin (11) who found more o,p-isomer in the surface layers of forest soils exposed to DDT. The analytical methods used by these authors are not as reliable as those described here, however.

Technical DDT is composed of about 4% TDE (8), which corresponds to the ratios shown in Tables II and III. This result suggests that the TDE found in the orchard soils originated in the technical mixture applied to the crop and not by microbial action in the soil, as recent reports might indicate (1,5).

Residues of kelthane [1,1-bis(p-chlorophenyl)-2,2,2-trichlorethanol] were found in the soil of both orchards and in the water collected at Hood

River. This pesticide has been used against orchard pests since 1956 with a total of approximately 14 and 10 pounds having been applied to the Hood River and Medford orchards, respectively. The amount remaining in the soil represents about two-thirds of that applied.

Table II. Vertical Distribution of DDT Analogs and Metabolites, Medford Orchard Soils, 1965 [a]

Soil level, inches		Pesticide Concentration, p.p.m.					Ratio p,p-DDT to:	
	p,p-DDT	o,p-DDT	DDE	TDE	Kelthane	o,p-DDT	DDE	TDE
0– 6	25.1	3.81	1.83	1.00	3.2	6.6	13.7	25.1
7–12	2.7	0.37	0.45	0.12	0.4	7.3	6.0	22.5
13–24	0.39	0.04	0.03	0.03	0.09	9.8	13.0	13.0
25–36	0.10	0.01	0.01	0.01	0.03	10.0	10.0	10.0

[a] Average of five composite samples analyzed by electron capture gas chromatography. Samples collected from drip zone of tree.

Table III. Vertical Distribution of DDT Analogs and Metabolites, Hood River Orchard Soils, 1965 [a]

Soil level, inches		Pesticide Concentration, p.p.m.					Ratio p,p-DDT to:	
	p,p-DDT	o,p-DDT	DDE	TDE	Kelthane	o,p-DDT	DDE	TDE
0– 6	60.9	6.75	5.11	2.36	4.97 [b]	9.01	11.9	25.8
7–12	3.4	0.50	0.46	0.46	0.03 [c]	6.8	7.4	7.4
13–24	1.2	0.82	0.19	0.51 [c]	——	14.6	6.2	23.4 [c]
25–30	0.39 [b]	0.04 [c]	0.04 [b]	0.02 [c]	——	9.8 [c]	9.8 [b]	19.9 [c]

[a] Average of six or more composite samples unless specified. Analyzed by electron capture gas chromatography. Samples collected from drip zone of tree.
[b] Average of two composite samples.
[c] One composite sample.

Water samples collected in February, March, June, and August from a small spring near the Hood River orchard were analyzed, and the results are shown in Table IV. The analyses were performed so as to reveal the total pesticide present, that in solution as well as that suspended. In a few cases the residues were separated into filterable and nonfilterable portions. In these cases about 75% of the pesticide appeared in the suspended form.

The pesticide content of the water samples collected early in the year was generally lower and more constant in amount than that found later in the season. The increased concentrations found in June and July coincide with spray applications and with irrigation periods and are

Table IV. DDT Analogs and Metabolites in Ground Water Draining from Hood River Orchard, 1965 [a]

	Residues, parts per trillion				
Date	p,p-DDT	o,p-DDT	TDE	DDE	Kelthane
Feb. 15	95	33	—	31	103
Feb. 22	90	26	42	38	42
Mar. 1	112	38	79	23	—
Mar. 8	121	22	6	43	—
Mar. 16	120	61	26	10	—
Mar. 22	126	10	48	10	—
June 8	1104	130	68	63	220
June 15	429	49	29	15	36
June 16	275	56	27	25	98
June 29	513	61	22	22	365
Aug. 4	310	208	9	6	—
Aug. 11	942	46	37	14	15
Aug. 17	697	75	11	13	36

[a] Based on analysis of single one-gallon samples.

probably caused by increased leaching brought on by these operations. Three DDT-containing sprays were applied during the time of these water collections.

Soil samples collected from waste lands downwind and downhill from the Hood River orchard were analyzed for DDT and its analogs. The results indicated the extent to which spray drift during application and surface runoff during rainfall or irrigation had contaminated these areas with pesticides. The samples were collected at distances up to 200 yards from the edge of the orchard. The average DDT content of ten 0–6-inch samples was 2.64 p.p.m. (total of DDT plus isomers), with the range 0.36–8.3 p.p.m. On a pound per acre basis, this amounts to approximately 5 pounds of total pesticide per acre.

Within 3 years after DDT was used commercially in the two orchards, concern over its possible accumulation in the soil had developed. Investigations of DDT concentrations in the surface layers of the orchard soils began in 1947 and continued for the next five years. A summary of these analyses is given in Table V. Build-up of residues was rapid at first, with levels equivalent to approximately 60 pounds per acre attained by 1951. Comparing these estimates with those from the more recent analyses shows that the amount accumulated during the last 14 years (1951–1965) is approximately the same as that deposited in the first six years (1945–1951). Several factors can be suggested as causes for this decline in rate of accumulation. The older methods of application resulted in more waste by spray runoff from the trees. Some of this waste was eliminated when the newer methods were adopted. Downward leaching and increased degradation may be cited as additional factors reducing the rate of residue build-up.

Since the total amount of DDT applied to the two orchards in the 20-year period is known and that still present in the orchard soils has been estimated from the analyses, it is of interest to consider the fate of the remainder—about 60%. A small portion, possibly 2–3%, has drifted or drained into adjacent areas. This estimate assumes that drift for distances over 600 feet is negligible.

A second source of loss is the crop itself, which carries a portion of the pesticide as a residue. Assuming that the apples or pears shipped from the orchards carried DDT residues at the legal limit of 7 p.p.m. and that an average yield of fruit is 20 tons per acre, one can calculate that 5.6 pounds of DDT have left the orchard by this route. This accounts for about 1.5% of the pesticide applied to the Hood River orchard and about 3% of that applied to the Medford orchard.

Table V. DDT in Hood River and Medford Orchard Soils, 1947–1951

	DDT, p.p.m.[a]		
	Hood River Orchard		*Medford Orchard*
Year	*0–3-inch level*	*4–6-inch level*	*0–3-inch level*
1947	18.7	—	—
1948	33.3	21.1	—
1949	43.6	12	—
1950	20.6	—	32.9
1951	38.7	26	44

[a] Composite samples collected from drip zone of trees, average of two to 11 samples.

A third route of loss from the orchards is by leaching downward and laterally into underground water systems. Using the data of Table IV, which show that total DDT in ground water may amount to 1 p.p.b., and assuming an annual percolation of water amounting to 60 inches, the 20-year loss would be less than 0.3 pound per acre of DDT. Confirmation of the minor role played by water leaching is shown by the soil profile analyses, which show that only traces of DDT have percolated to the 3-foot depth.

Losses of DDT by drift and surface runoff, by leaching, and by removal of crops thus account for only a small percentage of the pesticide applied. The two remaining sources of loss—volatilization and degradation—must account for the rest. The role played by each of these factors probably defies evaluation.

The conclusions which can be drawn from this study of two commercially operated orchards with histories of extended treatments with DDT are as follows.

(a) Contamination of land immediately adjacent to that treated is not a serious problem except in the event that forage crops are involved. Only a small percentage of the DDT applied to the orchard drifts or drains to such land.

(b) Similarly, losses by solution or suspension in drainage water are minor.

(c) Approximately 40% of the DDT applied remains as DDT and related compounds in the soil of the orchard, most of this being present in the top 12 inches of the soil profile.

(d) The remainder of the insecticide, about 50%, has disappeared from the orchard—a small amount as residue on the harvested crop and the rest by routes such as degradation and evaporation.

Acknowledgment

This research was supported in part by U.S. Public Health Service Grant No. ES0040–01. The valuable assistance of John Lamberton, who performed many of the analyses, is gratefully acknowledged.

Literature Cited

(1) Barker, P. S., Morrison, F. O., Whitaker, R. S., *Nature* **205**, 621 (1965).
(2) Foster, Arthur C., *USDA Tech. Bull.* **1149** (1956).
(3) Ginsburg, Joseph M., Reed, John P., *J. Econ. Entomol.* **47**, 467 (1954).
(4) Ginsburg, Joseph M., *J. Agr. Food Chem.* **3**, 322 (1955).
(5) Kallman, Burton J., Andrews, Austin K., *Science* **141**, 1050 (1963).
(6) Kovacs, M. F., Jr., *J. Assoc. Offic. Agr. Chemists* **46**, 884 (1963).
(7) Lichtenstein, E. P., *J. Econ. Entomol.* **50**, 545 (1957).
(8) Metcalf, Robert L., "Organic Insecticides," p. 129, Interscience Publishers Inc., New York, 1955.
(9) Murphy, R. T., Fahey, Jack E., Miles, E. J., *Proc. North Central Br. E.S.A.* **19**, 144 (1964).
(10) Witt, J. M., Bagatella, G. F., Percious, J. K., *Pesticide Res. Bull.* **2**, 4 (1962).
(11) Woodwell, G. M., Martin, F. T., *Science* **145**, 481 (1964).

RECEIVED October 27, 1965. Oregon Agricultural Experiment Station Technical Paper No. 2057.

Persistence of 2,6-Dichlorobenzonitrile in Aquatic Environments

CHARLES C. VAN VALIN

U.S. Department of the Interior, Bureau of Sport Fisheries and Wildlife, Fish-Pesticide Research Laboratory, Denver, Colo. 80225

In two experiments 2,6-dichlorobenzonitrile was added to aquatic systems, and the residue levels were followed for about 6 months. A granular formulation applied to a farm pond at 0.6 p.p.m. produced highest residues in water and fish about 2 weeks following treatment whereas vegetation and soil samples had the highest levels within 1 or 2 days. Residues were still measurable after 188 days. In ponds treated with a wettable powder formulation at 10, 20, and 40 p.p.m., residues in water and fish were highest within 3 days after treatment. The concentration in water 11 days after treatment was about 2% of the three-day level. Fish whole-body residues dropped nearly as fast but were still measurable at 112 days.

Dichlorobenil (2,6-dichlorobenzonitrile) is used for weed control in cranberry marshes, in nursery stock and woody plants, for pre-emergent control in crops, and for aquatic weed control. The acute toxicity of dichlorobenil to fish has been measured at the Fish-Pesticide Research Laboratory in Denver; the 24-hour-LC_{50} values are 22 p.p.m. active ingredient to bluegills (*Lepomis macrochirus* Rafinesque) at 24°C. and 23 p.p.m. to rainbow trout (*Salmo gairdneri* Richardson) at 13°C.

The herbicidal effects have been documented, and there has been some work published regarding the persistence of dichlorobenil in the soil. Barnsley and Rosher (1) measured the persistence of dichlorobenil under both tropical and temperate conditions, using plant bioassay to measure residues. They found that dichlorobenil disappeared rapidly, within a few days, when it was applied to the soil surface but was not worked in. However, when the chemical was incorporated in the soil, it persisted for several weeks. These persistence characteristics were attributed to the high vapor pressure of 5×10^{-4} mm. Hg at 20°C. and the relatively low solubility in water of 20 p.p.m. at 25°C. Massini (2) studied the movement of dichlobenil in soils and in plants. In addition to the volatility and solubility effects, he found that it was strongly adsorbed on lignin, humic matter, and lipid material.

Aly and Faust (3) investigated the physical, chemical, and biological factors which influence the persistence of 2,4-D compounds in natural surface waters. They found that esters of 2,4-D in aerobically incubated lake waters were hydrolyzed biologically to the free acid and corresponding alcohol within 9 days and that 2,4-D was decomposed 81–85% within 24 hours by lake muds after microbial adaptation.

Ebeling (4) states that the disappearance of most pesticide residues appears to depend on first-order reaction kinetics, but unfortunately residue data cannot be extrapolated from one environment or dosage range to another. Involved are the nature of the compound, absorption and metabolism by microorganisms, adsorption to mineral and organic colloids, absorption by higher organisms, chemical and photochemical alterations, the temperature, and dispersal by air and water movement (5,6).

Sheets (5), in reviewing the disappearance of substituted urea herbicides from soil, found that inactivation occurs under soil conditions favorable for the growth of microorganisms but takes place slowly or not at all in dry or autoclaved soil. Burschel and Freed (6), reviewing work relating to 2,4-D and amitrole as well as monuron, state that the data indicate that ultimate breakdown is caused by microbiological attack.

The persistence of dichlobenil in an aquatic environment had not been studied, however. Therefore, studies were undertaken in experimental ponds at Tishomingo, Okla. and a farm pond near Denver.

Procedure and Methods

Eight 0.1-acre experimental ponds at Tishomingo were stocked with bluegills and were treated June 5, 1964. A wettable powder formulation was used which was calculated to yield dichlobenil concentrations of 0, 10, 20, and 40 p.p.m. Fish and water were sampled beginning 3 days following treatment. The final water sample was taken 85 days, and the final fish sample 112 days after treatment. Bottom soil samples beginning 1 month after treatment were supplemented by samples taken after the ponds were drained.

The farm pond near Denver had a surface area of about two-thirds of an acre, with an average depth of 5 feet and a maximum depth of 11 feet. The fish present were predominantly bluegills, but there were also numerous largemouth bass, (*Micropterus salmoides* (Lacepede)), green sunfish, (*Lepomis cyanellus* (Rafinesque)), and yellow perch (*Perca flavescens* (Mitchill)). Several kinds of weeds were present, principally a species of *Chara*, unidentified filamentous algae, and sago pondweed (*Potamogeton pectinatus* L.). The pond was treated by personnel of the Weed Investigations Laboratory of the Agricultural Research Service, U. S. Department of Agriculture on April 29, 1964, with a 4% granular formulation of dichlobenil at the rate of 10 lb. active ingredient per surface acre, or about 0.6 p.p.m. Samples of fish, water, vegetation, and soil were collected before treatment and at scheduled intervals thereafter, beginning 6 hours after application and continuing through 188 days. An additional soil sample was obtained on July 8, 1965.

All samples obtained were analyzed for dichlobenil by modifications of procedures developed by the Thompson-Hayward Chemical Co. (7). Water samples were composites of portions taken from four different points in the ponds. The water was extracted by vigorously shaking 500 ml. in a 1000-ml. separatory funnel with solvent for 2 minutes for each of three portions—50, 25, and 25 ml.—of solvent. Benzene was used for most samples, although petroleum ether (30°–60°C.) was used for the first samples and worked equally well. The combined extracts were dried by passing through a 10-gram column of anhydrous sodium sulfate, the volume of effluent was measured, and the dichlobenil was determined by electron capture gas chromatography.

Pond bottom soil samples were composites of handfuls of soil taken from four different locations in the ponds and were extracted as obtained without draining or drying. The wet soil, weighing 100–150 grams, was extracted three times with a total of about 250 ml. of benzene by shaking the mixture vigorously in a round-bottomed flask. After allowing the solid material to settle, the supernatant benzene was filtered. The filtrate was rinsed through a column consisting of 3–5 grams of anhydrous sodium sulfate on top of 10 grams of a 1:1 (w/w) MgO-Celite mixture in a 20 x 400-mm. chromatographic tube. After the benzene portions had drained through, the column was rinsed with about 20 ml. of benzene. The total effluent volume was measured, and the solution was analyzed by gas chromatography.

Wet vegetation was ground in an Oster homogenizer with three times its weight of anhydrous sodium sulfate to obtain a free-flowing powder. The sample size used was usually about 40 grams. The ground mixture was extracted 5–7 hours with benzene in a Soxhlet extractor, and the extract, followed by 20 ml. of benzene, was passed through 10 grams of a 1:1 MgO-Celite mixture prior to gas chromatographic analysis. Because of the difficulty of obtaining a uniform wet weight for reporting, the results for soil and vegetation are reported on a dry weight basis.

Frozen whole fish bodies were chopped into small pieces and ground in the Oster homogenizer with anhydrous sodium sulfate at the rate of one or two parts by weight of sodium sulfate per part of fresh tissue, depending on the dryness of the resulting mixture. To obtain a free-flowing powder, the mixture was usually frozen and reground twice after the initial grinding. A sample of 100 grams of the mixture was extracted with benzene for 5–7 hours in a Soxhlet extractor, and the extract was passed through a 10-gram MgO-Celite column. The column was rinsed with about 20 ml. of benzene, and the effluent volume was measured. A 50-ml. portion was treated with 1 ml. of concentrated sulfuric acid by shaking vigorously for 1 minute in a 60-ml. separatory funnel. The acid layer was separated and discarded, and the benzene solution was filtered through a 1-inch sodium sulfate pad. Analysis was by gas chromatography, with the results based on wet weight.

For these analyses a Wilkens Model 204 gas chromatograph equipped with electron capture detectors and 1-mv. recorder was used. Either of two column packing materials was used, Dow Corning QF-1 or DC-11 (5% w/w) on Chromosorb W (60–80 mesh) in 5-foot by ⅛ inch borosilicate glass columns. Injector, column, and detector temperatures were 170°, 164°, and 175°C., respectively. Nitrogen carrier gas flow was about 40 ml. per minute. Five to 10 μliter injections of the sample were made with a 10-μliter No. 701N Hamilton syringe. Dichlobenil was retained about 1.5 minutes on the QF-1 column and about 0.8 minute on the DC-11. Quantitation was based on recorder peak area measurements by a Disc integrator.

The volume of extract for the four types of sample ranged from about 125 to about 300 ml. Because of the high sensitivity of the electron capture detectors, it was not necessary to concentrate the samples except for the soil sample which was taken on July 8, 1965. The extract in this case was condensed to about 5 ml. in a Kuderna-Danish evaporator.

There was no detector response at the dichlobenil retention time with any of the pre-treatment samples. Recoveries of 90% for soil, vegetation, and water and 83% for fish were established by adding known amounts of dichlobenil to unprocessed samples and then carrying these samples through the entire process. Recovery in the Kuderna-Danish concentration step was 90%.

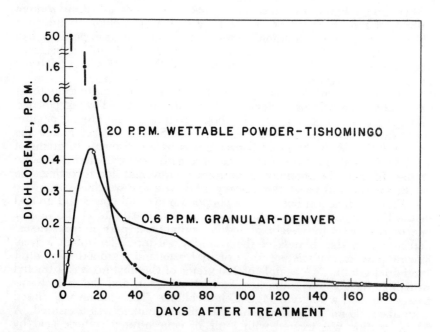

Figure 1.   Dichlobenil in water

Results and Discussion

Analysis results from samples taken from only the 20-p.p.m.-treated Tishomingo ponds are considered in this report. These are typical of the six treated ponds at Tishomingo; the patterns of herbicide build-up and removal are similar for all treatment levels, with quantitative differences proportional to the initial treatment.

Owing to the properties of the formulations used and the characteristics of the ponds tested, the patterns of accumulation and decline of residues in the two experiments were considerably different, as illustrated in Figure 1. The concentration of dichlobenil in water in the Tishomingo ponds treated with wettable powder was highest in the sample taken 3 days following treatment. A level of 50 p.p.m. was measured, which was two and one-half times treatment level. We cannot explain this anomalous level; error in treatment does not appear likely, nor does stratification or localization of the dichlobenil within the pond, especially since the water sample was a composite of portions taken at four different points. The only possibility that seems worth considering is that some of the powder from the formulation could have been floating at the surface where it could easily have become part of the sample.

The concentration of dissolved dichlobenil declined rapidly so that the 11-day levels averaged about 2% of the 3-day levels. In contrast, the highest concentration in the farm pond near Denver was measured nearly 3 weeks after treatment, at a level of 0.43 p.p.m. or about three-fourths of the theoretical maximum. Presumably, this lag in peaking was caused by the slow dissolution of the granular formulation. The much more gradual decline of the dissolved dichlobenil in this pond was probably caused by pond characteristics, such as temperature and bacterial activity.

The last water samples from the Tishomingo ponds, taken 85 days after treatment, showed that the residue level had decreased to 1.23 p.p.b. Dichlobenil remained in the Denver pond 188 days following treatment at a level of 1.05 p.p.b. A heavy rainstorm on July 30, 1964, one day before the 93-day sample was collected from the Denver pond, probably caused the dilution apparent in this and succeeding water samples. There was some overflow observed. After the rainstorm, water samples were collected from the pond below the dichlobenil-treated pond by personnel of the Weed Investigations Laboratory. Their analyses of these samples showed 0.03 p.p.m., indicating, on the basis of water volumes in the two ponds, that a considerable portion (perhaps as much as one-third) of the water in the dichlobenil-treated pond had been exchanged.

Figure 2 shows a pattern of residues in fish similar to that for water. Fish in the Tishomingo ponds treated with 20 p.p.m. of the wettable powder quickly absorbed high amounts of the herbicide; whole-body

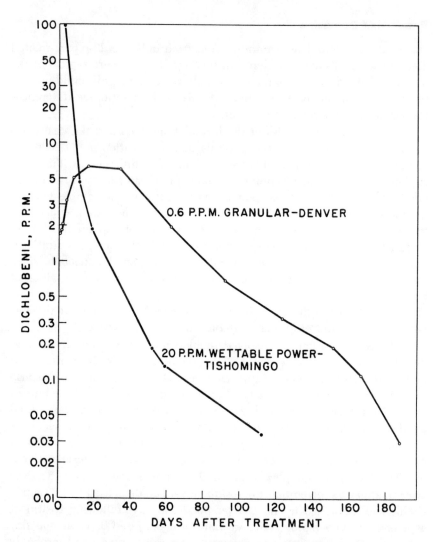

Figure 2.   Dichlobenil in fish

dichlobenil residues average 98 p.p.m. 3 days after treatment, twice the amount measured in water. The decline was rapid thereafter, similar to the water samples. Residue accumulation took place much less quickly in fish in the granular formulation-treated pond. Whole-body residues increased during the first 2 weeks of exposure to above 6 p.p.m., and this level apparently persisted for about 3 weeks since samples taken 35 days following treatment contained a level of 6 p.p.m. At this date the dichlobenil concentration in water had declined to about one-half the maximum level, and the fish whole-body residues were over 20 times the concentration in water. Bluegill and green sunfish residue levels were approximately equal and consistently about 50% higher than those found in bass or perch.

Pond mud at Tishomingo was first sampled about 1 month after treatment. Residue levels then were about 0.2 p.p.m., and this concentration gradually declined until the ponds were drained in October. Dichlobenil then was present at about 0.03 p.p.m.

The residue pattern for soil from the granule-treated pond is shown in Figure 3. Predictably, concentrations are highest within the first few

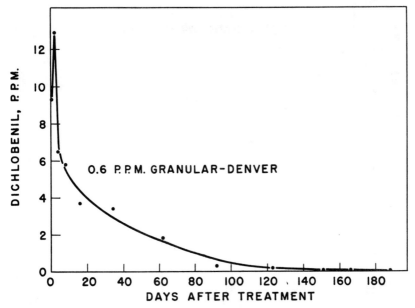

Figure 3.   *Dichlobenil in pond bottom mud*

days, with the peak concentration of almost 13 p.p.m. found in a sample taken 2 days after treatment. About half that level occurred in the sample taken 2 days later, but the decline thereafter was more gradual. The last soil sample, taken over 14 months after treatment, contained 0.08 p.p.b.

The high treatment levels in the Tishomingo ponds completely eliminated any plant growth. The 0.6-p.p.m. treatment in the Denver farm pond killed all vegetation except the filamentous algae, and this was severely inhibited for several weeks. The results illustrated in Figure 4 were obtained from the filamentous algae. *Chara* samples were obtained in the first 8 days following treatment and were close to the algae in residue amounts. The peak concentration measured for the algae was in the sample taken one day after treatment, with the surprising level of

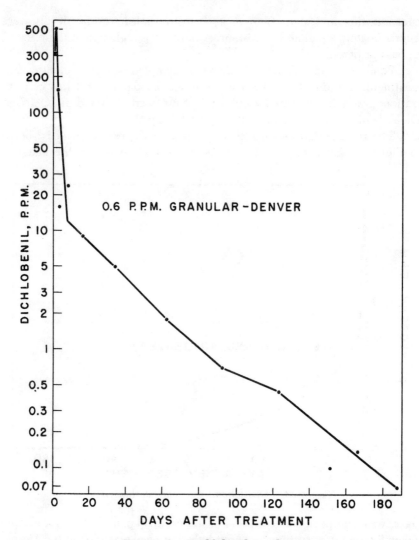

Figure 4.   Dichlobenil in algae

over 500 p.p.m. Within the next 7 days the residue level dropped to about 25 p.p.m. Following this sharp decline was the more gradual drop in residue concentration, typical of the patterns for water, fish tissue, and soil as well.

Numerous samples taken from the farm pond were analyzed for 2,6-dichlorobenzoic acid (7), as well as for dichlobenil. Although the presence of the benzoic acid derivative was expected as a metabolite, none was found. Interestingly, Massini (2) did detect one metabolite of dichlobenil but proved that it was not 2,6-dichlorobenzoic acid.

Acknowledgment

The author gratefully acknowledges the assistance of Oliver B. Cope, W. R. Bridges, Herman Sanders, Joseph McCraren, and others of the staff of the Fish-Pesticide Research Laboratory, and Peter A. Frank of the Weed Investigations Laboratory, Agricultural Research Service, U. S. Department of Agriculture.

Literature Cited

(1) Barnsley, G. E., Rosher, P. H., *Weed Research* 1, 147 (1961).
(2) Massini, P., *Weed Research* 1, 142 (1961).
(3) Aly, O. M., Faust, S. D., *J. Agr. Food Chem.* 12(6), 541 (1964).
(4) Ebeling, W., "Residue Reviews," Vol. 3, p. 116, Academic Press, N. Y., 1963.
(5) Sheets, T. J., *J. Agr. Food Chem.* 12(1), 30 (1964).
(6) Burschel, P., Freed, V. H., *Weeds* 7(2), 157 (1959).
(7) Shadbolt, C. A., Thompson-Hayward Chemical Company, Kansas City, Kansas, private communication.

RECEIVED October 13, 1965.

23

Sorption of Organic
Pesticides from Aqueous Solution

WALTER J. WEBER, Jr. and JOSEPH P. GOULD

Department of Civil Engineering, College of Engineering,
The University of Michigan, Ann Arbor, Mich.

*Adsorption on active carbon is an effective means for re-
moving organic pesticides from water. Capacities ranging
from approximately 40–53% by weight of the active carbon
have been realized. Capacities of this magnitude make
adsorption attractive from the standpoint of economics and
effectiveness of removing trace quantities. Rates of removal,
as well as total capacities, are remarkably similar for a broad
spectrum of classes of organic pesticides including thiophosphates, carbamates, dinitrophenols, and chlorophenoxy
acids. Thermodynamic studies indicate that the rate of
removal of organic pesticides by porous carbon is an endothermic process, in accord with a postulated intraparticle
transport rate-control mechanism while the equilibrium
position is controlled by an exothermic reaction, as is expected for adsorption.*

Dispersal of organic pesticides in the environment has been a matter
of widespread concern recently. One significant aspect of the
increased use of pesticides in agricultural, domestic, and industrial
applications has been the consequent increase in the occurrence of these
materials in waters which receive residue-containing wastes or land drainage. When such waters serve as drinking water supplies or for recrea-
tional purposes, the presence of pesticide materials represents a potential
hazard for the health and well being of the general public. Evidence of
the magnitude of the problem may be found in annual production figures;
for example, during the one-year period ending December 1962, more
than 350,000 tons of organic pesticides were produced (7).

If present trends toward increased use of pesticides and related compounds continue, it is quite possible that quantities of these materials

reaching our natural water courses may become large enough to represent a potential health hazard in the near future. Further, one must consider the possibility of cumulative toxicity even at current levels of concentration in ground and surface waters. These considerations make urgent the need for methods for extracting pesticide materials from waters and waste waters. In any consideration of treatment methods, the considerable stability of most synthetic organic pesticides must be recognized. Chlorinated hydrocarbons, the most stable class of pesticides, may remain essentially unchanged in natural water for years. For other classes of pesticides, such as the organic phosphate compounds, partial decomposition may often yield substances (e.g., paraoxon of parathion) of greater toxicity than the parent compounds.

As might be deduced from their chemical properties, most synthetic organic pesticides are quite resistant to conventional biological treatment. Other conventional water and waste treatment operations are also generally ineffective in removing pesticides. Coagulation and filtration, for example, are of variable effectiveness and thus are unreliable (6). Various oxidizing agents, including chlorine, permanganate, chlorine dioxide, and ozone, exhibit some quantitative differences in their respective abilities to oxidize pesticides but are qualitatively similar in behavior (6). In general, the chlorinated hydrocarbons are affected little by chemical oxidants, and the organic phosphates are converted in varying degrees to oxidation products which may be more toxic than the precursors.

Adsorption on carbon has attracted considerable attention as a possible alternative method for treating water and waste water to remove organic pesticides. Active carbon has long been known as an effective adsorbent for slightly soluble ring-type compounds, and several studies have indicated that the sparingly soluble cyclic pesticides are no exception. Studies by Hyndshaw on adsorption of a number of chlorinated hydrocarbons, chlorophenoxyacetic acids, and organophosphates have demonstrated reductions of 90% or more in pesticide concentrations, for initial concentrations in the range of 50 p.p.m. and lower, with carbon dosages of 20 p.p.m. and less (4). Aly and Faust have reported capacities for powdered carbon ranging from about 10% by weight for the free acid form of 2,4-dichlorophenoxyacetic acid to about 25% by weight for the isopropyl ester (1). Cohen *et al.* have indicated similar degrees of adsorption for the fish poisons, toxaphene and rotenone (2).

Objectives of this study were to investigate the adsorption of several of the important classes of organic pesticides and to establish precise physical and thermodynamic parameters. An effort has been made to shed some light on the relatively neglected question of rates of adsorption of pesticides. Further, initial attempts to correlate chemical structure with rate and capacity for adsorption have been made.

As Table I illustrates, the chemical classes represented by the pesticides studied include thiophosphates [O,O-diethyl-o-p-nitrophenyl phosphorothioate], carbamates [1-naphthyl-N-methylcarbamate], dinitrophenols [2,4-dinitro-o-sec-butylphenol and 2,4-dinitro-o-cyclohexylphenol], and chlorophenoxy acids [2,4-dichlorophenoxyacetic acid, 2,4,5-trichlorophenoxyacetic acid, and 2-(2,4,5-trichlorophenoxy)propionic acid]. In addition, a number of molecularly related nitrophenols have been studied to establish the effects of molecular geometry and substituent groups on adsorption of pesticide-type materials.

The O,O-diethyl-o-p-nitrophenyl phosphorothioate (parathion) was obtained from the American Cyanamid Co., and the 1-naphthyl-N-methylcarbamate (Sevin) was obtained from the R. A. Taft Sanitary Engineering Center, U. S. Public Health Service. The Dow Chemical Co. provided

Table I. Selected Organic Pesticides and Some Molecularly Related Nitrophenols

Compound	Common Name or Abbrev.	Primary Application as Pesticide	Molecular Weight	Approx. Solubility[a] of Neutral Molecule in Water at 25°C., mg./liter
2,4-Dichlorophenoxyacetic acid	2,4-D	herbicide	221.0	900
2,4,5-Trichlorophenoxyacetic acid	2,4,5-T	herbicide	255.5	280
2-(2,4,5-Trichlorophenoxy) propionic acid	Silvex	herbicide	269.5	180
2,4-Dinitro-o-sec-butylphenol	DNOSBP	herbicide, insecticide	240.2	52
2,4-Dinitro-o-cyclohexylphenol	DNOCHP	acaricide, insecticide	266.2	10
1-Naphthyl-N-methylcarbamate	Sevin	insecticide	201.2	99
O,O-Diethyl-o-p-nitrophenyl phosphorothioate	Parathion	acaricide, insecticide	291.3	24
4-Nitrophenol	PNP	related nitrophenol	139.1	16,000
2,4-Dinitrophenol	DNP	related nitrophenol	184.1	6,000
2,4-Dinitro-o-cresol	DNC	related nitrophenol	198.1	v.sl.s.
2,4-Dinitrothymol	DNT	related nitrophenol	240.2	v.sl.s.
2,6-Dinitro-p-cyclohexylphenol	DNPCHP	related nitrophenol	266.2	v.sl.s.

[a] All of these compounds except Sevin and parathion form soluble salts.

2,4-dichlorophenoxyacetic acid (2,4-D), 2,4,5-trichlorophenoxyacetic acid (2,4,5-T), 2-(2,4,5-trichlorophenoxy)propionic acid (Silvex), 2,4-dinitro-*o-sec*-butylphenol (DNOSBP), and 2,4-dinitro-*o*-cyclohexylphenol (DNO-CHP). The 2,6-dinitro-*p*-cyclohexylphenol (DNPCHP) was obtained from the Mallinckrodt Laboratories, Harvard University; the 2,4-dinitro-thymol (DNT) from Eastman Chemical Products, Inc.; the 4-nitrophenol (PNP), 2,4-dinitrophenol (DNP), and 2,4-dinitro-*o*-cresol (DNC) from the Matheson Co. All compounds as obtained were described by the suppliers as being chemically "pure" relative to the active chemical agent.

Columbia LC carbon, a coconut carbon with high resistance to attrition, was used as the adsorbent in all experiments (8). Prior to experimentation, the adsorbent was separated by thorough sieving into uniform particle sizes, after which portions of suitable size range were washed in distilled water to remove leachable impurities and adherent powder and dried at 105°C. The size range chosen for the present studies included those particles passing a U. S. Standard Sieve No. 50 and being retained on a No. 60 sieve; the mean particle diameter for this size range is 273 microns. All studies were conducted with carbon from the same manufacturer's lot to avoid batch-to-batch variations.

To eliminate from the experimental systems all extraneous material which might have introduced sources of error and interference, all solutions used in the experimental systems were prepared with twice-distilled water. Tap water was first distilled in a conventional tin-lined still, and the condensate was transferred into an all-glass still for redistillation. Preliminary boiling with escape of steam was used to purge the water of dissolved carbon dioxide and chlorine before collecting the condensate from the redistillation.

Experimental

Analytical Methods. Of the substances investigated, only parathion does not exhibit a characteristic absorption spectrum suitable for direct measurement of concentration within the ranges used in these experiments. Spectrophotometric data for the other pesticides and related dinitrophenols are listed in Table II.

The analytical method used for parathion takes advantage of the ease with which the phosphorus-oxygen bond in that material is cleaved by hydroxide. The hydrolysis produces a mole of 4-nitrophenol for each mole of parathion originally present in solution. Because 4-nitrophenol has a well-defined absorption spectrum with a high molar absorptivity at the wavelength of maximum absorption (400 mμ) and because the reaction to form 4-nitrophenol from parathion is rapid and quantitative, the method provides a reliable and sensitive means for analyzing parathion.

For fairly concentrated samples (1–100 μM), about 10 ml. of 1N KOH were added to 50 ml. of sample. The mixture was refluxed for 1

Table II. Analytical Data for Organic Pesticides and Molecularly Related Nitrophenols

Compound	Wavelength of Maximum Absorption, λ, mμ	Molar Absorptivity liter/mole.-cm.
2,4-Dichlorophenoxyacetic acid	284	1,900
2,4,5-Trichlorophenoxyacetic acid	289	2,500
2-(2,4,5-Trichlorophenoxy)propionic acid	289	2,500
2,4-Dinitro-o-sec-butylphenol	375	14,520
2,4-Dinitro-o-cyclohexylphenol	376	14,000
1-Naphthyl-N-methylcarbamate	279	5,900
4-Nitrophenol	anion—400	17,980
(also for parathion)	neutral—315	10,000
2,4-Dinitrophenol	360	14,820
2,4-Dinitro-o-cresol	373	14,040
2,4-Dinitrothymol	394	15,240
2,6-Dinitro-p-cyclohexylphenol	447	7,075

hour, allowed to cool, diluted to 100 ml., and then the absorbance at 400 mμ was measured in a cell of appropriate length. For more dilute samples, three KOH pellets were added to a 100-ml. sample, then the procedure outlined above was repeated. The lower limit of the method is about 50 nanomoles/liter using a 10-cm. cell.

After measuring the absorption spectrum for each solute with a Beckman model DK-2 spectrophotometer, the absorption maximum for solutions of each of the substances was located precisely with a Beckman model DU spectrophotometer by measuring intensities of absorption for a localized region on both sides of the wavelength of maximum absorption indicated by the spectra obtained with the DK-2 model. Subsequent spectrophotometric measurements were made with the DU model.

Experimental Methods. Agitated nonflow experiments were used to investigate both the kinetics and equilibria of adsorption. The batch technique was selected because of its relative simplicity. Advantages of this type of system include its freedom from complex hydraulic parameters indigenous to flow-through systems, its adaptability to small volume work, ease of investigating variation of conditions, and general facility of operation.

Although column operation seems likely to be used for large scale technical applications of carbon adsorption to waste treatment, evaluation of the fundamental characteristics of adsorption is simpler with a batch technique. Furthermore, once suitable functional relationships for the variables have been established, extrapolating data from batch systems to predict behavior in continuous systems should be feasible.

The reaction vessels for the kinetic studies were 4000-ml. resistant glass bottles, in which solutions were agitated with Teflon-coated stirring rods extending directly into the adsorbate solution and connected to synchronous motors operating at 1550 r.p.m. Previous kinetic studies in similar systems had shown that rate of adsorption is independent of stirring rate at rotations greater than a few hundred r.p.m. (8). Temperature control for the rate studies was maintained by immersing the reaction vessels in water baths, thermoregulated to $\pm 0.5°C$. All kinetic studies have been conducted at 28°C.

For each experiment on rate of adsorption, an 8-liter volume of adsorbate solution was prepared at a concentration slightly higher than that desired for the kinetic experiment. To insure that the nitrophenols studied were present as the anions in the experimental systems, sufficient KOH was added to give a final pH between 9 and 10. Spectrophotometric measurement of the exact concentration of solute in the solution was then made, and the original 8-liter volume was diluted appropriately to give a solution closer to the desired concentration. Exactly 3000 ml. of the adjusted solution were then placed in each of two 4-liter reaction vessels. The reaction vessels were then placed in a water bath for approximately 24 hours to allow the solution to attain the desired temperature and reach adsorptive equilibrium with the surfaces of the vessels. Before introducing a suitable, accurately weighed quantity of carbon to each vessel, an initial sample was removed and analyzed for concentration of adsorbate. This gave an accurate check on the preparation of the solution and served as the reference concentration for the rate study. The carbon was then introduced into the vessel and was rapidly dispersed by the motor-driven stirrer operating at 1550 r.p.m. At appropriate intervals the stirring was briefly interrupted while samples of the supernatant solution were pipeted from each of the reaction vessels; the samples for analysis resulted in some small decrease in total adsorbate available to the adsorbent, but the cumulative error of 2–3% was not significant for this type of experiment. The running of two parallel experiments, identical in all details, provided a check on the reproducibility of the data.

To investigate adsorptive capacities and equilibria, large volumes of adsorbate solution were prepared, and 250-ml. measures of this solution were dispensed into 300-ml. resistant glass reaction flasks. A suitable, accurately weighed amount of adsorbent was then added to each flask, the weight being varied to cover the range of equilibrium solute concentrations of interest. For each study, several flasks of solution were left without carbon for use as blanks. The ground-glass stoppered reaction flasks were then sealed and placed in an oscillating shaker to be shaken for approximately 2 weeks; the time required for equilibrium to be obtained was determined previously for each type of system. Samples from each of the solutions were analyzed at the end of the appropriate period; the amount of adsorption was computed from the difference between the concentration of adsorbate measured for the blanks and for each treated solution. Most studies were conducted in a room that was maintained at a reasonably uniform temperature so that fluctuations in the temperatures of the solutions were no more than 2–3°C. over the duration of the study. The mean temperature for the equilibrium studies was 25°C.

Adsorption Rates

Previous investigations have indicated that the rate-limiting step for removal of organic solutes from dilute aqueous solution by porous active carbon in agitated nonflow systems is one of intraparticle transport of the solute in the pores and capillaries of the adsorbent (*10*). For systems in which intraparticle transport is the rate-limiting step, data for uptake of solute from solution should give a linear plot as a function of the square root of time from the time the adsorbent was introduced to the system (*3*). In accord with this, the data for our experiments have been plotted as a function of the square root of time.

Representative rate data for 2,4,5-T and parathion for the experiments on adsorption of pesticides on active carbon are presented in Figures 1 and 2. The $(C_0 - C)/m$ values in these plots represent the amount of solute, both in micromoles and milligrams, removed from solution per gram of carbon. Good linearization of the data is observed for the experiments, in accord with expected behavior for intraparticle-transport rate control. Similar linearization was obtained also for data for the other pesticides. The linear traces facilitate comparison of relative rates of adsorption of pesticides, and such comparison is made in column 1 of Table III, using the square of the slope of each plot as the relative rate constant for the experiment.

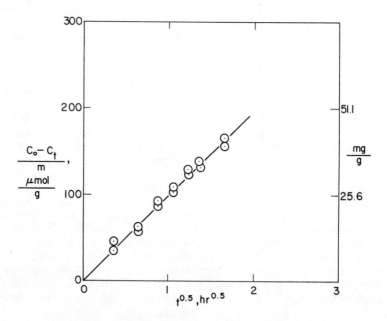

Figure 1.   Rate of adsorption of 2,4,5-T
Adsorption of 2,4,5-T on 273-micron Columbia LC carbon. Initial concentration, C_0, is 9.8 µmoles/liter, and the carbon dose, m, is 25 mg./liter. Temperature is 28°C. Cumulative uptake of 2,4,5-T per gram of carbon is plotted as a function of the square root of time for linearization of the data. Uptake is given in terms of µmoles per gram of carbon on the left ordinate and mg. per gram on the right ordinate.

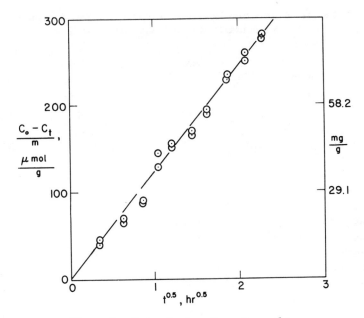

Figure 2. *Rate of adsorption of parathion*
Cumulative uptake of parathion from a 10.0-μmolar solution by 25
mg./liter on 273-micron Columbia LC carbon.

It is of interest that the rate constants for adsorption of the various organic pesticides on the 273-micron carbon are remarkably similar. The data suggest that even for a rather broad spectrum of different types of organic pesticides, similar rates of removal from solution should result. Thus, the effectiveness of active carbon as it relates to rate of removal of organic pesticides from solution should be relatively independent of the type of organic pesticide, at least within the classes of compounds and conditions used for the present experiments.

Pesticide Concentration. In these experiments we have observed that the concentration of pesticide has a significant effect upon rate of removal by active carbon. The rate data listed in Table III are for experiments conducted with a solution containing solute in initial concentration of about 10 μmoles/liter. Figure 3 illustrates some data for experiments conducted with some of the pesticides at concentrations greater than and slightly less than 10 μmoles/liter. The uppermost curve in Figure 3 is for adsorption of 2,4-D from a 52.2-μM solution. The middle curve in Figure 3 is for a 45.2-μM solution of Silvex, and the lower curve is for adsorption of DNOCHP from a solution with an initial concentration of 7.7 μmoles/liter.

For 2,4-D the 5.1-fold increase in initial molar concentration resulted in a new rate constant of 16.0 × 10⁴ (μmoles/gram)²/hr. as compared

Table III. Adsorption Constants for Organic Pesticides and Molecularly Related Nitrophenols

Compound	Relative Rate [a] Constant, k [$(\mu moles/gram)^2/hr.$] $\times 10^{-4}$	Langmuir Equilibrium Constants [b]	
		X_m, $(\mu moles/gram)$ $\times 10^{-3}$	b, $(1/\mu moles)$
2,4-Dichlorophenoxyacetic acid	1.44	1.75	0.095
2,4,5-Trichlorophenoxyacetic acid	1.00	1.75	0.150
2-(2,4,5-Trichlorophenoxy) propionic acid	0.71	1.72	0.145
2,4-Dinitro-o-sec-butylphenol	1.35	1.85	0.145
2,4-Dinitro-o-cyclohexylphenol	1.12	1.88	0.148
1-Naphthyl-N-methylcarbamate	1.64	—	—
O,O-Diethyl-o-p-nitrophenyl phosphorothioate	1.49	1.82	1.22
4-Nitrophenol	anion—0.52	—	—
	neutral—1.21	—	—
2,4-Dinitrophenol	0.87	—	—
2,4-Dinitro-o-cresol	1.12	—	—
2,4-Dinitrothymol	0.67	—	—
2,6-Dinitro-p-cyclohexylphenol	0.90	—	—

[a] Experimental conditions: C_o = 10 μmoles/liter, 25.0 mg./liter, 0.273-mm. Columbia carbon, 28°C.
[b] Experimental conditions: 0.273-mm. Columbia carbon, 25°C.

with a value of 1.44×10^4 (μmoles/gram)^2/hr. for experiments in which the initial concentration was 10.3 μmoles/liter. The experiment at high concentration with Silvex, representing a 4.6-fold increase in initial molar concentration, yielded a new relative rate constant of 7.56×10^4 (μmoles/gram)^2/hr. as compared with a value of 0.71×10^4 (μmoles/gram)^2/hr. for experiments with an initial molar concentration of 9.8 μmoles/liter.

It is interesting to note that the ratio of the relative rate constants for the two solutes, 2,4-D and Silvex, obtained from experiments at low concentration is 2.03 while the ratio of the relative rate constants obtained from experiments at high concentration is 2.11. Thus, it appears that the effect of initial concentration upon the rate at which organic pesticides are removed from water by active carbon is relatively uniform, at least for similar classes of organic pesticides.

While the effect of concentration is qualitatively evident, it is essential for purposes of engineering design and operation of adsorption processes that rather precise prediction of concentration or "load" effect be possible. Previous findings relative to the concentration dependence of

rate of uptake of certain other pollution materials by active carbon indicate a linear relationship between the relative rate constant expressed in
units of μmoles/gram-hr.   and the square-root of initial concentration (8).
To evaluate more quantitatively the dependence of rate of adsorption
upon initial pesticide concentration and to test the generality of the conclusions reached in the previous work cited, a series of experiments was
performed in which the initial concentration of a selected pesticide,

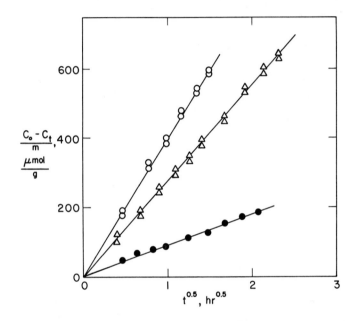

Figure 3.   Rates of adsorption of 2,4-D, Silvex, and
DNOCHP from solutions of different initial concentrations
○—2,4-D from a 52.2-μM solution
△—Silvex from a 45.2-μM solution
●—DNOCHP from a 7.7-μM solution

DNOSBP, was varied from 1.1 to 96.9 μmoles/liter. Relative rate constants, expressed in units of (μmoles/gram)^2/hr., derived from the present
experiments are plotted in Figure 4 *vs.* initial concentration of solute.
The linearity of the trace so obtained indicates good agreement with the
concentration dependence of adsorption rate noted previously for sulfonated alkylbenzenes (8). Thus, the previous and present experiments
suggest that the nature of the effect of concentration may well be general
and quantitatively as well as qualitatively predictable.

The data plotted in Figure 4 indicate a dependence of the relative
rate constant on concentration of 1180 (μmoles/gram)^2/hr. for each

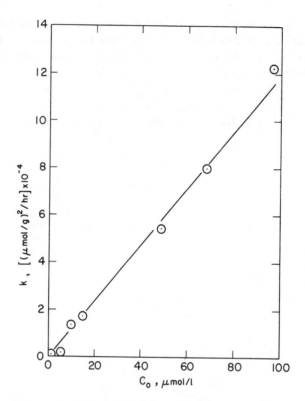

*Figure 4. Effect of initial concentration on adsorp-
tion of DNOSBP*
Rate constants obtained from a number of experiments
with different initial concentrations are plotted vs. initial
concentration to give a linear trace. Concentrations of
DNOSBP range from 1.1 to 96.9 μmoles.

μmole/liter or 1180 μmoles-liter/gram²-hr. Preliminary experiments with
initial concentrations of DNOSBP in the nanomolar range suggest reasonably close adherence to this rate dependence even at extremely low
concentrations.

Molecularly Related Nitrophenols. To define more explicitly the
relative influences of molecular structure and hydrophobic character upon
rate of adsorption of pesticide materials by porous carbon, a number of
pure dinitrophenols molecularly related to DNOSBP and DNOCHP
have been studied. The molecular structures of DNOSBP, DNOCHP and
the molecularly related dinitrophenols—DNP, DNC, DNT, and DNPCHP
—are illustrated in Figure 5.

As noted in Figure 5, the first four compounds of this series—DNP,
DNC, DNOSBP, and DNOCHP—are 2,4-dinitrophenols with various substituent groups in the remaining ortho position. The fifth member of the

series—DNT—is a 2,4-dinitrophenol isomeric with the DNOSBP but possessing two alkyl groups rather than one, while the sixth member—DNPCHP—is a dinitrophenol isomeric with the DNOCHP.

Relative rate constants for adsorption of these compounds on the experimental carbon are tabulated in Table III.

Because all six members of the dinitrophenol series were studied as the highly soluble anions, solubility effects can be largely neglected in comparing relative rates of adsorption. Primary considerations then would be hydrophobic character, affecting the rate at which solute transferred from liquid to solid phase, and molecular geometry, affecting rate of intraparticle transport through the influence of steric effects.

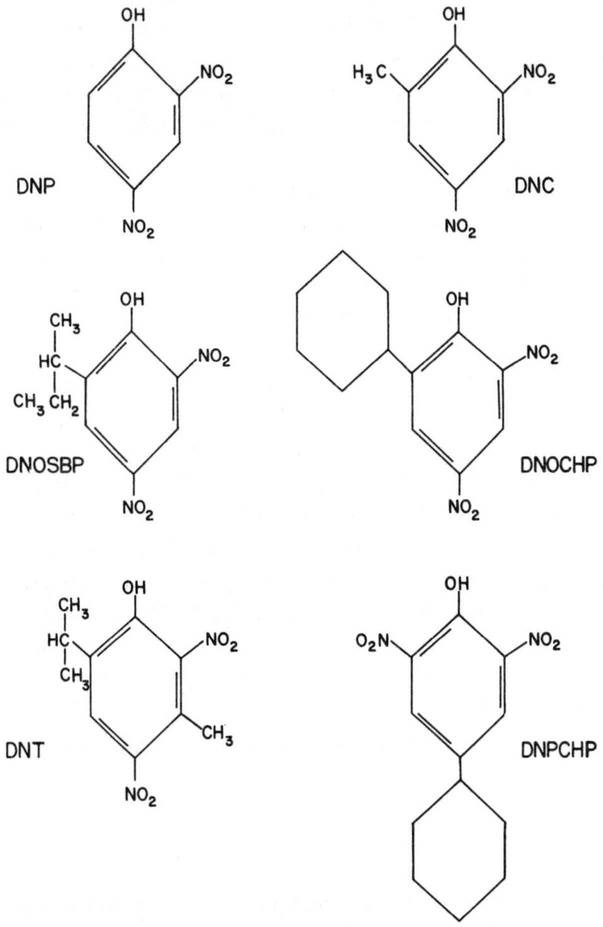

Figure 5.   Molecular structures of related dinitrophenols

One may note by comparing the relative rate constants listed in Table III that rate of adsorption increases rapidly in the series DNP-DNC-DNOSBP, suggesting that increasing hydrophobic nature increases the adsorption rate over this range more rapidly than the increasing molecular area can act to retard rate. However, by further comparing the rate constant for DNOSBP with that for the more hydrophobic DNOCHP, one observes a substantial decrease in rate of adsorption, suggesting that the geometric difference between the relatively small and easily deformed sec-butyl group and the larger and comparatively rigid cyclohexyl group is enough to override the influence of the increase in hydrophobic character. The structure of the sec-butyl group permits bending of carbon-carbon and carbon-hydrogen bonds in such fashion as to permit more rapid migration into the pore structure of the carbon while such bending or deformation is rather limited for the cyclohexyl group.

In studying the two pairs of isomers, DNOSBP-DNT and DNOCHP-DNPCHP, it is possible to neglect hydrophobic character—which will be essentially constant among isomers—and concentrate on molecular geometry. Comparing the structures of DNOSBP and DNT, one may deduce that the DNT molecule, with its fairly rigid alkyl groups, might present a larger effective cross-sectional area for diffusion than will the DNOSBP with its single and relatively easily deformed alkyl group. The correctness of this deduction is confirmed in the experimental observation that the rate of adsorption for DNOSBP is twice that for DNT.

An explanation of the observed difference between adsorption rates for DNOCHP and DNPCHP is not as straightforward as for the DNOSBP-DNT isomer pair. One possibility is that the cyclohexyl group is less able to fold out of the way when in the para position than when in the ortho position, thus presenting a less compact form for pore transport. In addition, it is likely that the concentration of three quite inductive groups on adjacent carbon atoms in the DNPCHP molecule tends, through resulting electrostatic interaction with functional groups at the surface of the carbon, to retard transport while in the DNOCHP molecule the relatively wide positional spacing of the three inductive groups decreases their influence. A third possibility is that, owing to steric interactions, the two nitro groups in DNPCHP are forced apart out of the plane of the ring and to opposite sides of it, increasing further the steric hindrance to pore transport.

Adsorption Equilibria

The extent to which the full surface area of an active carbon can be used for adsorption depends on the concentration of solute in the solution with which the carbon is mixed. The specific relationship between concentration of solute and degree of removal from solution, at constant temperature and for conditions of equilibrium, defines the adsorption isotherm. The preferred form for representing the adsorption isotherm is to express the quantity of solute absorbed per unit weight of adsorbent as a function of C, the equilibrium concentration of solute remaining in solution.

A number of different types of adsorption relationships prevail under different circumstances. The most common relationship between the amount of solute adsorbed per unit of adsorbent and the equilibrium concentration in solution is obtained for systems in which it appears that adsorption from solution leads to the deposition of only a single layer of solute molecules on the surface of the solid. This type of adsorption equilibrium is best represented by the Langmuir model for adsorption, which assumes that maximum adsorption corresponds to a saturated monolayer of solute molecules on the adsorbent surface, that the energy of adsorption is constant, and that there is no movement of adsorbate molecules in the plane of the surface after initial adsorption (5).

The form of the Langmuir adsorption isotherm is

$$X = \frac{X_m bC}{1 + bC} \tag{1}$$

in which C indicates the measured residual concentration in solution at equilibrium, X_m is equal to the number of moles of solute adsorbed by one gram of carbon in forming a complete monolayer on the carbon surface, X represents the number of moles of solute adsorbed per gram of carbon at concentration C, and b denotes a constant related to the energy of adsorption. The reciprocal, $1/b$, is the concentration at which adsorption attains half its limiting X_m value.

Two convenient linear forms for the Langmuir equation are:

$$\frac{1}{X} = \frac{1}{X_m} + \frac{1}{bX_m C} \tag{2}$$

and

$$\frac{C}{X} = \frac{1}{bX_m} + \frac{C}{X_m} \tag{3}$$

Either Equation 2 or Equation 3 may be used to linearize the data that conform to the Langmuir equation. The form chosen usually depends on the range and spread of the data and on the particular range of data to be emphasized.

All the organic pesticides tested exhibit equilibrium adsorption on the experimental carbon in reasonable accord with the Langmuir model for adsorption. Representative data for the isothermal equilibrium adsorption experiments are plotted in Figures 6 and 7 for 2,4,5-T and parathion, respectively. Figures 8 and 9 are plots of the same data according to the linear form of the Langmuir adsorption isotherm given by Equation 2. The ordinate intercept of the line drawn through the data in each of Figures 8 and 9 represents the reciprocal of the ultimate capacity for adsorption, $\dfrac{1}{X_m}$, and the slope of each plot represents the reciprocal of bX_m. From the intercepts and slopes of such linear plots, values for the Langmuir constants for each solute have been calculated; these values are listed in Table III.

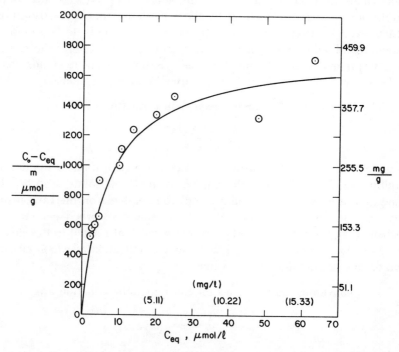

Figure 6.   Adsorption isotherm for 2,4,5-T
Capacity for adsorption of 2,4,5-T on 273-micron Columbia LC carbon at
25°C. is plotted as a function of residual concentration, C_{eq}, at equilibrium.
The left ordinate gives capacity in units of μmoles of solute per gram of carbon
and the right ordinate in units of milligrams of solute per gram of carbon.
The points represent experimental data; the line drawn through the data is
the calculated Langmuir isotherm.

As was the case for the relative rate constants for the different organic pesticides, values of X_m listed in Table III are quite similar in magnitude for the different adsorbates—on the order of 1800 μmoles of solute per gram of carbon. Thus, the ultimate capacity appears to be

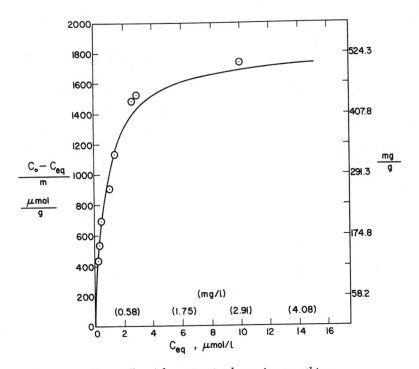

Figure 7.   Adsorption isotherm for parathion
Capacity for adsorption of parathion on 273-micron Columbia LC carbon at
25°C. is plotted as a function of residual concentration, C_{eq}, at equilibrium. The
left ordinate gives capacity in μmoles of solute per gram of carbon and the right
ordinate in units of mg. of solute per gram of carbon. The points represent
experimental data; the line drawn through the data is the calculated Langmuir
isotherm.

relatively independent of the type of organic pesticide tested, at least
within the experimental ranges. With the exception of the parathion,
values for the parameter b, which is a measure of the energy of adsorption, are quite similar for the organic pesticides. The fact that the value
for b for parathion is an order of magnitude higher than values of b
for the other organic pesticides indicates that this material has a high
energy of adsorption and attains adsorptive capacities near the ultimate
capacity at relatively low equilibrium concentrations.

Thermodynamic Constants

Equilibrium capacity for adsorption of organic solutes on carbon
can be predicted to increase with decreasing temperature since adsorption reactions are exothermic. The differential heat of adsorption, ΔH, is
defined as the total amount of heat evolved in the adsorption of a definite
quantity of solute on an adsorbent. Heats of vapor phase adsorption

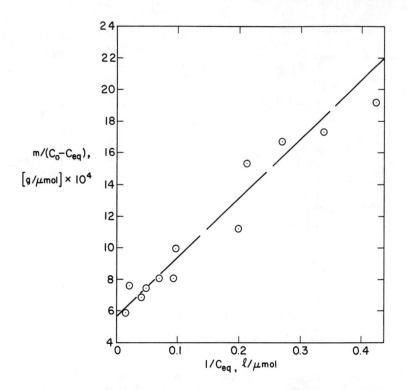

Figure 8.   Langmuir plot for 2,4,5-T
In accord with the Langmuir model for adsorption equilibrium, a linear
trace is obtained for the isotherm for 2,4,5-T when $(X)^{-1}$ is plotted vs.
$(C_{eq})^{-1}$. Intercept of plot is $(X_m)^{-1}$, and the slope is $(bX_m)^{-1}$.

generally are several thousand calories per mole, but because water must be desorbed from the surface during adsorption from aqueous solution, heat changes tend to be somewhat smaller than for vapor phase adsorption.

The differential heat of adsorption may be calculated from maximum levels of adsorption at two or more different temperatures and the van't Hoff equation in the form,

$$\Delta H = \frac{RT_1T_2}{T_2 - T_1} \left(\ln X_{m1} - \ln X_{m2} \right) \tag{4}$$

where R is the universal gas constant, T_1 and T_2 are the absolute temperatures of two otherwise identical systems, and X_m is for this example the limiting monolayer adsorption value for the Langmuir adsorption model. A plot of values for the logarithm of X_m vs. the reciprocal of absolute temperature for a given system should then yield a linear trace with a slope equal to $\Delta H/RT_1T_2$.

While the temperature dependence of equilibrium capacity for adsorption is defined by the parameter ΔH, the dependence of rate of adsorption is usually expressed in terms of activation energy, E. Rate of adsorption is related to the activation energy by the equation,

$$k = Ae^{-E/RT} \tag{5}$$

where k is the absolute rate constant, T the absolute temperature, and A is a temperature-independent factor sometimes called the frequency factor. Equation 5, the Arrhenius equation, may be written

$$\ln k = \ln A - \frac{E}{RT} \tag{6}$$

which implies a linear relationship between $\ln k$ and $\frac{1}{T}$ with a slope of E/R. Equation 6 may be written for any two rates, k_1 and k_2, corresponding to absolute temperatures T_1 and T_2, respectively, and the difference expressed as

$$E = \frac{RT_1 T_2}{T_2 - T_1} (\ln k_1 - \ln k_2) \tag{7}$$

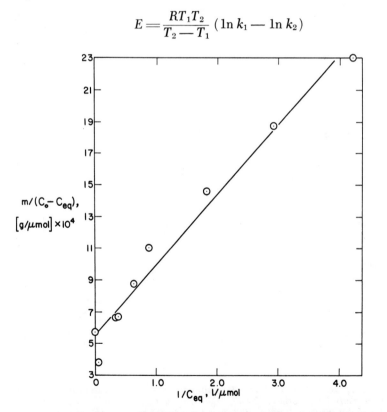

Figure 9. Langmuir plot for parathion

which has the same form as Equation 4. From this relationship E can be evaluated for any system in the same way as ΔH.

For uptake of solute from solution by porous solids the rate will be endothermic rather than exothermic if intraparticle transport is the rate-limiting mechanism. Because diffusion is an endothermic process while adsorption is exothermic, rate of uptake of solute by porous solids will often increase with increasing temperature while for the same system the equilibrium position of adsorption or adsorption capacity will decrease with increasing temperature.

Plots of the relative rate constants *vs.* T^{-1} for three different classes of the pesticides studied, along with those for the neutral and ionic

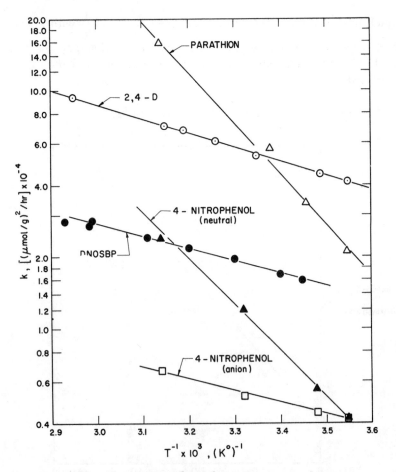

Figure 10.   Temperature dependence of rate of adsorption
Rate constants for parathion, 2,4-D, DNOSBP, and the neutral and anionic species of 4-nitrophenol are plotted on a logarithmic scale vs. the reciprocal of temperature, °K.

species of 4-nitrophenol, are given in Figure 10, and the corresponding
values for the respective energies of activation are listed in Table IV. It
should be noted that the activation energies derived from the present
experimental data, unlike previous values calculated for sulfonated alkylbenzenes, are based on relative rate constants expressed in units of

Table IV. Thermodynamic Constants for Adsorption

Compound	Activation Energy,[a] E^* cal./gram-mole	Heat of Adsorption, ΔH, cal./gram-mole
2,4-D	2740	— 4160
DNOSBP	2380	— 4190
Parathion	9650	—
PNP (neutral)	8890	—
PNP (anion)	2260	—

[a] Based on *relative* rate constant, k.

(μmoles/gram)^2 per hour. It is felt that the thermodynamic constants
so calculated more closely represent absolute rate theory values. In accord
with expectations for intraparticle transport as the rate-limiting mechanism, the experimental activation energy values tabulated in Table IV are
all positive. Thus, the kinetics of uptake of the pesticides by porous
carbon is endothermic.

Comparison of the values of E for the various pesticides and the
neutral and anionic species of the simple nitrophenol indicates that a
much higher activation energy is associated with adsorption of neutral
molecules (parathion and the neutral nitrophenol) than with adsorption
of anions (2,4-D, DNOSBP, and the anionic nitrophenol). This observation suggests the possibility of two different rate-limiting steps in the
intraparticle transport mechanism. Current studies are being directed
toward more detailed exploration of the observed thermokinetic phenomena.

The effects of temperature on the equilibrium capacity of active
carbon for adsorption of 2,4-D and DNOSBP have been studied. The
data are plotted in Figure 11, and the experimentally determined heats
of adsorption are listed in Table IV. The values for ΔH for the 2,4-D
and DNOSBP are remarkably similar, and as one would anticipate from
considering the thermodynamics of adsorption, both values are negative.
In view of the general range of the values for ΔH it may be anticipated
that normal temperature variations in practical applications will not
significantly affect ultimate capacity for sorption of organic pesticides
on carbon.

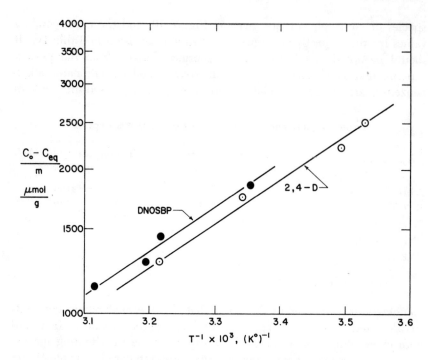

Figure 11. Temperature dependence of capacity for adsorption
Equilibrium capacities for adsorption of DNOSBP and 2,4-D are plotted on a
logarithmic scale vs. the reciprocal of temperature, °K.

Summary and Conclusions

Comparison may be made between the adsorption capacities, in terms of the Langmuir constants X_m and b, for the organic pesticides and those obtained in previous studies for sulfonated alkylbenzenes and other pollution materials (9). Results of some of the previous studies along with those from the present investigation are summarized in Table V.

It is apparent from the X_m values listed in Table V that capacities for adsorption of the organic pesticides on active carbon are quite large, greater on a molar basis than phenol and sulfonated 2-dodecylbenzene, and greater on a weight basis than any of the three other compounds. On the other hand, the b^{-1} values, except for parathion, indicate approach to saturation adsorption only at relatively high residual concentrations.

By way of comparing the capacity data derived from the present experiments with capacity data obtained by other investigators for the same solute, a plot of an experimental isotherm presented by Aly and Faust for adsorption of 2,4-D on powdered carbon indicates an adsorption capacity of 80 mg./gram corresponding to a residual concentration of 0.5 mg./liter (*1*). One may calculate from the Langmuir data presented in Table V that the present experiments predict a capacity of 70 mg./gram, at the 0.5 mg./liter residual concentration level, for adsorption on the comparatively large 273-micron experimental carbon. A considerably higher capacity is to be expected for the fine carbon used by Aly and Faust, according to previous observations on the effect of particle size on equilibrium capacity (*9*). Indeed, one would anticipate a capacity somewhat in excess of 80 mg./gram for carbon of the size used by Aly and Faust (95% passing a 325-mesh sieve). However, in light of the differences in carbon type and carbon size, the agreement may be considered rather good.

The capacity figures presented in Table V are probably most significant for column operation since counter current operation makes realizable those capacities corresponding to initial concentrations rather than to allowable effluent concentrations. The b^{-1} values indicate the anticipated sharpness of the breakthrough front and to some extent provide guidance for the optimum depth of column for satisfactory removal of the contaminant, although rate of adsorption is an equally important factor in this respect. Larger b^{-1} values in general would call for greater depths of adsorption column.

Table V. Comparison of Langmuir Equilibrium Constants for Organic Pesticides and Selected Adsorbates

Compound	X_m		b^{-1}	
	mmoles/gram	mg./gram	μmoles/liter	mg./liter
2,4-D	1.75	387	10.5	2.32
2,4,5-T	1.75	448	6.7	1.71
Silvex	1.72	464	6.9	1.86
DNOSBP	1.85	444	5.8	1.39
DNOCHP	1.88	500	6.8	1.81
Parathion	1.82	530	0.82	0.24
Phenol	1.09	103	9.3	0.87
Sulfonated 2-dodecylbenzene	0.40	139	0.22	0.078
1-Chloro-4-nitrobenzene	2.52	400	1.4	0.22

Analysis of this type can give only qualitative conclusions with regard to the pesticides for it is obvious that the basic assumption of the Langmuir treatment—i.e., that only a monomolecular layer of adsorbed material is formed—does not hold when one is considering weights of adsorbed material in the neighborhood of 40% of the weight of adsorbent. While the Langmuir formulation does adequately represent the data for adsorptive equilibrium over a large and relatively high concentration range, it seems likely that more refined experimentation in a lower concentration range (say 1–100 p.p.b.) would show considerably greater adsorption of the pesticides than that predicted by the Langmuir constants presented here. Indeed, experimental results for the lower end of the concentration range for equilibrium adsorption of DNOSBP and DNOCHP, shown in Figures 12 and 13 respectively, provide some evi-

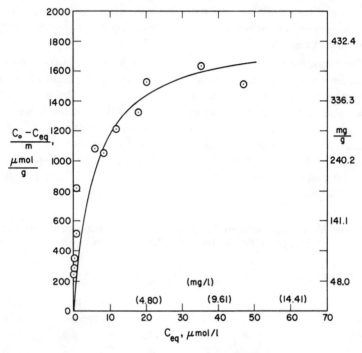

Figure 12.   Isotherm for DNOSBP
Equilibrium capacity for adsorption of DNOSBP is represented in terms of μmoles per gram of carbon on the left ordinate and in terms of mg./gram on the right ordinate. A calculated Langmuir isotherm is drawn through the experimental data.

dence of this. It seems likely that two different Langmuir formulations such as those found for phenol in lower and higher ranges of concentration (9) may be needed for more exact description. There the value of X_m for phenol at higher concentrations was found to be 3.32 μmoles/gram or 310 mg./gram rather than the figures recorded in Table V. From the previous work the phenol concentrations giving the higher capacity were from 6–14% of the saturation values in water. Many of the pesticides were studied in about this range of fractional concentrations of their saturation values. In addition, carbons of particle sizes smaller than the

273-micron carbon utilized for the present work will yield higher adsorption capacity values, as has been demonstrated by Weber and Morris (9).

Consequently, cleanup of small concentrations of pesticides by activated carbon seems likely to be considerably more efficient than indi-

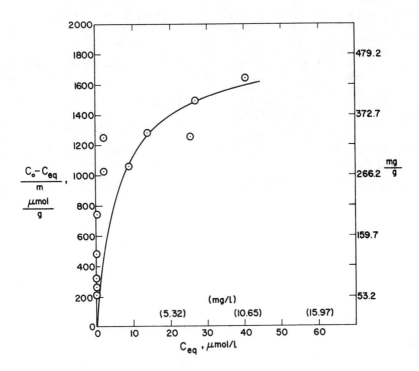

Figure 13.   Isotherm for DNOCHP
The curve drawn through the experimental data for equilibrium adsorption
of DNOCHP is a calculated Langmuir isotherm.

cated by the Langmuir constants obtained in these studies. Problems of initial leakage of these materials are not expected to occur when beds of adequate depth (5–10′) of active carbon are used for water and wastewater treatment.

Acknowledgments

The research reported herein has been supported in part by U. S. Public Health Service AWTR Contract SAph 76495 and in part by a Research Grant, WP-00706, from the Division of Water Supply and Pollution Control, U. S. Public Health Service.

Literature Cited

(1) Aly, O. M., Faust, S. D., *J. Am. Water Works Assoc.* **57**, 221 (1965).
(2) Cohen, J. M., Rourke, G. A., Woodward, R. L., *J. Am. Water Works Assoc.* **52**, 1551 (1960).
(3) Crank, J., "The Mathematics of Diffusion," Clarendon Press, London, 1965.
(4) Hyndshaw, A. Y., *J. Am. Water Works Assoc.* **54**, 91 (1962).
(5) Langmuir, I., *J. Am. Chem. Soc.* **40**, 1361 (1918).
(6) Robeck, G. G., Dostal, K. A., Cohen, J. M., Kreissl, J. F., *J. Am. Water Works Assoc.* **57**, 181 (1965).
(7) U.S. Tariff Commission, "Synthetic Organic Chemicals, United States Production and Sales, 1962," USTC Pub. No. 114, U.S. Government Printing Office, Washington, D.C., 1963.
(8) Weber, W. J., Jr., Morris, J. C., *J. Sanit. Eng. Div., Am. Soc. Civil Engrs.* **SA2**, 3483, 31 (1963).
(9) Weber, W. J., Jr., Morris, J. C., *J. Sanit. Eng. Div., Am. Soc. Civil Engrs.* **SA3**, 3952, 79 (1964).
(10) Weber, W. J., Jr., Rumer, R. R., Jr., *Water Resources Res.* **1**, 3, 361 (1965).

RECEIVED October 13, 1965.

INDEX

305